CDM 2007

A guide for clients and their advisors

Books are to be returned on or before
the last date below.

AVRIL ROBARTS LRC

7 – DAY
LOAN

LIBREX–

WITHDRAWN

**RICS
BOOKS**

LIVERPOOL
JOHN MOORES UNIVERSITY
AVRIL ROBARTS LRC
TITHEBARN STREET
LIVERPOOL L2 2ER
TEL. 0151 231 4022

Acknowledgements

The author and publishers wish to thank the following for permission to reproduce copyright material:

© Crown copyright material is reproduced with the permission of the Controller of HMSO and Queen's Printer for Scotland:

- L144, *Managing Health and Safety in Construction, Approved Code of Practice* (CDM 2007) (Construction, Design and Management Regulations 2007) ISBN 978 0 71766 223 4;
- HSG 65, *Successful Health and Safety Management,* ISBN 0 71761 276 7;
- *Summary of responses to Revitalising health and safety in construction,* www.hse.gov.uk/consult/disdocs/dde20.summary.pdf;
- *Developing guidelines for the selection of designers and contractors under the Construction (Design and Management) Regulations 1994,* 'The Carpenter Report', Research Report, 422; and
- primary and secondary legislation.

The CIC project stages are the copyright of the Construction Industry Council and are reproduced here with permission from the Construction Industry Council.

The project stages from the RIBA Outline Plan of Work 2007, copyright Royal Institute of British Architects (RIBA), are reproduced here with permission from the RIBA.

The quote from the foreword of CIRIA Guide C652, *Safer surfaces to walk on – reducing the risk of slipping* (CIRIA, London, 2006, www.ciria.org) is reproduced with permission from CIRIA.

Extracts of case material given in a presentation by Michael Appleby are reproduced with permission.

Specimen copies of an HSE improvement notice, an HSE prohibition notice and an F10 Notification of construction project are copyright HSE and are reproduced here with permission.

The text of *Procurement decisions* is copyright Davis Langdon. It is from an article that was originally written by Simon Rawlinson of Davis Langdon, first published in *Building magazine* on 10 February 2006, and is reproduced here with permission.

The text of *Appendix B: Insolvency and CDM* was written by David Jones FCIOB FASI MRICS MaPS of London Borough of Bromley and is reproduced here with permission.

Published by the Royal Institution of Chartered Surveryors
under the RICS Books imprint
Surveyor Court
Westwood Business Park
Coventry CV4 8JE
UK

www.ricsbooks.com

ISBN 978 1 84219 327 3

Typeset in Great Britain by Columns Design Ltd, Reading, Berkshire
Printed in Great Britain by Latimer Trend and Company

FSC
Mixed Sources
Product group from well-managed
forests and other controlled sources
Cert no. SGS-COC-2482
www.fsc.org
© 1996 Forest Stewardship Council

Contents

(RRFSO 2005, which came into effect on 1 October 2006. The *Building Regulations* also apply (Part M and Part B).

Requirements relating to work at height are now shifted to the centre of the triangle reflecting the fact that sections were taken out of both the CHSW Regulations and the *Workplace Regulations* 1992 and incorporated in the new *Work at Height Regulations* 2005.

Work at Height Regulations 2005
These Regulations implement Directive 2001/45/EC of 27 June 2001, amending Council Directive 89/655/EEC concerning the minimum health and safety requirements for the use of work equipment by workers at work.

Workplace (Health, Safety and Welfare) Regulations 1992
Although the *Workplace Regulations* have been in place since 1992 (with previous requirements dating back to 1963 – *Offices, Shops and Railway Premises Act 1963* – and earlier) they have not always been expressly considered by designers as part of the design process, except where the requirements of the *Building Regulations* have coincided with those contained within the *Workplace Regulations* 1992.

Designers now have an explicit duty under CDM 2007 to deliver a building design that meets the requirements of the *Workplace Regulations* 1992 (see CDM regulation 11).

Contractually this has always been the case, as the client has been entitled to a building that is fit for purpose and capable of occupation and use under more general legal principles.

> *CDM 2007 regulation 11*
> Regulation 11(3) 'Every designer shall in preparing or modifying a design which may be used in construction work in Great Britain avoid foreseeable risks to the health and safety of any person:
> ...
> (e) using a structure designed as a workplace.'
> Regulation 11(5) 'In designing any structure for use as a workplace the designer shall take account of the provisions of the *Workplace (Health, Safety and Welfare) Regulations* 1992 which relate to the design of, and materials used in, the structure.'

The definition of 'workplace' covers a wide range of workplaces not only factories, shops and offices but, for example, schools, hospitals, hotels and places of entertainment. The term also includes the common parts of shared buildings, private roads and paths on industrial estates and business parks, and temporary work sites (but not construction sites).

The *Workplace Regulations* 1992 also relate to the occupation of the premises and cover such issues as area of workspace, ventilation and lighting (which to a certain extent are dependent upon the occupancy of the premises and can vary with the density of occupation as well as the purpose to which the premises are put).

CDM 1994 and CDM 2007
CDM 2007 is built upon 12 years of experience in the industry and is intended to redress some of the criticisms of the original CDM Regulations, for example, that they introduced unnecessary bureaucracy into the construction process, lacked clarity and were not easily understood. They were also subject to misinterpretation and the bad practice which followed.

The publication of HSG224 (the Approved Code of Practice for the *Construction (Design and Management) Regulations* 1994) in 2001 reinforced the point that CDM is intended to encourage the integration of health and safety into the management of projects. Any paperwork should contribute to the management of health and safety.

This is reinforced by the Approved Code of Practice (ACOP), *Managing health and safety in construction: Construction (Design and Management) Regulations 2007*[4], issued with CDM 2007, in paragraph 3:

> 'These regulations are intended to focus attention on planning and management throughout construction projects, from design concept onwards. The aim is for health and safety considerations to be treated as an essential, but normal part of a project's development – not an afterthought or bolt on extra.'

The 'construction triangle' (shown in figure 2) demonstrates that CDM should not be considered in isolation: there are too many other issues to be taken into account, especially at the design stage, and it is essential that CDM be considered in the wider context, as part of the integrated risk management process.

LIABILITY

An important point to remember is that in the event of an incident where there is a breach of health and safety law (a criminal offence) due to the failings of the employer, there is also potential for a claim under civil law.

Under criminal law it is only necessary to establish that there has been a breach of the legislation: the HSE can secure a prosecution even if there has not been an accident or an injury. The fact that someone has been exposed to a risk, or there is a potential for someone to be exposed to a risk is sufficient in itself for a prosecution to be brought.

For example, if employees are found to be working on a roof without edge protection then that could be sufficient grounds for the HSE to bring a prosecution. In the 'construction blitzes' undertaken by the HSE over recent years several construction companies were successfully prosecuted for failures to provide adequate edge protection – even though none of the workers on the site had sustained a fall or an injury.

RISK TRANSFER

Traditional forms of construction procurement have tended to push risk down the supply chain (often to those least able to manage the risk). This tendency has been redressed more recently by newer methods of procurement, such as partnering arrangements (e.g. PPP – Public Private Partnership), which have placed the emphasis on risks being shared by the partners.

Under such arrangements the partners share both the benefits (e.g. cost savings engineered into the project) and the liabilities or losses (e.g. increased material costs).

Under a contract it is possible to deal with risk in a number of ways: retaining, transferring or sharing risks. The risk may be avoided (e.g. by declining a project because the risk profile is too high or by using a different form of construction which is inherently safer, such as constructing a road around a hill rather than boring a tunnel through it).

(See Chapter 6 *Buying the construction work* for further information relating to procurement of construction works.)

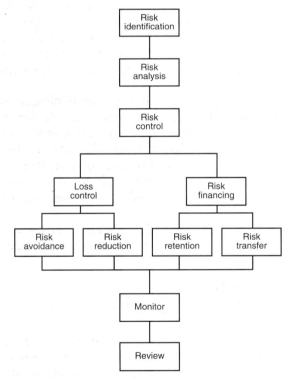

Figure 3: Risk management

MANAGING RISK

However, the important aspect of risk management is that the risk should be recognised and appropriate measures implemented in order to mitigate and control the risk. In order to do so, information relating to hazards and risks must be an integral part of the information flows.

It is not acceptable for risks to be passed on to other parties within the project, or further down the supply chain, without all parties being exposed to that risk being provided with information as to the nature and extent of the risk or with information as to how it is proposed to reduce or control the risk.

Risk cannot be avoided but it can be managed. CDM 2007 requires all duty holders to be provided with the right information at the right time, thus ensuring that risk is adequately managed throughout the life of the project (and beyond). The setting up and maintenance of procedures and tools for ensuring adequate flows of information is an integral part of CDM 2007.

Figure 4 gives an indication of how the information flows can be managed.

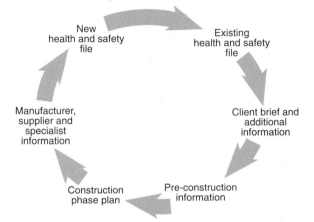

Figure 4: Information flows are a continuing cycle

INTEGRATION OF CDM INTO THE BUSINESS

For clients, CDM is only part of the management process that needs to be in place in order to successfully manage a business.

Most of the duties outlined in CDM 2007 already existed, to a greater or lesser degree, in other Regulations, with CDM referring to clients and other legislation referring to employers.

The *Health and Safety at Work etc. Act* 1974 places an overriding duty upon employers to safeguard the health, safety and welfare of employees as well as those not in their employ.

The *Management Regulations* 1999 require employers to manage their activities in much the same way as the CDM Regulations, and many key words, such as planning, organisation, monitoring and review, co-operation and co-ordination are to be found in both sets of Regulations.

(Further guidance and information relating to health and safety legislation, and enforcement procedures and prosecutions together with a summary of health and safety legislation can be found in Chapters 11 and 12.)

The Health and Safety Executive (HSE) publication HSG65 *Successful health and safety management*[5] provides a practical guide for directors and managers who wish to improve health and safety within their organisations and sets out the principles for achieving successful health and safety management.

Where adequate procedures are already in place and businesses are already managing health and

safety, and risk, then the integration of CDM procedures into the management process should have a
fairly minimal impact on the business.

Procedures for vetting contractors, monitoring performance, maintaining asbestos registers and requirements for operating and maintenance manuals will
already be an integral part of the company procedures.

CDM – PROPORTIONALITY

The HSE has stated that it is not its intention to place
additional burdens on business and the government's
Better Regulation Task Force is committed to reducing the burden on small to medium enterprises
(SMEs).

In the Regulatory Impact Assessment (RIA) which
formed part of the submission to the Health and
Safety Commission (HSC), it was stated that the aim
of CDM 2007 is to reduce construction accidents and
ill health by:

- being flexible and accommodating the wide range
  of contractual arrangements to be found in the
  construction industry;
- emphasising the need to plan and manage work
  rather than the bureaucracy associated with it;
- emphasising the communication and co-ordination advantages of duty holders working in integrated teams; and
- simplifying the way duty holders assess competence.

It was also anticipated that health and safety benefits would flow from the explicit requirement for
designers to consider the risks associated with structures intended as a place of work and the risks posed
to those workers undertaking maintenance in a building.

The RIA also considered the benefits of incorporating CHSW 1995 into CDM 2007: although no immediate financial savings were anticipated, it was felt that
having a single set of Regulations for the construction
industry would provide tangible benefits in future to
new entrants to the industry.

SMALL BUSINESS CLIENTS

Smaller clients whose work is not primarily focused
on the construction industry were not well repre-
sented in the formal consultation process: the HSE
commissioned a report by Tim Kind of the Forum for
Private Business to solicit their views and made some
amendments to both the Regulations and the ACOP
to address these concerns.

However, one area identified in this report but not
addressed was the fact that there is a lack of integration with the planning and building control regimes.

Most small clients are aware of the local planning
and building control processes (as are designers dealing with smaller projects) and it was suggested that
there was scope for greater integration at local level for
smaller projects.

This is an issue that still requires resolution but the
HSE has agreed to work with Communities and Local
Government (CLG) to look for ways to achieve better
integration of the planning, building control and
CDM regulatory regimes, with a view to bringing forward a simplification proposal should discussions
identify changes which would reduce the burdens on
small businesses.

Whilst this issue has been left open for future
debate, the Health and Safety Commission accepted
the proposals for the new Regulations as they stood,
with the proviso that the HSE would continue to
explore ways in which the process can be made easier
for small business clients.

A paper was submitted to the Health and Safety
Commission in January 2007, *Construction Programme's existing SME work and development of future
strategy*[6], in which it was reported that a significant
number of small to medium enterprises (SMEs),
including contractors and construction professionals,
work only for domestic clients or small business
clients and generally do not receive exposure to health
and safety advice.

The HSE recognises that it is extremely difficult to
communicate with this group and even harder to
influence them to improve health and safety standards. It is thought that this group's better understanding of the building control and planning regimes
provides an opportunity for HSE to work more
closely with building control officers in order to reach
SMEs.

It is possible therefore that further changes will
occur as the result of the drive towards better regulation.

BUREAUCRACY AND AUDITABLE TRAIL

A major criticism in the past has been that CDM has
been responsible for the creation of mountains of
paperwork, much of it generic and often missing the
real issues relating to the project.

Where documents have obviously been copied
from a previous project, or those preparing the plan
or file have not understood the purpose of the documents, then at best they add little value, at worst they
can be completely misleading about the risks that
might be encountered on the site.

All documents produced for a project need to be
project specific, i.e. produced specifically to deal with
the particular project planned for that site, identifying
the nature of the works and the specific hazards and
risks that are likely to be encountered on that site or
project.

There is little point in having sections that refer to electricity pylons or working next to the canal when neither feature is to be found within a five mile radius of the site. However, the requirement for cranes and piling rigs to have navigation lights if they are on the final approaches to the regional airport could be important information. The information provided must be accurate and relevant.

A further criticism has been the reams of paper-work produced by clients and their advisors for assessing the competence and resources of contractors. The criticism is not necessarily aimed at the individual client with a single bespoke questionnaire but at the requirement, especially for contractors, to respond to competency questionnaires every time they submit a tender.

The need for a reduction in bureaucracy has been stated but nevertheless it is important that the documentation produced for a project is capable of providing an auditable trail.

In the event of failure 'gold plated arrangements' are likely to be used in evidence in order to demonstrate that a duty holder had failed to comply with their own policies and procedures. Therefore it is more sensible to document arrangements which are applicable and achievable.

The aim of this book is to provide clients and their advisors with a clear understanding as to what is required under the new CDM Regulations, where they differ from the old Regulations, and how best practice can help to improve the performance of clients in managing their projects.

Temporary or mobile construction sites

Reference is made throughout the book to Directive 92/57/EEC[3] which sets out the minimum safety and health requirements at temporary or mobile construction sites and upon which the UK legislation is based.

Each of the Member States is free to implement the Directive into domestic law in the manner which accords with local custom. In the case of the UK this has been by way of Regulations made under HASAW 1974.

Where references are made to the Articles or Annexes to the Directive, they provide a baseline from which comparisons can be made between the original objectives and intentions of the Directive and the manner in which they have been interpreted and transposed into UK law.

Although the UK is required to comply with the Directive, there are some differences (some would say significant differences) in interpretation and implementation.

It should also be recognised that the UK legal system based on common law, without a written constitution, has evolved in a different way to the European systems based on the Napoleonic Code. One major difference, the concept of 'reasonably practicable' is not recognised in mainland Europe and is, at the time of writing, being tested in the European Courts.

The Commission of the European Communities has made an application to the European Court for a declaration that the UK has failed to fulfil its obligations under Article 5(1) and (4) of Directive 89/391/EEC of 12 June 1989 on the introduction of measures to encourage improvements in the safety and health of workers at work. Advocate General Mengozzi delivered an 'Opinion' on the merits of the case[7] on 18 January 2007 in which he supported the UK position, with a recommendation that the Court dismiss the application. Subsequently the European Court has found in favour of the UK.

Additional information about the *Temporary or Mobile Construction Sites Directive*[3, 8] can be found in Chapter 11.

2 Setting the scene

This chapter examines the impact of intervention by the enforcing authorities, recent developments in legislation both in Europe and the UK, and the effects of failures in safety on site (including recent health and safety statistics).

WHERE HAS THE INDUSTRY STRUGGLED?

Statistics of fatal injuries

HSE publishes annual statistics[9] of accidents and fatal injuries and the latest figures available at the time of publication show the lowest level of fatal injury on record.

In 2005/06, 212 people were fatally injured, down from 223 in 2004/05. This rate is the lowest on record, with an incidence rate of 0.71 fatalities per 100,000 workers.

Two industries (construction and agriculture) account for just under half of all fatal injuries – although both industries saw significant reductions in the number and rate of fatalities during this period. Construction saw fatalities reduced by 14 per cent, giving the lowest number of fatalities since records began.

UK construction

Health and safety performance in the UK construction industry is improving. In the last 40 years there has been an overall reduction in the number of people killed each year whilst working in the industry – from a historical peak of 285 in 1966/67 to 59 in 2005/06 (see figure 5).

Furthermore an incident rate can be calculated, taking into account the actual number of construction workers. This shows that, due to the rising numbers at work in the industry, the fatal injury rate per 100,000 workers has declined more steeply (see figure 6).

Whilst this is a significant improvement, there were still 59 families in the year 2005/06 that lost a parent, sibling or child.

The provisional figure for 2006/2007 indicates a rise

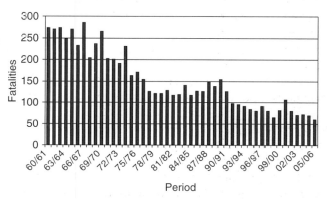

Figure 5: Improving performance over time

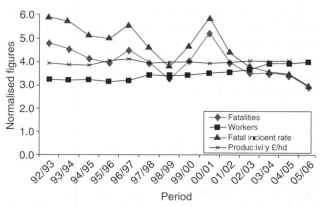

Figure 6: Improving performance incidence rate

back up to 78 fatalities for the year: preliminary enquiries suggest that this increase is due, at least partially, to the sharp increase in 'non-English' speaking entrants into the UK construction industry and the problems associated with poor communication on site.

The financial burden

We should not forget that for every person who was killed in 2003/04, construction industry employers reported another 67 workers who suffered a major injury and a further 125 who lost more than 3 days from work due to accidents caused at work.

The financial toll on the workers and their families, and the burden on the state, can only be imagined, especially taking into account the fact that 75 per cent of the construction workforce were self-employed (prior to the introduction of the new CIS Tax Scheme).

This financial waste also reduces the competitiveness of the UK construction industry.

Furthermore the Labour Force Survey indicates that only about half of the accidents that should be reported to the Health and Safety Executive are actually reported, so the numbers for major injuries and other reportable injuries can be doubled. The Health and Safety Commission has indicated that those failing to report are mainly the self-employed.

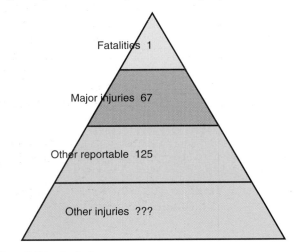

Figure 7: Triangle of misery

Work-related illness

Although accidents may make the headlines, the incidence of ill health in the industry goes largely unreported.

Asbestos is responsible for some 3000–4000 work-related deaths a year, but there is still little recognition that workers in the repairs and maintenance sector are still being exposed to asbestos when carrying out minor works (with carpenters, electricians and plumbers/heating engineers being generally at most risk).

Recent cases have also involved spouses and children who have come into contact with the asbestos fibres on their (generally male) partners'/parents' clothes when they have returned home from work.

It was estimated that up to 86,000 people suffered work-related ill health in the construction industry in 2005/06 which led to them having time off work.

Labour Force Survey

Another report, produced by the HSE, provides information on the two million British workers suffering from ill health which they believe was caused or made worse by work.

The report *Self-reported work-related illness in 2004/05: results from the Labour Force Survey*[10] high-

lights the fact that musculoskeletal disorders (MSDs) are the biggest cause of ill health, resulting in employees taking time off work or being unable to perform the tasks that they normally carry out.

An increasing problem being reported is stress, with around half a million people estimated as suffering from work-related stress.

The costs of accidents and ill health

Whatever figures are used, the cost of accidents and work-related ill health to the UK economy is tremendous, not only in relation to the reduction in output caused by work absence, but in the costs that are borne by us all in the additional burden placed upon the NHS, the emergency services, and the personal cost to those affected.

The costs of **accidents and ill health to the UK economy** has been estimated at £32 billion.

Because a large proportion of construction industry workers are self–employed, are reluctant to report injuries, and there are financial implications of them taking time off work to recover from injury or ill health, there is every indication that a significant proportion of the workforce on construction sites are suffering from ill health or injuries that should be treated.

A recent study[11] by the University of Liverpool suggests that only 30 per cent of reportable accidents in the workplace are notified to the HSE under the *Reporting of Injuries, Diseases and Dangerous Occurrences Regulations* 1995 (RIDDOR 1995).

The study investigated the under-reporting of accidents to the HSE by comparing the attendance of patients at the Royal Liverpool University Hospital with cases reported to the HSE and then following up the patients to establish the amount of time lost from work and the type and severity of the injuries.

The report found that the main reason accidents were reported was time lost from work and that other factors were ancillary. If a major injury led to lost time from work then it was more likely to be reported than those instances where people were able to return to work, even if the injuries were fairly major or led to the workers being placed on light duties whilst they recovered from their injuries.

The study also found that the self-employed were least likely to lodge reports under RIDDOR 1995, with a reporting rate of 12 per cent compared with 32 per cent for employed workers.

The *Constructing Better Health* pilot[12] that was carried out in Leicester estimated that in the construction industry in Great Britain in 2006 around 11,500 people were absent from their job with work-related illness every day.

They also found that a significant number of people who were on site had undiagnosed health problems ranging from high blood pressure to, in one case, an operator of a piece of mobile plant who was clinically blind.

One third of all those who were given free health checks under the scheme were referred to their GP for further diagnosis and treatment.

Accidents involving members of the public

The accident toll includes members of the public injured by activities on construction sites and by incidents affecting people outside the site boundaries.

In 2005/06, five members of the public were killed by construction activities and approximately 50 times that number received some form of injury.

Recent incidents have included members of the public being killed by a crane collapse in Central London, a youngster falling from a scaffold, and injuries to both people and vehicles from scaffolding collapsing across the public highway.

Accidents involving young people gaining entry onto construction sites, especially during school holidays, is a persistent problem. However such incidents are deemed forseeable and clients are expected to ensure that the contractor's arrangements take account of such matters.

For more examples of incidents, see the case reports in Chapter 12.

Highways Economic Note No1

Another interesting source of information is the annually updated document *Highways Economic Note No1* (HEN1)[3], produced by the Department for Transport. It is used to calculate the official value for a human life and as a criteria against which the decisions to improve roads where fatalities have occurred are measured.

The current figure is calculated at £1.4 million (as the value of life on British roads) but the principles can be applied to other forms of transport or even to industry (including the nuclear industry where a figure of up to £14.3 million applies – this being justified by the fact that an incident involving the nuclear industry is likely to have far more reaching effects than an accident on the roads).

These figures provide a benchmark against which to measure the cost of providing safety measures on construction sites. Generally the costs associated with an accident on site far outweigh the paltry savings achieved by skimping on accident prevention.

Construction skills shortage

Partly due to the misery that injury and ill health causes to workers and their families and the resulting poor reputation that the industry has earned, the construction industry in the UK faces a real skills shortage.

Sir Michael Latham, Chairman of CITB Construction Skills, reported in 2006 that their research indicated that the industry, which employs 2.5 million workers, needed to recruit 83,000 new workers each year over the next five years.

Whilst some of this shortfall is due to a more active industry that has seen the workforce increase from 1.5 million workers in the early 1990s, the largest part of the current deficit is caused by workers leaving the industry for safer jobs or being invalided out.

Although some of the shortfall has been met by migrant workers, this is not sustainable. The shortfall has led to an increase in labour rates and therefore overall construction costs. This will only be exacerbated when the home economies of these migrant workers improve and they return home.

The most significant ways to reverse this shortfall are:

● to ensure that there is a reduction in the number of workers being invalided out and leaving or retiring early; and
● to improve the industry's reputation so that people actually want to come and work in it.

Business impact

The *Movement for Innovation (M4i) Demonstration Projects*[14] showed that, where health and safety was addressed correctly by the client, design team and contractor, accidents rates were 61 per cent lower and costs were 6 per cent lower, resulting in an increase in profits for contractors of 2 per cent.

Clearly the long term benefits of good health and safety risk management by all involved in a project will result in a more competitive construction industry. Conversely poor health and safety risk management by those involved in a project can leave health and safety difficult to manage on sites.

Aside from the toll of misery that this exacts from construction workers and their families, poor health and safety risk management can have a significant impact on a project.

If the HSE is inclined to dwell on a site when it visits, the site management will be tied up for about a day with the conversation with the inspector and taking subsequent corrective action.

If the HSE issues a prohibition notice, the site is likely to be out of action for a minimum of three days: the imposition of a prohibition notice on a crane hire company at the beginning of 2007 affected several hundred sites and left many of them without alternative lifting capability for several weeks or more.

In the event of a fatality on a construction site, the site is likely to be closed down completely for several weeks whilst initial investigations are carried out.

Enforcement Policy Statement

The Health and Safety Commission issued its *Enforcement Policy Statement for the Construction Industry* (HSC15) in January 2002. This Policy created the Construction Division within the Health and Safety Executive and increased the number of inspectors.

Along with this was a policy to take interventions further up the chain.

This has two significant implications for project teams.

- If an inspector goes to site and finds something about which he or she is not happy, in addition to speaking to the contractor, the inspector can take the project team to task about why the risk had not been identified and eliminated or reduced.
- In addition, inspectors are at liberty to intervene with designers and construction clients about their general performance, not in relation to a specific project.

The Policy Statement indicated that the average number of inspections per construction inspector in 2003 should be 106.

In industry in general in 1994 the target had been 380.

Health and Safety Executive inspectors in the construction industry have been allocated more time to pursue interventions than other inspectors.

Responding to interventions

Responding to these interventions can be time consuming for senior managers if things have not been done correctly and there are no records to show what has been done.

Whilst an inspector's first inclination will be to encourage better performance, if there are shortcomings in a company's performance the inspector may be inclined to issue an improvement or prohibition notice.

Where these are not addressed correctly, the Health and Safety Executive may be inclined to prosecute.

HSE enforcement

Clients should be aware of the sanctions that are available to the HSE where health and safety legislation is being breached:

- improvement notices;
- prohibition notices; and/or
- prosecution.

Prosecutions database

Since 1999 the Health and Safety Executive has had a name and shame policy: this is supported by a publicly accessible database where all prosecutions are lodged with details of the defendant and the case.

The visibility of this database is increased by the production of annual Offences and Penalties Reports and publicity by pressure groups like the Centre for Corporate Accountability.

See Chapter 12 for additional information on enforcement.

R v F Howe and Son

Judges said in the Court of Appeal case of Howe (*R v F Howe and Son (Engineers) Ltd* [1999] 2 All ER 249):

- 'Any fine should reflect not only the gravity of the offence but also the means of the offender.'
- 'The objective of prosecutions for health and safety offences in the workplace is to achieve a safe environment for those who work there and for other members of the public who may be affected. A fine needs to be large enough to bring that message home where the defendant company is a company not only to those who manage it but also to its shareholders.'
- 'Although in general we accept that [the fine should not be so large enough to imperil the earnings of employees or create a risk of bankruptcy] there may be cases where the offences are so serious that the defendant ought not to be in business.'

In addition to the serious impact on senior managers' productivity that an intervention from the Health and Safety Executive may have, there is a serious potential for damage to the reputation of a company.

This can also be reflected in:

- a significant reduction in the share price of quoted companies; and
- a reduction in future business.

The requirement for listed companies to report upon health and safety issues means that they cannot hide such information from their shareholders.

See also the Turnbull Report on page 12.

The effect on smaller businesses can be equally dramatic with a significant impact on profits and future business, and may result in smaller businesses losing major clients.

The Health and Safety Executive has been taking more targeted enforcement action and devoting additional resources to investigation to push up their prosecution success rate.

Since the Court of Appeal case of Howe, courts have been taking a more robust and innovative approach to fines and it should be remembered that a conviction under health and safety law, including the *Construction (Design and Management) Regulations*, leaves the guilty party with a criminal record.

HSE Designer Initiative

Although clients may be aware that improvement and prohibition notices may be served upon contractors, they may not be so aware of the fact that they can also be served upon designers and clients.

An initiative was undertaken over a three-year period by the HSE (Construction Division) from their offices in Scotland, the Northwest and Newcastle upon Tyne[15] whereby HSE inspectors conducted a number of in-depth audits of firms of designers and also undertook site visits, with the designers invited to attend.

The broad aims of this initiative were to assess designer performance, and gather intelligence concerning both good and bad design practice, with special emphasis on issues relating to work at height.

In 2005, a total of 128 design practices (mainly architects and structural engineers) were assessed, 14 follow up visits were made, and 3 improvement notices were served.

HSE investigations

It is now current practice, in those cases where HSE is called upon to investigate accidents or incidents on site, for the HSE Construction Inspector to follow the trail back through the designers to the client in order to ascertain whether the designers or client have contributed to any failings in the design, the allocation of resources (including time) or failure to communicate information down the line.

With the role of the client enhanced under CDM 2007 by, for example, the requirements to ensure an adequate period for mobilisation and to provide welfare facilities throughout the project, it can be anticipated that this type of intervention by the HSE will become more commonplace.

Enforcement by other agencies

Clients should also be aware of and take account of the powers of other agencies to take enforcement action, such as:

- Environmental Health – in respect of breaches of environmental legislation such as the *Environmental Protection Act 1990* regarding noise, dust and fumes emanating from the site;
- Planning Authority – in respect of breaches of planning law, such as hours of work, tree preservation orders (TPOs), etc.;
- Environment Agency – in respect of discharges of substances, such as oils or chemicals, into the sewers or watercourses;
- Highways Authority – in respect of any obstructions to the highway;

- Defra – in respect of disturbance to wildlife, such as badgers (licences are required to move badger setts), slow worms, newts, etc.

Even where no direct action is taken against the developer, or client, any form of enforcement action has the potential to disrupt the programme and may have a detrimental effect on the client's business. A recent case, where a crane hire company was served with a prohibition notice following fatalities on sites in Battersea and Liverpool arising from the collapse of tower cranes, created major disruption on a large number of sites – some of these tower cranes were out of action for several weeks whilst checks were undertaken in order to comply with the prohibition notice.

Further information relating to enforcement can be found in Chapter 12.

THE JOURNEY TO CDM 2007

Construction health and safety legislation developed over time in an ad hoc fashion, generally being framed and enacted in response to serious incidents – with the aim of preventing people from being harmed by that type of accident again.

Douglas Short, a Health and Safety Executive Factory Inspector, is credited as the force behind the pulling together of the Construction Regulations in the 1960s. These included:

- the *Construction (General Provisions) Regulations 1961*;
- the *Construction (Lifting Operations) Regulations 1961*;
- the *Construction (Working Places) Regulations 1966*; and
- the *Construction (Health and Welfare) Regulations 1966*.

Since then there has been a steady decline in the harm that is being done to construction workers.

The Robens Report

In response to the report of the Robens' Committee, the *Health and Safety at Work etc. Act 1974* was enacted on 31 July 1974.

Amongst other things the Act sets high level goals for employers in relation to the well-being of their workers, whether they be employed or self-employed, and those affected by their undertaking.

Health and Safety Commission Executive
The Health and Safety Commission (HSC) and the Health and Safety Executive (HSE) were both set up by the *Health and Safety at Work etc. Act 1974* as non-departmental bodies with specific statutory functions in relation to health and safety.

The Health and Safety Commission comprises a body of up to ten people, appointed by the Secretary of State, Department of Work and Pensions and representing all parts of industry including employers and trade union representatives. The HSC is the policy making body.

The Health and Safety Executive comprises a body of three people appointed by the Commission and advises and assists the Commission in undertaking its own duties as well as being responsible (along with local authorities) for the enforcement of health and safety law.

Additional information can be found in *The health and safety system in Great Britain*[16].

At the time of writing there are proposals for the two bodies to be amalgamated.

Framework Directive (89/391/EEC)

In 1989 the European Commission passed the *Framework Directive* (89/391/EEC)[17] which had requirements largely similar to those of the *Health and Safety at Work etc. Act* 1974 with respect to employers and workers (employed and the self-employed) and the impact of undertakings on the public.

In response to the *Framework Directive* the UK government enacted the *Management of Health and Safety at Work Regulations* 1992 (which have since been replaced by the 1999 Regulations of the same name).

These reflect the 'general principles of prevention' which give the structured, hierarchical, approach that should be taken in the management of health and safety risks.

The general principles show that the first action that should be taken to protect workers and the public is to avoid risks, and the last resort is to give employees appropriate instructions.

General principles of prevention

The general principles of prevention (set out in Schedule 1 of the *Management of Health and Safety at Work Regulations* 1999 and Article 6(2) of Directive 89/391/EEC) are as follows:

'(a) avoiding risks;
(b) evaluating the risks which cannot be avoided;
(c) combating the risks at source;
(d) adapting the work to the individual, especially as regards the design of workplaces, the choice of work equipment and the choice of working and production methods, with a view, in particular, to alleviating monotonous work and work at a predetermined work-rate and to reducing their effect on health;
(e) adapting to technical progress;
(f) replacing the dangerous by the non-dangerous or the less dangerous;
(g) developing a coherent overall prevention policy which covers technology, organisation of work, working conditions, social relationships and the influence of factors relating to the working environment;
(h) giving collective protective measures priority over individual protective measures; and
(i) giving appropriate instructions to employees.'

There was a realisation across Europe that the provisions of the *Framework Directive*, as nationally enacted, were not working in the construction industry.

Whilst two thirds of construction site fatalities were brought about by decisions that were made before the works started on site, predominantly by clients and designers, these people did not appear to be clear about their obligations to consider the implications of their decisions on construction workers. The subsequent research was reported in *From Drawing Board to Building Site*[18].

Temporary or Mobile Construction Sites Directive

In response to these findings the *Temporary or Mobile Construction Sites Directive* (92/57/EEC)[3] was passed.

This was enacted in Great Britain by two Statutory Instruments:

- the *Construction (Design and Management) Regulations* 1994; and
- the *Construction (Health, Safety and Welfare) Regulations* 1996.

The publication of the Regulations was supported by an Approved Code of Practice (ACOP) and various guidance documents.

The two particularly aimed at clients were Construction Information Sheet 39 *The Role of the Client*[19] and MISC193 *Having Construction Work Done*[20].

The Turnbull Report

Another significant milestone, albeit from the world of commerce, was the publication of the *Turnbull Report*[21] in September 1999.

The Turnbull Report had been commissioned by the Institute of Chartered Accountants in England and Wales (ICAEW) and the London Stock Exchange (LSE) to provide clarification on the requirements and implementation of a previous document produced by Hampel (*Principles of Good Governance and Code of Best Practice*[22]).

Turnbull, in his report, confirmed that the Code called for effective internal control systems and risk management processes. He also highlighted the need for all risks to be managed on an ongoing basis and for significant risks to be disclosed and reported on formally.

Firms listed on the London Stock Exchange are now required to formally report upon the effectiveness of their internal controls and disclose any significant risks in their annual reports.

CDM 1994 amended

A decision by the Court of Appeal in the case of *Paul Wurth SA*[23] concerning duties of designers led to an amendment of the CDM Regulations in 2000. This amendment closed a loophole whereby design carried out by persons other than the appointed designer (the duty holder) did not attract duties under the CDM Regulations existing at that time.

Regina v Paul Wurth SA

The HSE had alleged that Paul Wurth SA had failed in their duties as designer under regulation 13(2)(a) of CDM 1994 when dealing with the design of a conveyor belt for installation at the British Steel Port Talbot Works in South Wales.

Following a successful prosecution by the HSE, the Court of Appeal set aside the conviction in the lower court.

The judgement made it clear that the wording of CDM 1994 meant that no designer duty arose when a designer arranged for other persons, including his or her employees, to prepare designs.

Paul Wurth SA had entered into a contract for the design, installation and commissioning of a slag granulation plant at Port Talbot Steelworks. Paul Wurth had subcontracted the design for the conveyor to Fairport, who in turn had subcontracted the manufacture to another company called Universal – it was

this company that had produced the production drawings for the machinery involved in the incident at British Steel in September 1997. Universal produced the construction drawings (without incorporating a locking pin) which were submitted to Paul Wurth for approval.

During the installation of the conveyor a man, who was working on its installation, received fatal crush injuries when the conveyor fell over because the latching devices were not suitably secured by a locking pin.

This case led to an amendment to the existing CDM Regulations in order to deal with this anomaly in the form of the *Construction (Design and Management) (Amendment) Regulations* 2000, which came into effect on 2 October 2000.

These amendments changed the definition of designer in regulation 2(1) and introduced a new regulation 2(3A) stating that:

'... any reference to a person preparing a design shall include a reference to his employee or other person at work under his control preparing it for him ...'.

Revitalising Health and Safety

In 1999, the 25th anniversary of the *Health and Safety at Work etc. Act* 1974, there was a concern that the improvements in health and safety performance in Great Britain had plateaued.

In response to these concerns an initiative, called Revitalising Health and Safety, was launched which set targets for improvement in the health and safety performance of UK industry.

In late 2000, the Deputy Prime Minister called the construction industry to account for its poor record and at a summit in early 2001 the industry set targets for its improvement in the subsequent ten years.

The industry felt that it had more opportunity to improve than other industries and therefore the more challenging targets shown below were set.

Revitalising Health and Safety

Measure	Performance	Reduction* All industries	Reduction* Construction
Working days lost from work-related injury and ill health	25m days lost per year	30%	50%
Incidence of people suffering from work-related ill health	2m suffer (5% of pop)	20%	50%
Fatal and major injury rate	29,000 (98/99)	10%	66%

*Reduction by 2010 (half by 2004)

Strategy – three sectors (agriculture, construction, health service) and five risk areas (falls, workplace transport, stress, musculoskeletal disorder, and slips, trips and falls)

HSG224, *Managing Health and Safety in Construction*

On 4 September 2001, the Health and Safety Commission, with the consent of the Secretary of State, passed for use new documentation on the *Construction (Design and Management) Regulations* 1994, HSG224, *Managing Health and Safety in Construction*[24].

This came into force on 1 February 2002 and contained both Approved Code of Practice (ACOP) material and guidance.

This was generally accepted as a significant improvement on the previous ACOP.

'Re*vitali*sing Health and Safety in Construction'

Following the setting of the 'Re*vitali*sing targets' and the publication of HSG224, in August 2002 the Health and Safety Executive published a discussion document, *Revitalising Health and Safety in Construction* (DDE20)[25], a review of the health and safety performance of the construction industry.

This document presented a view of the industry gained from analysis and interview and posed some serious questions about how the industry wanted to progress and the tools that could be used to create a movement for change.

In *Revitalising Health and Safety in Construction* the perceptions of the construction industry were summarised.

Three strands are evident from this.

- The **workforce** is perceived as being composed of transient casual workers, with little engagement in the work, working for poor pay, having little in the way of prospects and with low trade union membership (possibly related to the fragmented nature of the work). Corresponding with this the industry is portrayed as having little respect for its workers and being unhealthy to work in. It is therefore not surprising that there are also skills shortages in the construction industry.
- There are some **highly positive perceptions** attributed to construction. It is seen as a hardworking, dynamic, creative and innovative industry, quick to adapt and good at problem-solving.
- However, too much energy is engaged in **firefighting rather than a planned approach**, as demonstrated by perceptions that the industry cuts corners, takes risks, focuses on trimming costs, has low profit margins, is poor at planning and slow to change – and litigation is often the ultimate price paid for the lack of planning and the failure to deal effectively with potential risks.

Response to the discussion document

There were over 300 responses[26] to the questions posed in the discussion document. Respondents identified that the most significant thing that could be done to bring about improvements in the industry was training. Second to this was the issue of clients and time.

Positive changes suggested: clients/time
'The role and involvement of clients was also seen as a key issue.'

What was also interesting was that when clients were mentioned, usually the issue of timescales was linked.

- 'Clients not accepting the cheapest tender and giving realistic construction periods.'
- 'Clients that insist on good health and safety standards build this requirement into their tender processes and do not impose unrealistic time scales on projects.'
- 'More monitoring on site by client, demanding higher standards on their projects.'
- 'Clients have to accept that unreasonable time-scales or budgets can have detrimental effect on safety and that their attitude to safety is crucial.'
- 'The problem is that as soon as money gets tight or there is a delay on site, which is going to cost money, then because accidents are relatively rare, risks are taken to bring the job back on track.'

© *Crown copyright material is reproduced with the permission of the Controller of HMSO and Queen's Printer for Scotland.*

The overall consensus was that the *Construction (Design and Management) Regulations* 1994 were about right and minor tweaks were required to encourage better performance in the industry.

In 2003 the Construction Industry Advisory Committee (CONIAC) set up a Working Group to take forward the revisions to the CDM Regulations and in March 2005 a consultation document, CD200 (see www.hse.gov.uk/consult/2005.htm), was published.

This invited comment from the industry by the end of July 2005 but in the event the deadline was extended to the end of August 2005.

Draft regulatory package – October 2006

Following the consultation, a draft regulatory package was put together and passed by the Health and Safety Commission at its meeting on 17 October 2006 for introduction on 6 April 2007.

The *Construction (Design and Management) Regulations* 2007 (CDM 2007) combined the requirements of the *Construction (Design and Management) Regulations* 1994 (CDM 1994) and the *Construction (Health, Safety and Welfare) Regulations* 1996 (CHSW 1996) into one set of Regulations.

This should provide a simplified set of construction regulations, making it easier for duty holders to know what is expected of them and providing flexibility so that they work across a range of contractual arrangements.

The stated aim of the HSE/HSC is to reduce the

bureaucracy associated with the previous CDM Regulations and to concentrate more on ensuring that:

- projects are properly managed;
- risks are controlled; and
- information flows are better maintained, with information reaching those who need it at the time that they need it (at the appropriate stage of the project).

To this end the pre-construction health and safety plan has been replaced with the pre-construction information, which should be made available to those who need it, including designers and contractors.

Approved Code of Practice (ACOP) and guidance

The Health and Safety Commission published an Approved Code of Practice[4] with the Regulations but the construction industry was left to produce the detailed guidance that was required.

CONIAC set up an Industry Guidance Working Group to oversee the production of the new industry guidance.

Six main publications were produced, aimed at each of the duty holders and the workforce with a general overview. These are separate sets of guidance for:

- clients,
- CDM co-ordinators,
- designers,
- principal contractors,
- contractors and
- workers.

The new Regulations – CDM 2007

The application of the Regulations was simplified, the Regulations applying to all construction works with additional duties on clients, designers and contractors and the need to appoint a CDM co-ordinator and a principal contractor when the works were notifiable.

> *Notifiable project*
> '… a project is notifiable if the construction phase is likely to involve more than:
>
> (a) 30 days; or
> (b) 500 person days,
>
> of construction work.'
> CDM 2007 regulation 2(3)

Duty holders' responsibilities are covered elsewhere in this book, however, it is worth noting at this point that the Regulations now place an explicit duty on designers to extend their coverage of those that they consider to those who are using a structure as a workplace when undertaking their design.

CDM 2007 also now makes it explicit that designers should take into account the requirements of the *Workplace Regulations* 1992 so that there is no ambiguity about duty holders' obligations.

> *Who should we be thinking about?*
>
> ### CDM 2007 regulation 11(3)
> '… any person:
> (a) carrying out construction work;
> (b) liable to be affected by such construction work;
> (c) cleaning any window or any transparent or translucent wall, ceiling or roof in or on a structure;
> (d) maintaining the permanent fixtures and fittings of a structure; or
> (e) using a structure designed as a workplace.'

CDM 2007 – a management process

The emphasis of CDM 2007 is about the management of the process and on planning at the various stages of delivery and throughout the whole of the project.

Information flows are key to the whole process: from client to designers; from designers back to the client and to contractors; from contractors to subcontractors; and then back to the client upon completion of the project.

For notifiable projects the CDM co-ordinator completes the jigsaw and becomes the conduit for the main information flows and management of the CDM process.

Interwoven into these flows of information are the pre-construction information, the construction phase plan and the health and safety file.

There are also a number of significant 'gateways' where the client needs to be satisfied that matters are in place before the project proceeds to the next stage.

To provide some form of structure, the key stages used and built into the programme by the Royal Institution of British Architects (RIBA) (Stages 1 – 5) are generally used and recognised throughout the construction industry and these are shown, together with the Construction Industry Council (CIC) Project Stages in Chapter 4 (see the comparison on page 40).

Surveyors undertaking design

A point of interest to surveyors undertaking design work is that regulation 11(5) requires the designer to take account of the requirements of the *Workplace Regulations* 1992.

These Regulations relate to the safety of the building in use and deal with issues such as ventilation, temperature and lighting, room dimensions and space, provision of safe flooring (non-slip surfaces), windows, skylights and ventilators, and the ability to clean windows safely.

They also cover the provision of safe circulation routes for pedestrians and vehicles whether within the premises (in the case of warehouses or factories) or within the site. Provision of welfare facilities, toilet accommodation, washing facilities, facilities for changing clothing and for rest and to eat meals are also covered in these Regulations. Designers also need to consider the relationship with other Regulations such as Building Regulations, DDA and the new Fire Safety Order (RRFSO).

European initiatives

With health and safety legislation throughout Europe being derived from the *Framework Directive*[17], a number of initiatives have been promoted with the aim of sharing experiences and best practice.

The major initiative has been the launch of the European Week for Safety and Health at Work, which in 2004 focused on the construction industry and was the largest occupational safety and health campaign ever to take place in Europe – with over 30 countries taking part.

This campaign culminated in the 'European Construction Safety Summit'[27] in Bilbao, Spain on 22 November 2004, hosted by the European Agency for Safety and Health at Work. At the summit a number of workshops were held, including those on:

- procurement, design and planning;
- management of occupational safety and health on construction sites; and
- prevention of ill-health problems in construction.

The Bilbao Declaration resulted in the formation of the European Construction Safety Forum (ECSF) comprising the original six signatories and RICS. Members were tasked with making a contribution to health and safety which could be shared by the partners and, more importantly, put in practice across Europe.

A subsequent event held in Brussels on 21 September 2006 at the premises of the European Economic and Social Committee (EESC) provided an opportunity for those involved in the construction sector to report upon progress and achievements since the signing of the Bilbao Declaration in November 2004. The follow-up event *Building in Safety – 2 Years After* was organised by the European Construction Safety Forum (ECSF) and the European Agency for Safety and Health at Work (EASHW). Topics covered included:

- Occupational Safety and Health (OSH) statistics in Europe – the type of accidents and occupational diseases and the differences in accident rates across the enlarged European Union; and
- the principal causes of accidents.

However, it became clear that, because of differences in the way that figures are collected and compiled, it is difficult to arrive at direct comparisons between Member States. For example, figures collected by the International Labour Organisation (ILO) by way of member surveys may differ from the official reported figures – although it is possible to detect trends by either method.

Representatives from the European Construction Safety Forum (ECSF) all spoke on the various partners' contributions since Bilbao, mainly in the form of industry specific guidance (which included the designers' guide noted below).

The partners in the ECSF are: the Architects' Council for Europe (ECA); the European Builders Confederation (EBC); the European Council of Civil Engineers (ECCE); the European Federation of Building and Woodworkers (EFBWW); the European Federation of Engineering Consultancy Associations (EFCA) the European Construction Industry Federation (FIEC) and the Royal Institution of Chartered Surveyors (RICS).

Designers' guide

A useful guide for designers *Designing for Safety in Construction*[28] was produced by the Architects' Council for Europe (ECA) and European Federation of Engineering Consultancy Associations (EFCA).

The publication concentrates on the responsibilities placed by the Directive on designers and provides practical examples which are intended to assist them in complying with their requirements. It includes guidance on general principles of prevention; recording decisions (i.e. how to keep records of the hazards they have identified and how they have dealt with the associated risks); and how information has been passed on to other duty holders, such as contractors.

This broadly covers the same areas as designers are required to deal with in the UK under the CDM Regulations.

Future challenges

One of the major challenges is the expansion of the European Community and the increasing mobility of the labour market. This raises issues of language barriers and common standards. European legislation applies throughout all Member States but standards and local practice vary immensely.

Further initiatives have included a number of conferences specifically targeted at improving health and safety performance in construction following the enlargement of the European Union in 2006 with events in Northern Cyprus and Zagreb.

3 CDM 2007 at a glance

The *Construction (Design and Management) Regulations* 2007 (CDM 2007) came into effect on 6 April 2007. CDM 2007 is structured into five parts:

- **Part 1 – Introduction** Citation and commencement (regulation 1), Interpretation (regulation 2) and Application (regulation 3);
- **Part 2 – General management duties applying to construction projects** (regulations 4 to 13);
- **Part 3 – Additional duties where a project is notifiable** (regulations 14 to 24);
- **Part 4 – Duties relating to health and safety on construction sites** (regulations 25 to 44); and
- **Part 5 – General** Civil liability (regulation 45), Enforcement in respect of fire (regulation 46), Transitional provisions (regulation 47) and Revocations and amendments (regulation 48).

The draft also contains five Schedules (which set out particular administrative requirements):

- **Schedule 1** – Particulars to be notified to the Executive (or Office of Rail Regulation);
- **Schedule 2** – Welfare facilities;
- **Schedule 3** – Particulars to be included in a report of inspection;
- **Schedule 4** – Revocation of instruments; and
- **Schedule 5** – Amendments.

PART 1 – INTRODUCTION

Part 1 follows the usual format for UK legislation and covers:

Regulation
1 Citation and commencement
2 Interpretation
3 Application

Interpretation (regulation 2)

This provides a legal definition of the terms used throughout the Regulations and, in the event of a prosecution or a civil claim, provides the interpretation that would be applied by the courts.

Some of these terms will have been derived from previous legislation and much of the terminology is common to other construction-related legislation but the term 'client' is unique to CDM Regulations: in all other health and safety legislation reference is made to the employer.

It is to this regulation that we look for definitions of terms such as 'construction site', 'construction phase' and 'construction work'. (See the definitions section in Chapter 6 for more detail.)

Regulation 2(3) provides an interpretation as to when a project becomes notifiable:

'… a project is notifiable if the construction phase is likely to involve more than

(a) 30 days; or
(b) 500 person days,
of construction work.'

Additional duties are required in respect of notifiable projects (under Part 3).

Application (regulation 3)

Regulation 3(1) 'These Regulations shall apply (a) in Great Britain; and (b) outside Great Britain [where allowed under] the *Health and Safety at Work etc. Act 1974 (Application Outside Great Britain) Order* 2001.'

Northern Ireland
Northern Ireland has a separate set of legislation with Regulations made under the *Health and Safety at Work (Northern Ireland) Order* 1978. The *Construction (Design and Management) Regulations (Northern Ireland)* 2007 (SR 2007/291) take effect from 9 July 2007.

For information specifically about Northern Ireland, see the contact details in Appendix G: *Useful sources of information.*

PART 2 – GENERAL MANAGEMENT DUTIES APPLYING TO CONSTRUCTION PROJECTS (4–13)

The duties under Part 2 apply:

- to all construction projects, and
- to all duty holders undertaking construction works, i.e. to clients, designers and contractors.

These duties apply whatever the duration, type or size of the project (subject to the definitions of construction site and construction work as set out in regulation 2).

Summary of Part 2 regulations

Regulation
4 Competence
5 Co-operation
6 Co-ordination
7 General principles of prevention
8 Election by clients
9 Client's duty in relation to arrangements for managing projects
10 Client's duty in relation to information
11 Duties of designers
12 Designs prepared or modified outside Great Britain
13 Duties of contractors

The requirements relating to competence, co-operation and co-ordination, and the duties of designers and contractors (covered in Part 2) will apply to all those smaller projects not previously regarded as CDM projects.

For building surveyors this will have an impact on the management of future projects – including external redecoration and repairs of blocks of flats, small extensions and refurbishment projects. In many instances the building surveyor will be deemed to be the designer by virtue of preparation of a specification or bill of quantities and will be required to comply with regulation 11 (Duties of designers), which includes a requirement to be satisfied that the client is aware of its duties under these Regulations. In practice, this may mean that the designer needs to advise the client as to what its duties actually are.

In addition, they need to avoid forseeable risks to the health and safety of any person not just carrying out construction work but also:

- cleaning or maintaining the permanent fixtures and fittings of a structure;
- using a structure designed as a workplace; or
- liable to be affected by such construction work.

Competence

CDM 2007 requires that clients appoint competent companies and individuals to the various duty holder roles – a client should ensure under regulation 4 that 'he has taken reasonable steps to ensure that the person to be appointed or engaged is competent'.

Regulation 4 also applies to any person appointing or engaging another duty holder, such as a designer subcontracting out design work, or a principal contractor engaging other contractors.

Regulation 4(1)(b) places a duty upon any person accepting an appointment or engagement to only accept such an appointment if they are competent to do so.

The ACOP provides relevant information as to the standards required in respect of competence and how the client can carry out an assessment of competence. Duty holders will need to measure their knowledge and experience against the core criteria contained within the ACOP.

All duty holders need to be able to meet these requirements **now**: regulation 4 applies in full for any appointment made since 6 April 2007, when CDM 2007 came into force.

There are special arrangements in force for principal contractors and former planning supervisors whose appointments were already in place – these are covered later under regulation 47 (Transitional provisions).

See Chapter 7 for further information relating to competence.

Client's duties

The role of the client in relation to the new arrangements for managing projects is emphasised by regulation 9 and this demonstrates a significant shift towards making the client more accountable.

The client will need to be more thorough in checking out the arrangements made for managing the health and safety of the project including the allocation of sufficient time and other resources.

In practice many clients will not possess adequate knowledge to undertake their client duties, especially so in the case of 'one-off' clients and will be required to seek the help of 'experts' – which in many cases will be their property advisors.

Regulation 10 deals with the client's duty in relation to information already in his or her possession and information provided by designers. The client is also now required to specify the amount of time which will be allowed for mobilisation.

The pre-construction information will include (as appropriate to the type of project):

- reports on soil investigations and contamination;
- condition surveys relating to structures and buildings – especially important where defects in the structure could result in premature or unintended collapse;
- information relating to adjacent structures or premises which might be affected by the construction works;
- information relating to previous uses of the site, structure, or premises where this is likely to have an effect on the health or safety of those undertaking construction work;
- information relating to the presence of asbestos; and
- information relating to the intended use.

For notifiable projects this information should be passed on to the CDM co-ordinator.

Relevant information should be passed to those who need it: the flow of information should be more focused so that only relevant and useful information is passed on. For example, information regarding ground conditions will be relevant to the structural engineer and ground workers and those involved in the construction of the structural frame, but would not be needed by the fit-out contractors (who may require additional information that will be provided later in the project).

It should be stressed that the **General management duties applying to construction projects** covered under Part 2 apply to **all** construction work (as do the whole of Parts 1, 4 and 5).

For more detail about the role of the client see Chapter 4 *The client*.

PART 3 – ADDITIONAL DUTIES WHERE PROJECT IS NOTIFIABLE (14–24)

Part 3 only applies where a project is notifiable, i.e. if the construction phase is likely to involve more than:

(a) 30 days; or
(b) 500 person days;

of construction work.

Summary of Part 3 Regulations

Regulation
14 Appointments by the client where a project is notifiable
15 Client's duty in relation to information where a project is notifiable
16 The client's duty in relation to the start of the construction phase where a project is notifiable
17 The client's duty in relation to the health and safety file
18 Additional duties of designers
19 Additional duties of contractors
20 General duties of CDM co-ordinators
21 Notification of project by the CDM co-ordinator
22 Duties of the principal contractor
23 The principal contractor's duties in relation to the construction phase plan
24 The principal contractor's duties in relation to co-operation and consultation with workers

Part 3 sets out the additional duties placed upon the **client** (regulations 14, 15, 16 and 17); **designers** (regulation 18), **contractors** (regulation 19), and **principal contractors** (regulations 22, 23 and 24).

Note: Parts 1, 2, and 4 will also apply to any project to which Part 3 applies.

The client's role is extended significantly by CDM 2007 and where a client fails to appoint a CDM

co-ordinator or principal contractor then the client is deemed to be undertaking these roles and performing the duties set out in the Regulations for each of these duty holders. Clients can place themselves at considerable risk where they take on these roles without any knowledge or experience of construction.

These appointments should be confirmed in writing.

PART 4 – DUTIES RELATING TO HEALTH AND SAFETY ON CONSTRUCTION SITES (25–44)

Part 4 of these Regulations basically comprises the former *Construction (Health, Safety and Welfare) Regulations* 1996 which have been transposed into CDM 2007 but with a number of minor changes to both the wording and the order of the previous Regulations.

There are also about a dozen significant amendments to the old CDM Regulations including a new regulation 34 (Energy distribution installations) and the removal of the requirement for demolition works to be supervised by a competent person (although CDM 2007 regulation 4 does require the appointment of competent persons).

Part 4 mainly relates to the control of construction activities and to persons controlling such activities.

Summary of Part 4 Regulations

Regulation
25 Application of regulations 26 to 44
26 Safe places of work
27 Good order and site security
28 Stability of structures
29 Demolition or dismantling
30 Explosives
31 Excavations
32 Cofferdams and caissons
33 Reports of inspections
34 Energy distribution installations
35 Prevention of drowning
36 Traffic routes
37 Vehicles
38 Prevention of risk from fire, etc.
39 Emergency procedures
40 Emergency routes and exits
41 Fire detection and fire-fighting
42 Fresh air
43 Temperature and weather protection
44 Lighting

PART 5 – GENERAL

Summary of Part 5 Regulations

Part 5 follows the usual format for UK legislation and covers:

Regulation
45 Civil liability
46 Enforcement in respect of fire
47 Transitional provisions
48 Revocations and amendments

Civil liability

Regulation 45 covers the extent to which a breach of statutory duty confers a right of action in civil proceedings. The whole question of civil liability is dealt with in Chapter 12.

Fire

Regulation 46 clarifies arrangements in relation to fire legislation.

Transitional provisions

Regulation 47 covers the transitional arrangements, which only apply to the competence requirements relating to CDM co-ordinators and principal contractors in the period up to 6 April 2008 and the phasing out of client agents (where already appointed) in the period leading up to 6 April 2012.

Where a project began before the new CDM Regulations came into force all of the provisions of CDM 2007 shall apply to the project, subject to the modifications allowed for under regulation 47.

CDM co-ordinator and principal contractor

Where any planning supervisor (now CDM co-ordinator) or principal contractor had already been appointed under CDM 1994 then the client is allowed a period of up to 12 months to ensure that the CDM co-ordinator (CDM-C) and principal contractor (PC) are competent within the meaning of regulation 4(2).

Where already appointed under the old Regulations, in the absence of an express appointment by the client, both the CDM-C and the PC shall be treated as having been appointed under CDM 2007, and shall be required to take such steps as are necessary to ensure that they are competent.

These transitional arrangements recognise that additional training may well be required by duty holders to meet the enhanced requirements of the new Regulations.

Client's agent

Any agent already appointed under regulation 4 of CDM 1994 may continue to act as the agent until such time as the project comes to an end (subject to the proviso that such an appointment cannot extend beyond 2012).

The provision for election of an agent by the client has been removed from the new Regulations but clients are still able to enter into contractual arrangements with third parties (the traditional role of chartered surveyors to manage estates and undertake construction works on behalf of their clients remains and is permitted under CDM 2007).

However, such an arrangement does not permit a client to abrogate its criminal liability. In the event that the agent is in breach of the Regulations then the client will still retain responsibility for any breaches of the client's duties.

Revocations and amendments (regulation 48)

Basically this section of the Regulations (and the relevant Schedules) comprises a tidying up exercise whereby other related legislation is amended or earlier legislation is repealed.

It is important that the changes introduced by means of amendments and revocations are understood as they may have a significant impact on the wording or the application of earlier legislation or may completely replace previous legislation.

Revocations

Regulation 48(1) deals with revocations and these are listed in Schedule 4 to the Regulations.

CDM 2007 completely revokes:

- the *Construction (Design and Management) Regulations* 1994;
- the *Construction (Health, Safety and Welfare) Regulations* 1996; and
- the *Construction (Design and Management) (Amendment) Regulations* 2000.

Amendments

Regulation 48(2) deals with amendments to existing legislation and these are listed in Schedule 5.

Most related legislation currently on the statute books has been subjected to amendments, and it is important that the updated versions are used.

4 The client

CLIENT – HEAD OF THE PROCUREMENT CHAIN

As head of the procurement chain the client is in a unique position to influence the way in which the project is run and to establish the right safety culture for both the project team and those undertaking construction works.

The decisions that the client takes can affect everyone in the supply chain and can help to deliver a safer project that is on time and on budget.

The client is able to exert considerable influence and control whatever the size of the project, so it is important that the client understands that decisions made early on in the life of the project will set the tone for the way in which the project works in the later stages.

It is the client who procures the services of the consultants that make up the project team and it is the client who decides the budget and selects the contractors who will undertake the construction works.

This chapter looks at who clients are and the various issues relating to the type of client, funding arrangements, structure of client organisations, the role of their advisors, client agents and the application of CDM.

We also look at the case of domestic clients, who are not deemed to be 'clients' under CDM 2007 and, therefore, do not have any duties under these Regulations.

THE CLIENT HOLDS THE KEY

There can be no doubt that the client holds the key to the success of efforts by the construction industry to reduce the harm that is caused to people.

At the simplest level this is because without the client there would be no construction activity.

It is the importance that clients place on health and safety that determines the culture in the team and therefore the attention paid to health and safety in their work.

That is not to say that clients should not be able to rely on the construction industry to work with procedures and processes that achieve safe and healthy outcomes. However, where clients take an interest in health and safety and set the standard, outcomes for workers and the public are always better.

Clients might express their desired health and safety standards explicitly, but if their actions do not match their words, if they do not 'walk the talk', all the other members of the team will follow the example set and not the clients' words. The client who does not provide adequate health and safety information about the site, brushes aside the design team's concerns about health and safety or turns up on site and walks around in a long overcoat and street shoes undermines any fine words about health and safety!

Of course where clients are explicit about their aspirations **and** follow through with their actions, then those involved in the project will be in no doubt about what is really expected.

Clients on some of the most successful projects, from a health and safety point of view, have made their wishes with respect to health and safety quite clear and then monitored everyone's performance on a regular basis to ensure that their goals were achieved.

Whilst there is no explicit legal requirement on clients to monitor the performance of their service providers, there is an implied requirement in regulation 9(2) and additional expectations contained within the ACOP.

CDM 2007 regulation 9 – Client's duty in relation to arrangements for managing projects
(1) 'Every client shall take reasonable steps to ensure that the arrangements made for managing the project (including the allocation of sufficient time and other resources) by persons with a duty under these Regulations (including the client himself) are suitable to ensure … [the well being of construction workers and the public and any persons using the structure as a workplace and the adequacy of welfare facilities for construction workers]

(2) … are maintained and reviewed throughout the project.'

DEFINITION OF CLIENT

The definition of client provided in regulation 2 is fairly broad, and effectively embraces any company, organisation or individual for whom a construction project is carried out (apart from domestic projects as discussed later in this chapter).

This covers the procurement of any type of construction work from the smallest extension or refurbishment project up to major civil engineering schemes: new build schemes such as shops, warehouses, hospitals or schools; major infrastructure such as railway infrastructure – tunnels and bridges; airport terminals and power stations.

Construction work is defined in the Regulations (regulation 2 – definitions) and the ACOP (paragraphs 13 and 14) contains a list of works which do not fall within the definition, for example, moving demountable partitions.

A client is defined under regulation 2(1) as

'a person who in the course or furtherance of a business:
(a) seeks or accepts the services of another which may be used in the carrying out of a project for him; or
(b) carries out a project himself.'

Identification of the client (or clients) is required at an early stage in the project because they will need to be identified on the *F10 Notification of construction project* that is submitted to the Health and Safety Executive. A declaration by the client that he or she is aware of his or her duties under CDM is now a requirement under CDM 2007 (regulation 21 and Schedule 1).

It is the client who takes on the duties under Part 2 of CDM 2007 for all construction projects, regardless of size of the project, and, where a project is notifiable (i.e. likely to involve more than 30 days; or 500 person days) the additional duties under Part 3. (For more information see Section 2, *F10 Notification of construction project* in Chapter 9 *Provision of information*.)

Client duties under CDM 2007

PART 2 – General management duties applying to construction projects
8 Election by clients
9 Client's duty in relation to arrangements for managing projects
10 Client's duty in relation to information

PART 3 – Additional duties where project is notifiable
14 Appointments by the client where a project is notifiable
15 Client's duty in relation to information where a project is notifiable
16 The client's duty in relation to the start of construction phase where a project is notifiable
17 The client's duty in relation to the health and safety file

Regulation 9 – Client's duty in relation to arrangements for managing projects
Regulation 9(1) 'Every client shall take reasonable steps to ensure that the arrangements made for managing the project (including the allocation of sufficient time and other resources) … are suitable to ensure that:

(a) the construction work can be carried out so far as is reasonably practicable without risk to the safety of any person;
(b) the requirements of Schedule 2 [Welfare facilities] are complied with … ; and
(c) any structure designed for use as a workplace has been designed taking account of the provisions of the [*Workplace Regulations 1992*] which relate to the design of, and materials used in, the structure.'

Although the *Workplace Regulations* 1992 have been in force for 15 years and designers should already have been aware of their requirements, regulation 9(c) now makes this an explicit duty.

Regulation 10 – Client's duty in relation to information
10(2) 'The pre-construction information shall consist of all the information in the client's possession (or which is reasonably obtainable), including:

(a) any information about or affecting the site or the construction work;
(b) any information concerning the proposed use of the structure as a workplace;
(c) the minimum amount of time before the construction phase which will be allowed to the contractors appointed by the client for planning and preparation for construction work; and
(d) any information in any existing health and safety file, …'

Identifying the client

It is important that the client for any particular project is properly identified because it is that person who takes on the responsibilities and duties under the CDM Regulations for that project, and in addition any responsibilities and duties under other relevant health and safety legislation.

This will include, where applicable, the 'employer' duties under the *Health and Safety at Work etc. Act 1974* (HASAW 1974) and the *Management of Health and Safety at Work Regulations* 1999 (*Management Regulations 1999*), both of which are all embracing.

As noted earlier, the definition of client is fairly broad and potentially any business or organisation can be involved at some stage as a client for whom construction work is carried out.

The definition of client can include:

- individuals and partnerships, limited companies and corporations;
- the private and public sectors, development agencies, trustees and charitable organisations;
- the regular client; and
- the one-off client.

In recent years numerous methods of financing development schemes evolved, including Private Finance Initiative (PFI), Public Private Partnership (PPP) and a number of Special Purpose Vehicle (SPV) schemes.

Increasingly works in the public sector are being handed over to agencies (such as the Highways Agency) which are one step removed from central government. There is also increased involvement from regional development agencies.

With diverse sources of funding and a multitude of agencies and special purpose vehicles for effecting the development, it is often difficult to establish who the client should be.

CDM 2007 does not permit the appointment of a client's agent, but does allow election by clients where there is more than one client involved in a project (see *Election by clients* later in this chapter).

ALLOCATION OF RESOURCES

The other actions by clients that underpin their aspirations for health and safety on a project are how the two most important resources in the industry, time and money, are allocated.

Clients need to be clear from the start how much time and money they are prepared to expend on their project, i.e. their capital investment, and accept the constraints that these place on what can be achieved.

It should be remembered that the consideration of time and money should not be solely in relation to the construction phase – the build.

Adequate resources need to be provided for the team that are interpreting the client's aspirations and providing the definition information from which the structure can be built.

If these are in short supply the client will not get a satisfactory outcome.

It is all too easy to focus on getting the job done, the actual construction work, and to forget about the value that good design, health and safety co-ordination, planning and preparation can bring to a project.

> As the oft quoted Sir John Harvey Jones pointed out, doing is often much more fun than planning and often comes more naturally.

Lessons can be learned from the rail industry where many months of planning are required to programme and organise a planned possession of the rail infrastructure. For major projects, such as the Trent Valley Project (where 12 miles of railway are being four tracked) the planning phase has spanned several years, with possessions being planned up to two years in advance. In addition to laying 12 miles of new track, the scheme has involved the replacement of bridges over roads, rivers and canals, and has required meticulous planning in order to achieve the project objectives.

Good planning and good project management are essential tools for the provision of successful projects but such resources need to be provided at the front end of projects and allowed for in the overall budget.

ELECTION BY CLIENTS

CDM 2007 recognises the fact that for some construction projects there may well be several clients involved in the scheme and allows for these clients to elect one or more of those clients to be treated as the client for the purpose of these Regulations.

Such election must be in writing (as required under regulation 8).

The elected client(s) will be subject to all of the client duties: those who have opted out will only be subject to the duties to supply information in their possession under regulations 5(1)(b) Co-operation, 10(1) Client's duty in relation to information, and 17(1) The client's duty in relation to the health and safety file.

The option for election applies to all construction projects regardless of size and whether or not they are notifiable.

Case study – village store

The local village store and post office was taken over by a consortium of villagers when it was threatened with closure – with a number of people having a stake in the business.

A small group of villagers are involved in the overall strategy of the business but the day-to-day running of the store has been delegated to the manager.

An extension was required in order to expand the business and provide additional trading space. A retired accountant was elected to undertake the client role and manage the project.

Notifiable projects

For notifiable projects it is important that the client duty to appoint a CDM co-ordinator is discharged at the appropriate time: clients should not delay such appointments, even where they intend to make an election under regulation 8.

Special Purpose Vehicles

In the case of Special Purpose Vehicles (SPVs), such as PFI, PPP and similar forms of procurement, the role and responsibilities of the client can be transferred at various stages as the project proceeds.

The project originator is legally the *client* at the start of the project and should ensure that:

● a CDM co-ordinator is appointed; and
● the *F10 Notification of construction project* is completed; and
● the HSE is notified during the early design and specification phase.

The project originator cannot wait until someone else takes over the client role.

Paragraph 40 of the ACOP provides additional guidance:

'The role and responsibilities of the client can transfer from one party to another as the project proceeds. This is normally the case when the SPV is appointed to carry out detailed specification and delivery of the project. Any such transfer should:

(a) be clear to, and agreed by all those involved;
(b) be clearly recorded;
(c) provide the practical authority to discharge the client's duties.

If the project originator does not wish to remain a client in respect of the Regulations after the SPV has been appointed, they should make use of the election facility in regulation 8.

Without such an election, the project originator may retain some client responsibilities.'

Multiple clients – other examples

More conventional forms of procurement often involve more than one client, and where one or more 'partners' in the development are not directly involved in the day-to-day running of the scheme the election facility provides the obvious route for the 'sleeping partners'.

Case study – town centre, multiple parties

A major town centre development involved multiple parties (some of whom were existing landowners but did not wish to have a financial involvement other than their ownership of the site). It also involved several developers for different parts of the scheme (retail, leisure and residential) as well as alterations and improvements to the highways under a Section 106 Agreement (including new cycle lanes, pavings, traffic lights, etc.).

One developer took on the role of client, although responsibility to provide existing information about the site still resided with the original landowners who provided information that was already in their possession about asbestos, ground contamination and existing services.

Case study – multiple projects in a school

A scenario that often arises is where several projects take place at the same time.

● Major works may be undertaken in an educational establishment during the school holidays, funded and managed by the local authority with a scheme drawn up and tendered and due to start on the first day of the school summer holiday.
● At the same time regular maintenance works may be scheduled for the boilers, while a deep clean by a separate firm of specialist cleaners has been scheduled in other parts of the building.
● The school may also have arranged for a volunteer force to come in at the same time to redecorate some of the classrooms.

In this type of scenario the issue is one of control of the various contractors who will be working independently in the same premises.

The ultimate client needs to be quite clear as to how the various contractors will be managed.

> The aim must be for each individual contractor to be contained within their own designated area – where this cannot be achieved other options must be considered.
>
> It might be feasible for the principal contractor to take possession of the whole of the construction site and then programme the works of the various contractors to avoid potential conflicts and provide a proper sequence to avoid interference and duplication of effort. Issues such as control of access, security and separation of work areas would all need to be taken into consideration.

Where doubt remains as to who is legally the client then paragraph 41 of the ACOP provides the following guidelines.

'Take into account who:
(a) ultimately decides what is to be constructed, where, when and by whom;
(b) commissions the design and construction work ..;
(c) initiates the work;
(d) is at the head of the procurement chain;
(e) engages the contractors.'

Where it is not immediately obvious who is legally the client, then all of the possible clients who might be involved in the development can appoint one of them as the only client for the purposes of CDM 2007.

Key points
- Liability only moves after election.
- Preceding liability remains.
- Client duties under 5(1)(b), 10(1) and 17(1) continue.
- An **audit** trail should be established to document what actions were taken.

CLIENTS – TAKING ON ADDITIONAL DUTIES

It should be noted that clients can take on additional responsibilities either intentionally or unwittingly, in the following circumstances:
- Designer – if clients specify materials or methods of working they may well be construed as having taken on a designer role and responsibilities in accordance with CDM 2007.
- Contractors – where clients directly manage or carry out construction work they will be deemed to take on the contractor role and responsibilities.

Liability under other legislation

Other health and safety legislation, such as HASAW 1974 and the *Management Regulations* 1999, also applies, whether or not the client has taken advantage of the client election provisions under regulation 8.

The election by clients only relates to duties under CDM 2007 – it does not relate to any other duties or responsibilities, such as those that apply under sections 2, 3 and 4 of HASAW 1974.

Clients should be aware of their general duties under the Act and ensure that their activities take account of them – see below for an outline of duties under sections 2, 3 and 4 of HASAW 1974.

It should be noted that HASAW 1974 and most Regulations refer to employers, employees and the self-employed rather than clients, contractors, and designers.

Section 4 of HASAW 1974 refers to those having control of premises or undertakings; which may introduce other parties, for example, managing agents or landlords into the equation.

The CDM Regulations are unique in only referring to 'duty holders' although it should be pointed out that each of the duty holders can also be employers (or self-employed) at the same time as they are fulfilling their roles and duties under CDM.

For example, the main contractor would be appointed and take on the role of 'principal contractor' under CDM, where the project is notifiable, but would also undertake duties as an employer under HASAW 1974 and other legislation.

The HSE considers – in the *Regulatory Impact Assessment* (RIA) – that CDM 2007 strengthens the role of the client in ensuring that suitable health and safety management arrangements remain in place throughout the life of the project.

The changes invoked by regulation 9 make existing duties under HASAW 1974 and the *Management Regulations* 1999 more explicit, in that they put a duty on the client to take reasonable steps to ensure that there are, and continue to be, suitable management arrangements to ensure health, safety and welfare on site, and that the design of any structure intended as a workplace complies with the *Workplace Regulations* 1992.

> *HASAW 1974*
>
> Section 2 – General duties of employers to their employees
> '2(1) It shall be the duty of every employer to ensure, so far as is reasonably practicable, the health, safety and welfare at work of all his employees.
>
> 2(2) Without prejudice to the generality of an employer's duty under the preceding subsection, the matters to which that duty extends include in particular:
>
> (a) the provision and maintenance of plant and systems of work that are, so far as is reason-

ably practicable, safe and without risks to health;

(b) arrangements for ensuring, so far as is reasonably practicable, safety and absence of risks to health in connection with the use, handling, storage and transport of articles and substances;

(c) the provision of such information, instruction, training and supervision as is necessary to ensure, so far as is reasonably practicable, the health and safety at work of his employees;

(d) so far as is reasonably practicable as regards any place of work under the employer's control, the maintenance of it in a condition that is safe and without risks to health and the provision and maintenance of means of access to and egress from it that are safe and without such risks;

(e) the provision and maintenance of a working environment for his employees that is, so far as is reasonably practicable, safe, without risks to health, and adequate as regards facilities and arrangements for their welfare at work.

...'

Section 3 – General duties of employers and self-employed to persons other than their employees

'3(1) It shall be the duty of every employer to conduct his undertaking in such a way as to ensure, so far as is reasonably practicable, that persons not in his employment who may be affected thereby are not thereby exposed to risks to their health or safety.

...'

Section 4 relates to the general duties of persons concerned with premises to persons other than their own employees. This covers the duties and obligations of those persons having control of the premises to ensure that the premises and the means of access are safe and without risks to health.

THE CLIENT ORGANISATION – ARRANGEMENTS AND PROCEDURES

This section examines what arrangements the client organisation should have in place in order to discharge its own duties as an employer under general health and safety legislation and in the role as client under CDM.

There is a clear requirement under regulation 9 (Client's duty in relation to arrangements for managing projects) for the client to ensure that suitable arrangements are in place for managing the project and that these arrangements are maintained and reviewed throughout the project.

The ACOP refers to the client in the broadest terms, and acknowledges the fact that clients might be organisations or individuals, but does not offer much of an insight as to how individual companies or organisations should manage their own affairs: these fall within the scope of their own policy arrangements under the *Management Regulations* 1999.

It is important that the client has adequate management arrangements and procedures in place for dealing with the procurement of construction work: this should include all planning, design, management or other work involved in a project from inception until the end of the construction phase (as required under CDM 2007) and for the continuing occupation and, where applicable, the use of the premises or structure after completion of the construction project.

All companies should have a Health and Safety Policy, which should include the arrangements and procedures for purchasing and procurement of goods and services; and for control of contractors working within the companies' premises. It should also set out the organisational arrangements which identify who within the organisation is responsible for each of these areas.

In practice many companies do not have clear arrangements in place – especially where the procurement of construction works falls outside the core activities of the business. In many cases there is no explicit management process for dealing with CDM projects: without a clear command structure and defined roles and responsibilities it is difficult to achieve a successful outcome to the project.

Where management arrangements and procedures are inadequate, the level of exposure to risk increases: this applies to all types of risks including financial and industrial relations (including exposure to claims for discrimination), as well as health and safety.

Client representative

In order to discharge CDM duties effectively most organisations will need to identify an individual from within the organisation who is empowered to undertake the client role on behalf of the organisation with an adequate level of authority and access to resources.

How this is achieved will vary from company to company: depending upon the size and organisation. It may be the managing director in the case of a smaller organisation, or a project manager in the case of a larger company, public body or other organisation.

It is important that the person undertaking this role has an understanding of the duties imposed upon the client organisation under both CDM 2007 and other health and safety legislation. This person should also act as the interface between the client organisation and the rest of the project team.

Although the CDM co-ordinator is required to give suitable and sufficient advice and assistance to the client in respect of the measures required in order to undertake the project, this advice is limited to compliance with the requirements of CDM and should not be extended to advising the company or organisation on how to conduct its own business activities. The CDM co-ordinator does, however, need to have an appreciation of the business activities, the client brief for the project and the impact of the project on the operation of the business where works are being undertaken within the client's premises.

Where the arrangements for achieving compliance with CDM 2007 are not clearly set out in the Company Health and Safety Policy or in procedures documentation then it would be advisable to clearly set out the terms of reference for the person undertaking the role of client for the purpose of these Regulations.

Sponsors and nominated responsible person(s)

There are alternative models to those cited above that would allow a company or organisation to discharge its duties under CDM 2007, including the designation of sponsors (i.e. the department or part of the organisation that creates the demand for a building or structure) and nominated responsible persons (i.e. those appointed from within the organisation who would ensure that the client duties were complied with).

The sponsors would have control of the project brief and the budget but would delegate powers to the nominated responsible person(s) to ensure that company policy and procedures were being followed.

Other alternatives include outsourcing the client role to an external resource (such as a project manager or client's agent) who would undertake the tasks on behalf of the client.

However, the client still retains legal responsibility (see the section dealing with the client agent below).

Where an organisation has a large estate or number of properties to manage it is likely to have its own estates department which will deal with CDM projects or a managing agent who will deal with any construction-related project.

CLIENT AGENT

Historically, many chartered surveyors have been involved in the management of estates and have acted in the capacity of 'agent'.

In the case of large rural estates, the 'agent' would effectively run the estate and be in charge of the day-to-day management. Nowadays a lot of this work is carried out by professional practices who nevertheless act in the capacity of an agent.

There are also large urban estates, especially in London, such as those owned by the Duke of Westminster, and the Howard de Walden and Cadogan

estates. In addition, there are large numbers of residential properties, especially blocks of flats, which are managed by professional firms engaged as managing agents.

In each of the above cases the agent will be engaged in the day-to-day management of the estates, including works of repair and maintenance, improvements and larger capital schemes.

Much of this work will come within the scope of the CDM Regulations and the professional agent will effectively manage the scheme, often without any real reference to the client (or landowner/freeholder).

Client agent under CDM 1994

The previous Regulations, CDM 1994, allowed the client to appoint an agent to undertake the client role on his or her behalf and limit to a certain extent the criminal liability attached to the client role. However, these provisions were subject to a certain amount of misunderstanding in that the responsibilities placed upon clients under other legislation remained in place. (For further detail see *Client's agent under CDM 1994* below.)

Position under CDM 2007

The provisions for the appointment of a client agent are not included in CDM 2007 but clients are still at liberty to enter into contractual arrangements for the appointment of an agent.

Where the remit of the agent is extensive and effectively grants that agent day-to-day control of the estate, the landowner or owner of the estate is still identified as the client for the purposes of the CDM Regulations and cannot abrogate its duties and responsibilities under these Regulations.

It should also be made clear that the appointment of a CDM co-ordinator does not absolve a client of its liabilities either: the Directive 92/57/EEC, *Temporary or Mobile Construction Sites* is quite clear on this point in Article 7, paragraph 1, stating that where a person responsible for co-ordination is appointed, the project supervisor or client remains responsible for safety and health.

In other words the client is unable to escape CDM duties and liabilities by appointing a CDM co-ordinator or an 'agent'.

Client's agent under CDM 1994

Generally in UK criminal law, criminal liabilities cannot be transferred from one party to another by a civil contract but the client's agent provision allowed this to happen in respect of client's duties under CDM, i.e. it allowed the transfer of criminal liability in respect of the client's duties under CDM from one party (the client) to another (the client's agent).

Although the client's criminal liabilities under CDM were transferred when the client's agent provision was used, criminal liabilities arising under other legislation (e.g. under sections 3 and 4 of HASAW 1974 and under the *Management Regulations* 1999) **were not transferred**. So, some clients may have thought (erroneously) that, having appointed an agent, they no longer had any criminal liabilities in relation to a project.

The removal of the client's agent provision simply removes the ability for clients to transfer their criminal liabilities under CDM to a third party, thus bringing CDM into line with all other health and safety legislation.

This does not prevent clients from appointing a third party to discharge their duties. A client can still appoint a third party to 'manage' construction work on its behalf, but the client will still be criminally liable under CDM for failure to discharge the duties.

Client advisor

In practice many clients will already have a team of professional advisors who provide advice on an ongoing basis, and many existing professional relationships will allow the client to deal with CDM projects without the necessity of venturing outside of his or her established team.

Clients with extensive property portfolios or interests will often already have chartered surveyors dealing with their day-to-day business requirements and similar relationships with financial and legal advisors.

However, for many, especially for the inexperienced or one-off client, access to good professional advice might either be unavailable or not sought.

It is important that they are pointed in the right direction and that the initial source of advice has sufficient knowledge of legislation to alert clients to the need to comply with CDM 2007.

(See also Chapter 5 *Getting a project started*.)

Where a client initially seeks advice from a designer then it is to be anticipated that, at some stage, the client will be made aware of the requirements of the CDM Regulations.

Where the project is notifiable, i.e. it is likely to be for more than 30 days (or more than 500 person days), the client will need to appoint a CDM co-ordinator in accordance with the client duties under regulation 14.

THE CDM CO-ORDINATOR

For a lot of projects a client will be able to rely upon advice from traditional advisors and for Part 2 projects (i.e. those of short duration and therefore falling within the non-notifiable category) this is likely to be the case.

However, for Part 3 projects the client is able to call upon advice and assistance from the CDM co-ordinator – a new role created under CDM 2007 which replaces the old planning supervisor under CDM 1994.

This new role is more in line with the Directive requirements but does not split the role into the design stage and the construction phase (as is more commonly the case in the rest of Europe).

Article 2 sets out the requirements relating to the co-ordinator role (see below). This is the model followed throughout the rest of Europe and also in the new CDM Regulations recently introduced in Eire.

By splitting the role the problems associated with trying to find an individual, or organisation, that has expertise in the areas of design, construction and health and safety are lessened: the initial role being fulfilled by those with more bias towards design; the construction phase being dealt with by those from a construction background.

It should perhaps be noted that where design is ongoing during the construction phase the original design stage co-ordinator still carries on with this role, even though the construction phase co-ordinator has been appointed.

> *Directive 92/57/EEC requirements – Article 2*
> *Definitions*
> '(e) "co-ordinator for safety and health matters at the project preparations stage" means any natural or legal person entrusted by the client and/or project supervisor, during preparation of the project design, with performing the duties referred to in Article 5;
> (f) "co-ordinator for safety and health matters at the project execution stage" means any natural or legal person entrusted by the client and/or project supervisor, during execution of the project, with performing the duties referred to in Article 6.'

The CDM co-ordinator role

This section looks at what role the CDM co-ordinator fulfils under UK legislation.

Paragraph 84 of the ACOP states:

'The role of the CDM co-ordinator is to provide the client with a key project advisor in respect of construction health and safety risk management matters. They should assist and advise the client on appointment of competent contractors and the adequacy of management arrangements; ensure proper co-ordination of the health and safety aspects of the design process; facilitate good communication and co-operation between project team members and prepare the health and safety file.'

In paragraph 85, the ACOP recognises the importance of appointing the CDM co-ordinator at an early stage:

'through early involvement with clients and designers, a CDM co-ordinator can make a significant contribution to reducing risks to workers during construction, and to contractors and end users who work on or in the structure after construction.'

However, the contribution that can be made by the CDM co-ordinator is to a certain extent dependent upon the timing of the appointment.

Regulation 14(1) only requires that the CDM-C is appointed: '... as soon as is practicable after initial design work or other preparations for construction work have begun.'

It should be noted that until such time as this appointment has been made the client retains the role (see also Chapter 5 *Getting a project started*).

The later the appointment the less opportunity there is to influence the design, especially with regard to such matters as the building footprint, the location of a new structure in relation to its surroundings or to consider complex access issues. (Access may be a considerable issue in its own right. See the section on access rights in Chapter 5.)

As the design moves into the detailed design stages, or obtains planning consent, it becomes increasingly difficult, both for the design team and the CDM co-ordinator, to make fundamental changes.

Case study – retail unit

The initial design for a new purpose-built retail unit on a retail park located the store and warehouse adjacent to a railway line at the rear of the site in order to maximise the car parking provision at the front of the building.

This design created problems with the siting of cranes and a requirement for piling close to the rail infrastructure. Network Rail were unhappy with proposals for the piling rig to be working so close to the railway and the risks associated with plant and equipment overturning or otherwise falling onto the track and live overhead line equipment.

The CDM co-ordinator (or planning supervisor in this case) pointed out the merits of moving the building away from the rear boundary, closer to the front of the site.

This reduced the potential for risks to the rail infrastructure and also facilitated a one-way traffic

---

system for deliveries around [...] (by creating a new access ro[...] line of construction and the [...] segregated customers from d[...] deliveries were taking place.

The amount of available [...] remained the same but the new design provided a very real benefit in making the whole layout much safer and avoiding the requirement for delivery vehicles to reverse in an area accessible to the public.

What do CDM co-ordinators do?

A brief description of the role of the CDM co-ordinator (or CDM-C), as described in paragraph 84 ACOP, has already been provided above, and is covered in more detail as we progress through the various project stages.

The **main duties** of the CDM-C are covered by regulations 20 (General duties of CDM co-ordinators) and 21 (Notification of the project by the CDM co-ordinator). Primarily the role is to advise and assist the client in the furtherance of the client duties, as set out in paragraph 90 of the ACOP.

Regulation 20(1)(a) is fairly wide ranging:

'The CDM co-ordinator shall: give suitable and sufficient advice and assistance to the client on undertaking the measures he needs to take to comply with these Regulations during the project (including, in particular, assisting the client in complying with regulations 9 and 16);'.

Regulation 9 covers the client's duty in relation to arrangements for managing projects and regulation 16 covers the client's duty in relation to the start of the construction phase where a project is notifiable.

It is perhaps worth reminding readers that these measures include all of the client's duties as set out in both Part 2 and Part 3 of the CDM Regulations, i.e. both non-notifiable projects and those which are notifiable.

CDM-C summary of duties
Paragraph 90 of the ACOP states:

'CDM co-ordinators must:
(a) give suitable and sufficient advice and assistance to clients in order to help them to comply with their duties, in particular:
   (i) the duty to appoint competent designers and contractors; and
   (ii) the duty to ensure that adequate arrangements are in place for managing the project;
(b) notify HSE about the project (see paragraphs 15–19);

(c) co-ordinate design work, planning and other preparation for construction where relevant to health and safety;

(d) identify and collect the pre-construction information and advise the client if surveys need to be commissioned to fill significant gaps;

(e) promptly provide in a convenient form to those involved with the design of the structure; and to every contractor (including the principal contractor) who may be or has been appointed by the client, such parts of the preconstruction information which are relevant to each;

(f) manage the flow of health and safety information between clients, designers and contractors;

(g) advise the client on the suitability of the initial construction phase plan and the arrangements made to ensure that welfare facilities are on site from the start;

(h) produce or update a relevant, user friendly, health and safety file suitable for future use at the end of the construction phase.'

Who can undertake the role?

The CDM co-ordinator needs to be in a position to advise the client on various aspects of design, construction procurement and the construction process and have a knowledge of health and safety in construction.

As construction covers such a vast and diverse range – from the smallest extension and refurbishment projects up to major civil engineering projects such as the construction of new power stations or river crossings – it is apparent that the role needs to be fulfilled by someone with knowledge and experience in the specific sector of construction relating to the project being planned or carried out.

These issues and the question of competence are dealt with in Chapter 7.

PROFESSIONAL CLIENTS

Framework agreements

Framework agreements are now an accepted method of procurement, especially for organisations that generate a significant flow of projects over a given timescale.

A framework agreement enables the client to call off individual projects or packages of work as and when required throughout the lifetime of the agreement.

The number of contractors or suppliers involved in the framework agreement can vary to suit the circumstances as can the amount of work given to each contractor. The type and scale of the work can vary from routine maintenance and repairs up to major capital projects.

References and competency assessments should be undertaken as an initial part of the process and theoretically all contractors and suppliers included in the framework agreement will meet the assessment criteria.

However, there is a need to monitor the performance of any contractor where long term framework agreements are involved. This is evident from the experience on the railways – in recent years Network Rail has been forced to suspend or terminate the services of a number of contractors involved in routine maintenance works on the railway.

Clients need to monitor the performance of their contractors. In the event that clear evidence presents itself that the contractors are no longer compliant with their health and safety obligations, clients must take action.

DEVELOPERS

Developers clearly come within the scope of clients under regulation 2, whether they are involved with a one-off development, a residential refurbishment project, or the construction of a new industrial estate for let or sale.

Residential developments

In residential developments where individual properties are sold during the course of the development, the developer effectively remains as the client until such time as the properties are sold and purchasers take possession.

Purchasers in these circumstances do not take on the client role or responsibilities even where they have entered into a contract to purchase before the construction works are complete.

However, private individuals who 'dabble' in property (i.e. get involved with development as a business venture) and procure construction works will find that they **do** fall within the definition of a client and therefore take on the client role for the purpose of the Regulations.

Commercial developments

With commercial developments, units are often sold before the overall scheme is completed and the purchasers or tenants (in the case of both freehold and leasehold premises) may wish to take possession and enter the premises for the purpose of carrying out fit-out works.

In these cases they would become clients where the fit-out works are classified as construction works, and

the fit-out project become notifiable where it exceeds the threshold requirements.

Where builders take on the role of developer (builder-developer) then they can end up taking on all or some of the CDM duty holder roles, i.e. client, principal contractor, designer and CDM co-ordinator. Where this is the case they must comply with CDM 2007 for each of their respective roles.

Industry pressures

Clients are exposed to pressures from a number of sources including:

- planning;
- financial;
- legal;
- stakeholder; and/or
- Environment Agency.

Each of these can place restrictions and constraints upon the client and also expose the client to potential risk.

Take **planning** for example. Planners can place constraints upon the design through considerations such as height and massing of the building, treatment of elevations, the nature, type and size of components such as balconies, balustrading and handrails, or window openings and roofs. In the case of listed structures or buildings in conservation areas, the constraints can be more restrictive

CDM 2007 now changes the position inasmuch as planners are still able to dictate certain matters as long as they relate to planning matters within their statutory powers. Where they exceed their powers they are at risk of taking on liabilities under CDM for design.

Case study – listed property

In a Grade 1 listed property, used for commercial purposes, the balustrading to the balcony on the staircase at second floor level was only at waist height and well below the requirements of current legislation (*Building Regulations* and the *Workplace Regulations* 1992).

English Heritage would not permit any additional safety features, e.g. raising the height of the balustrade or providing a safety net within the stairwell.

In these circumstances English Heritage are influencing the design, by placing constraints on the project that affect health and safety and would therefore be deemed to take on design responsibilities under CDM 2007.

DOMESTIC CLIENTS

Domestic clients are a special case and do not have duties under CDM 2007.

The definition of a client under regulation 2 (Interpretation) makes specific reference to the client's activities being 'in the course or furtherance of a business', thereby excluding domestic householders as CDM duty holders.

Paragraphs 29–32 of the ACOP provide further clarification and confirm that domestic clients are not required to appoint a CDM co-ordinator or principal contractor for domestic work, even if the project is of such a size and duration to meet the normal threshold for notification.

Interestingly, contractors are no longer required to notify HSE of domestic projects even where under the old CDM 1994 such projects would have been notifiable by the contractor.

However, domestic property, including single occupation dwellings and flats can come within the full remit of CDM 2007 if owned by local authorities, housing associations, charities, or landlords with tenanted premises: these are all deemed to be clients whose activities are carried out 'in the course of or furtherance of a business'.

Leaseholders

Another group that is caught up in the umbrella of CDM is the otherwise domestic client who is a leaseholder of a flat and has formed a company jointly with the other leaseholders (normally jointly owning the freehold interest) to undertake maintenance of the common parts or elements of the structure.

As shareholders of the 'company' they are no longer deemed to enjoy exemption from the client duties and responsibilities. This will be the case even where the property is managed on their behalf by a managing agent or the construction works are administered on their behalf by a chartered surveyor or other construction professional.

Self-build schemes

In the case of self-build schemes the application of CDM will depend upon the way in which the scheme has been put together and the contractual arrangements for letting out the works packages.

Generally, unless the domestic 'client' is intending to sell, let out or use the property for commercial purposes, i.e. is involved in a business or undertaking, then he or she will be regarded as a domestic client and will not attract any duties under CDM 2007.

Domestic clients may hire contractors and designers as required in order to progress the scheme without attracting any client duties under CDM. They may also undertake work on someone else's plot in exchange for services, goods or money without attracting any client duties. However, in this scenario, those engaged in carrying out work in exchange for services, goods or money would be regarded as contractors, i.e. involved in an undertaking, and would attract duties under both CDM and general health and safety legislation.

Where there is a mix of those intending to build for their own occupation and those intending to build for sale, it is possible to have both CDM clients and domestic clients within the same scheme. The former will attract duties as a client under CDM but the latter will not.

Where domestic clients register for VAT in order to claim back the VAT element on purchases of materials then, provided they are not trading, then they would remain as domestic clients.

Where individuals or groups of individuals register for VAT purposes with the intention of trading then they would become clients within the meaning of client under regulation 2 (Interpretation) and would attract client duties under Part 2 of the CDM Regulations.

Where the construction works are likely to last more than 30 days then the additional duties under Part 3 would also apply.

Note: There is no definition of 'domestic client' under regulation 2.

The advice must be for each individual scheme to be assessed on its individual merits: where there is any doubt the advice of the HSE should be sought.

The European Directive – treatment of domestic clients

The intention of Directive 92/57/EEC is that where two or more contractors are involved in construction work on a given site, one contractor needs to take control of the site and provide effective management for the construction process.

Where the construction works are significant and involve works such as demolition, deep excavations for sewer connections or for underpinning of existing foundations, then it would seem reasonable for the requirements of the Directive to be implemented. See Annex II below.

UK derogation for domestic clients

The Directive allows for Member States to allow derogations in respect of the provisions under Article 3, i.e. the appointment of co-ordinators and the requirement to draw up a health and safety plan, except where the work concerned involves particular risks as listed in Annex II.

Directive 92/57/EEC Annex II
'1. Work which puts workers at risk of burial under earthfalls, engulfment in swampland or falling from a height, where the risk is particularly

aggravated by the nature of the work or processes used or by the environment at the place of work or site.

2. Work which puts workers at risk from chemical or biological substances constituting a particular danger to the safety and health of workers or involving a legal requirement for health monitoring.

3. Work with ionising radiation requiring the designation of controlled or supervised areas as defined in Article 20 of Directive 80/836/Euratiom.

4. Work near high voltage power lines.

5. Work exposing workers to the risk of drowning.

6. Work on wells, underground earthworks and tunnels.

7. Work carried out by [divers] having a system of air supply.

8. Work carried out by workers in caisson with a compressed-air atmosphere.

9. Work involving the use of explosives.

10. Work involving the assembly or dismantling of heavy prefabricated components.'

Most domestic projects, (e.g. small house extensions or internal remodelling of kitchens and bathrooms) would not involve such high risk activities, although it is quite possible for domestic projects to be located close to water or high voltage power lines.

Even in these cases, the UK legislation does not require the domestic client to appoint a CDM co-ordinator or prepare a plan.

The ACOP, at paragraph 31, confirms that there is no legal requirement for the appointment of a CDM co-ordinator or principal contractor when a domestic project reaches the notification threshold.

Case studies A and B below indicate the criteria that apply to distinguish between domestic and non-domestic projects.

In addition, the ACOP confirms that contractors are not required to notify the HSE of construction work for domestic clients, even if the project is large enough to reach the notification threshold.

However, in paragraph 21 the ACOP does recognise that where such high-risk activities occur there might be a need for a written plan (similar to the construction phase plan) in order to achieve a more rigorous approach to co-ordination, co-operation and planning by contractors involved with the project (but even here the client has no duties under CDM 2007).

Case study – domestic case A

This case study concerned a country residence occupied by the building owner and his family and involved extensive construction works to extend the existing dwelling, construct a swimming pool and create additional accommodation for the use of staff employed by the family.

The existing residence comprised a large country house with numerous outbuildings, stables and grounds of some 15 acres or more and the proposed works were programmed to last for 36 weeks at a cost of £2.5 million.

The building owner employed six staff including gardeners, chauffeur and housekeeper: all of the staff wages were paid from the owner's own income but did attract PAYE and NI, although they were regarded as domestic staff.

Although the construction works were extensive and lasted for about nine months the project was regarded as domestic and the owner was not regarded as a client under CDM.

The architect and the contractor were duty holders under CDM and had to comply with the regulations and the Part 4 duties applied in full during the actual construction works.

Case study – domestic case B

A similar project on a smaller estate of only 5 acres was undertaken by the same designer and contractor the following year on the recommendation of the building owner to one of his close neighbours.

However, in this case the building owner ran a successful livery stable with a small shop selling equine supplies to the general public.

The staff accommodation was for the use of the shop manager and various staff employed by the business who were therefore not regarded as domestic staff

The construction works involving the staff accommodation were clearly for the benefit of the business, the cost of these works being met by the business and included in the accounts, as were the ongoing costs of repairs and maintenance.

This part of the work, i.e. the staff accommodation was considered to be in connection with the business and therefore attracted client duties under Part 2 of the Regulations. Because the work took longer than 30 days the project was notifiable and therefore Part 3 duties also applied: the client appointing a principal contractor and CDM-C for this section of the works.

The domestic parts of the project, e.g. the swimming pool and extension to the house were not considered to be commercial in nature and no client duties applied. These works were accounted for separately and paid for out of the income of the building owner rather than through the business.

The test to be applied in these circumstances, regardless of the size of the project is whether or not the works are being carried out purely for use as part of the domestic accommodation or whether the works are carried out in connection with a business.

It is also important for the contractual arrangements to be clear. In case study B there are two separate clients:

- the domestic property owner having works carried out in his own name as a private individual; and
- the business having works undertaken in the name of the company.

From a contract administration point of view there must be two distinct contracts in order to avoid payments being made from the wrong account and the tax liabilities of the client becoming muddled. How issues such as shared site facilities are dealt with is a matter for consideration by the contract administrator and outside the scope of this book.

However, for a project of this size the client might well seek the advice and services of the CDM-C on both contracts.

Domestic clients – liability under other legislation

Domestic clients are not completely absolved of liability in respect of activities being undertaken within their own premises as they do owe a duty of care to persons who come onto their premises and to others who might be affected by activities being undertaken on their premises.

Under the provisions of the *Occupiers Liability Acts* 1957 and 1984, occupiers of domestic premises can be held liable for injuries to visitors (including trespassers) who suffer any injuries whilst on the occupiers' premises, including injuries sustained whilst construction works are being carried out.

See the case of *Moon v Garrett* in Chapter 12 *Enforcement and lessons to be learned*.

Insurance work – for domestic clients

The situation regarding works carried out under insurance and warranty claims is fairly straightforward. It remains unchanged under CDM 2007, and is covered by the ACOP in paragraphs 33–36.

Where an insurance company arranges for construction work to be carried out following a claim, e.g. for fire, flood or impact damage, then the insurance company is the client for the purposes of CDM. In these circumstances it will normally specify the work to be undertaken, instruct the contractor and make payments direct to the contractor, even if this is done by a third party such as a loss assessor (who would be appointed by and act on behalf of the insurance company).

Paragraph 35 of the ACOP states:

'It is common, with insurance-related work, for agents to be appointed to act on behalf of either the insured or the insurer. These agents resolve claims and may co-ordinate the remedial works. Such agents may legally be clients with all relevant duties.'

Where the insurance company specifies designers or contractors for certain aspects of the work, the insurer takes on the responsibility for ensuring that those appointed are competent.

Where remedial work is undertaken under a home warranty scheme, e.g. NHBC or Zurich, then it is the provider of the warranty that is the client for the purposes of CDM 2007.

However, there are some cases where the insurance company pays out the claim monies and leaves the home owner to arrange the works: in these circumstances the home owner would be regarded as a domestic client and would not attract client duties under CDM.

PROJECT FEEDBACK

Experience is mainly gained from working on projects and it is essential that lessons are learned from each project undertaken: this applies equally to all members of the project team.

The client should ensure that there are adequate arrangements for reporting and investigation of incidents and that the knowledge gained is shared amongst all members of the project team.

A useful tool is the project debrief, where all aspects of project performance can be examined and information as to both good practice and bad practice can be disseminated.

A key factor that is often overlooked are the lessons to be learned from the buildings or structure in use: the experience and knowledge gained by those involved in the day-to-day operation and how this can be fed back into the design process. The experience of those involved in facilities management should be fed into the project brief: such knowledge can avoid mistakes being repeated on future projects. This might involve something as simple as the cost of changing light bulbs, which when spread across a whole property portfolio runs into thousands of pounds, or the benefits of locating plant at ground floor level and the avoidance of expensive cranage operations every time a piece of plant needs changing.

The potential for significant cost benefits arising from reduced future maintenance costs provides a valid reason for holding a project debrief: any benefits that might arise from the safety perspective are an additional bonus.

It is important that such exercises (both feedback procedures and project reviews) are dealt with on the basis of a 'no blame' culture, where the overriding aim is for all members of the team, including clients, designers and contractors, to be able to participate and share experiences and for all to benefit from the shared knowledge.

5 Getting a project started

In this chapter we examine the issues that the client needs to consider in order to progress a project from initial concept through to obtaining planning and other necessary consents and getting to the stage where the construction package is ready to go out to tender.

We also look at the need for a proper client brief and at the dynamics behind the appointment of a team to deliver a project: the requirement for a mix of innovative skills and technical expertise that combines the creative and the practical.

The next stage, procuring the construction work, is dealt with in Chapter 6 *Buying the construction work*.

INTRODUCTION

For any project there are a number of key issues that have to be taken into consideration in order to make the smooth transition from initial ideas and concepts to a scheme that is ready to start on site.

This is true regardless of the size or complexity of the project: in fact, it is often the case that a seemingly small (in financial terms) project requires almost as much input as the much larger, seemingly more complex project.

For most projects the initial goal is obtaining planning consent for the initial scheme put together by the architect or engineer. In recent years this whole process has become far more complex and time consuming because issues such as sustainability, rights of light, environmental impact, etc. have taken on an increasingly important role in the planning process.

Initial feasibility studies will need to concentrate on the potential of the site or premises to provide the required development, as well as financial issues.

At this stage, it is important to develop a clear brief as to what the client requires: whether the scheme comprises the refurbishment of existing office premises or the demolition and redevelopment of the site.

For a smaller scheme (e.g. the redesign of a single office floor) a brief is still required, costings are still required and a contractor needs to be found to undertake the works. It may not be necessary to acquire planning consent (the consent of the landlord would be required in respect of leased premises) but issues such as asbestos, provision of pre-construction infor-

mation and consideration of the *Workplace Regulations* 1992 will all need to be taken into account.

For a slightly more complex scheme (e.g. one involving the demolition of existing premises and construction of new buildings) the requirements will be greater – with the involvement of the structural engineer, ground investigations and, perhaps, issues relating to works on or adjacent to the highway (e.g. scaffold licence or temporary suspension of parking bays).

Most work to existing premises (apart from detached properties) will involve issues relating to access and party wall matters.

(Access may be a considerable issue in its own right. See the section on access rights later in this chapter.)

INSPECTIONS, SURVEYS AND INVESTIGATIONS

An important aspect of many projects is gathering the initial information about the site, premises or structure, including condition and measured surveys, asbestos surveys, ground and soil investigations, and all manner of inspections and surveys which involve surveyors, engineers and designers visiting the site of the project.

Health and safety issues – inspections and surveys

Clients and those undertaking initial site inspections, surveys and investigations should be aware of the safety issues involved in carrying out such inspections:

- **Safety issues relating to surveyors, engineers and designers** – safety procedures, inductions and safe methods of working, training and information, personal safety, lone working policy and procedures, requirements relating to use of PPE.
- **Safety issues relating to the sites, premises and structures** – condition of premises and structures, derelict buildings and structures, dangerous structures, fire damage, hazardous chemicals and substances, asbestos, pests and vermin and associated diseases.

Both clients and their professional advisors owe a duty of care to those undertaking such inspections and should be aware of their obligations to both employees and others who may be engaged in this type of work. Information about the condition of sites, structures and premises should be provided to those required to undertake inspections.

Clients should also be aware of their liabilities under the *Occupiers Liability Acts* 1957 and 1984. The extent of their liability has been examined in various cases brought before the courts and the 1984 Act extended the liability to trespassers. Chapter 11 covers these issues in more detail.

Obtaining advice from specialists

Where specialists are brought in, by the very nature of the advice being sought, they will tend to focus on the issues that they have been asked to consider. For example, a surveyor reporting on rights of light is unlikely to give much consideration to safety issues during construction: indeed it is not part of his or her remit to do so.

Likewise, a specialist asked to consider energy provision or requirements, or sustainability issues, is not being asked to consider safety issues (except insofar as they relate to the installation or use of any plant, equipment or components as part of their proposals).

The issue here is that each of these specialists is preparing advice on various aspects of the scheme for consideration by the designer and it is the designer who will be considering the advice provided and making decisions based upon that advice. Once the specialists make direct input into the design process then they will be regarded as duty holders under CDM with all that implies.

The case study 'town centre development team' illustrates the extent of advice and the variety of specialists involved in a fairly straightforward planning application within an existing town centre which has seen considerable development over the last ten years.

Whilst much of the emphasis must, by necessity, be concentrated on the efforts to arrive at a scheme that is financially viable and meets the requirements of the planners (without planning consent there will not be a scheme) it is essential that, as part of the overall strategy, CDM procedures are embedded in the process.

A full CDM review of the project should be undertaken prior to the submission to the local planning authority. The review should, as necessary and appropriate, consider:

- the methods of construction appropriate to the site and type of structure;
- the building footprint and issues relating to access during construction and for future maintenance, cleaning and repair; and
- consideration of the *Workplace Regulations* 1992, i.e. the building or structure in use.

The requirement for a CDM review should also apply where the scheme comprises a 'master plan' for which planning consent is being sought. Those involved in the later detailed design and implementation of the approved scheme often encounter difficulties because issues such as access during construction and later during future maintenance and cleaning have not been properly thought through.

Case study – town centre development team

Prior to the planning application being issued to the planning authority the architects who were the lead designer for this particular project had called upon a considerable number of specialists in order to provide them with advice on various aspects of the scheme.

These included the following consultants:

- planning consultant;
- transport consultant;
- rights of light consultant;
- access and party wall surveyor;
- building surveyor;
- acoustic consultant;
- sustainability consultant;
- fire consultant.

Each of these consultants provided the architects with advice required in order to work the scheme up to a stage where it could be submitted to the local authority planning department with a reasonable chance of achieving planning approval.

Equally important though was the fact that it was developed on the basis of sufficiently informed decisions regarding access, impact on adjacent properties, etc. and that the scheme as submitted was capable of being built without significant change to the proposals.

These consultants were selected on the basis of their expertise in their particular specialities, not on the basis of health and safety assessments. They provided the architect with advice – he made the decisions relating to design, based upon the advice provided.

Other members of the project team – structural engineer, mechanical engineer and planning supervisor/CDM co-ordinator were all involved as duty holders under CDM and were assessed for competence as required by regulation 4.

ACCESS RIGHTS

Access is an issue that affects all construction projects – from the refurbishment of premises situated in the middle of an old town centre with narrow streets and inadequate parking for contractors vehicles or suppliers making deliveries, to the construction of new rail infrastructure where temporary access roads have to be made up across adjoining fields in order to provide sufficient access to the work site.

Apart from the logistical problems that need to be taken into account there are other considerations relating to legal rights of access which are often overlooked or only considered at too late a stage in the project and can lead to delays in the programme.

Those surveyors acquainted with property law will be aware of rights conferred on both building owners and adjoining owners (and the utility companies) by rights of way, easements and other rights, covered in legal documents forming part of the conveyance, that may not be immediately obvious to others involved in the project.

It is essential that any potential problems relating to access or other property-related issues are discovered at the outset rather than coming as a complete surprise once the project gets on site and the building owner is served an injunction by the adjoining owner or other parties enjoying rights on, over or under the land. This can bring a project to a complete standstill while matters are dealt with through the courts.

Whilst most of these issues might be covered by civil law, there is an area of legislation that should not be overlooked, i.e. that which relates to access to neighbouring land. This is covered by two important sets of legislation, namely:

- the *Party Wall etc. Act* 1996, and
- the *Access to Neighbouring Land Act* 1992.

The *Party Wall etc. Act* 1996 relates to works to party walls, and is restricted to issues relating to party walls. Provision is made in the Act for access onto neighbouring land or premises where it is required in order to carry out works to the party wall.

The *Access to Neighbouring Land Act* 1992 relates to the statutory rights of owners of land to apply to the courts for access to neighbouring land in order to be able to undertake works to their own building.

The access rights are limited to certain works, namely, works of preservation, i.e. repair works and only come into effect where a building owner has made an application to the courts for an 'access order'.

It should be noted that the above legislation applies, in the main, to situations where there are already buildings in existence.

Generally, these rights of access are not available for new build (unless existing buildings are being demolished) and it is an area where proper advice should be obtained from a surveyor specialising in this field.

The same applies to rights in respect of airspace, e.g. where clients wish to make use of a crane on their own property which is likely to oversail the airspace over an adjoining property or even the public highway.

Where works are undertaken on the approach to an airfield, it may be necessary to inform the airfield operator of the intention to use plant and equipment such as mobile or tower cranes, piling rigs, etc. that project above the general roof height and where necessary provide navigation warning lights.

Works adjacent to infrastructure

Additional problems can occur where construction works are proposed adjacent to a railway line, power cables, transmission masts or other situations where there is a potential risk to the rail infrastructure or the assets of the adjoining owner.

Similar issues can arise where construction works are undertaken adjacent to canals, waterways or harbours where by-laws exist in respect of use or access to the canals, waterways or harbours.

In all of the above cases, building owners should ascertain who owns or manages the adjoining property and whether there are any special conditions or licenses required in respect of the proposed construction works or in respect of access.

Case study – access for refurbishment

This case involved the conversion and refurbishment of existing premises to form a new bar and restaurant on a busy town centre frontage.

The building owner, a major brewery, assumed that the adjoining owners would allow access to a yard at the rear of the premises for the erection of a scaffold in order to allow the building owner to construct an additional storey at the rear of the premises.

When the contractor attempted to gain access to the rear yard the adjoining owner denied access to the contractor (partly because no one had bothered to make contact with him prior to the construction works starting on site or seek his permission to enter onto his land).

The contractor was forced to build the rear elevation brickwork overhand – this took slightly longer and made the work more difficult.

Case study – access for new hotel

In this case, the developer of new hotel premises assumed that access would be available for the duration of the construction works over an access road to the side of the premises for the siting of mobile cranes, erection of scaffolding and for deliveries.

Access was denied. The sequence of construction had to be changed, leading to considerable additional costs and the project suffered considerable delays to the programme.

Limited access was allowed outside of normal working hours in order to allow the assembly and dismantling of the tower crane used during construction – again this led to additional costs.

RIGHTS OF LIGHT

Another issue that has been highlighted after a recent decision in the Court of Appeal is the question of rights of light (*Regan v Paul Properties Limited* [2006] All ER (D) 327).

The case arose over a town centre development where an existing residential owner objected to the fact that a proposed mixed-use development would take away a significant amount of light to his living room.

Despite his objections the developer continued with the development but was served with an injunction which was granted on appeal.

APPOINTING THE TEAM

The basic dynamics for building a project team are applicable to all types of project whether they be IT, financial, manufacturing or construction. The techniques and principles for team building are well established across most industry sectors and can be adapted to reflect the type of project and the size of the team.

In construction we have seen various models in recent years such as those adopted for the Channel Tunnel Rail Link (CTRL – but now referred to as High Speed 1, or HS1) which have proved highly successful and have relied upon breaking down a complicated major civil engineering project into manageable packages: each with its own dedicated project team.

We have also seen projects such as the Wembley Stadium and the Scottish Parliament which have experienced delays and cost overruns (and incidentally have also been the subject of disputes, some of which have ended up before the courts).

The procurement model drives the team dynamics

As illustrated in the case study 'town centre development team' the nature of the project dictates the size and make up of the team. Construction covers a vast range of project types and the key thing is that the client selects a team that can deliver the project, no matter how large or small.

First appointments – application of regulation 14 (Appointments by client where a project is notifiable)

Before we move on to team selection, however, there is an important gateway that the client and the first appointee(s) have to consider.

The regulations do permit limited design ('initial design') to take place but once the initial design is complete the client needs to make a decision as to whether the project requires the appointment of a CDM co-ordinator, i.e. is the project notifiable or not.

The flow chart in figure 8 indicates the actions that must be taken at this stage.

It should perhaps be emphasised at this point that the duties placed upon the client under Part 2 of CDM 2007 **apply to all projects**.

The requirements placed upon the client to check competence under regulation 4, and the duties in relation to arrangements for managing projects and for providing information, apply to all projects whether they are notifiable or not.

The decision to be made by the client is simply whether or not the project is notifiable, i.e. if it is likely to be a project involving construction and lasting for 30 days or more (or alternatively if it will be of short duration but with a high input of labour and exceeding 500 person days).

If it is notifiable, all of the additional duties contained within Part 3 of the Regulations then come into play.

The designer has to be satisfied (regulation 11) that the client is aware of its duties. Where the project is of such a size that it is obvious it will be notifiable, designers may leave themselves vulnerable if they continue with the design beyond an initial design without ensuring that the client is aware of its duties in this respect.

Regulation 11 Duties of designers – '11(1) No designer shall commence work in relation to a project unless any client for the project is aware of his duties under these Regulations.'

Successful teams	
Competence (retrospective)	**Resources for your project**
Can they demonstrate expertise on previous projects? Project references	How does this expertise relate to your project? Have you worked with the project team before?
Professional membership: – corporate – individual (including CPD)	Who will be assigned to your project? Is this the only project they are working on? How will you ensure continuity of the management team and other allocated resources? What contingencies are there for holidays/sickness?

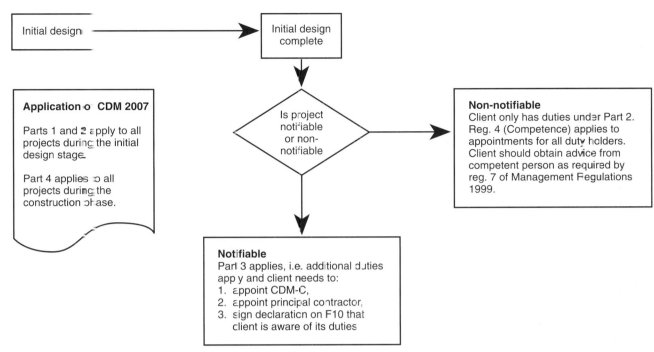

Figure 8: Notifiable and non-notifiable projects – actions arising

Appointing the CDM co-ordinator

The client must appoint a CDM-C where a project is notifiable 'as soon as is practicable after initial design work or other preparation for construction work has begun' (regulation 14(1)) and the appointment must be in writing (regulation 14(5)).

Once appointed the CDM-C needs to familiarise him- or herself with the client's proposals, the initial design proposals and any issues that are particular to the site, structure or premises.

The CDM Regulations require the client to appoint the CDM co-ordinator to, amongst other things, ensure proper co-ordination of the health and safety aspects of the design process.

It is suggested in the ACOP (at paragraph 86) that during 'initial design or other preparation for construction work' the client can 'appraise their project needs and objectives, including the business case and any possible constraints on development to enable them to decide whether or not to proceed with the project before appointing the CDM co-ordinator'. It then goes on to say that 'they should be appointed before significant detailed design work begins' including 'preparation of the initial concept design and implementation of any strategic brief'.

What is initial design work?

CDM 2007 does allow the client to defer the appointment of the CDM co-ordinator until such time as initial design has taken place, but for a notifiable project the appointment is still required and where the appointment is delayed the client is deemed to take on the role.

In some ways it is easier to regard the appointment of the CDM-C as a transfer of the role from the client: there is little advantage to be gained by delaying the appointment.

The HSE has given some guidance as to what comprises initial design work. It includes feasibility studies to enable the client to decide whether or not to proceed with the project, and any work necessary to identify the client's requirements or possible constraints on the development. Designers should encourage the appointment of a CDM co-ordinator at the earliest opportunity.

The following examples illustrate what is beyond preliminary design, and hence that which should not be progressed in the absence of a CDM co-ordinator:

(a) Work within and beyond RIBA Stage C;
(b) Work within and beyond CIC Consultant Contract 2006 Stage 3;
(c) Work beyond OGC Gateway 1; and
(d) Work within and beyond ACE Agreement A (1) OR B (1) 2002 Stage C3.

The ACOP recognises (in paragraph 124) that 'designers have to weigh many factors as they prepare their designs … including cost, fitness for purpose, aesthetics, buildability, maintainability and environmental impact'.

The requirement under regulation 11(5) for designers to take account of the provisions of the *Workplace Regulations* 1992 means that the CDM co-ordinator needs a better understanding of the client's requirements.

For its part, the client is now required, as part of the pre-construction information, to provide any information concerning the proposed use of the structure as a workplace (regulation 10(2)(b)).

RIBA project stages	CIC project stages
A Appraisal B Design brief	1 – Preparation
C Concept D Design development E Technical design	2 – Concept 3 – Design development
F Production information G Tender documentation H Tender action	4 – Production information
J Mobilisation K Construction to practical completion	5 – Manufacture, installation and construction information
L Post practical completion	6 – Post practical completion

The CIC project stages are the copyright of the Construction Industry Council and are reproduced here with permission from the Construction Industry Council.

The project stages from the RIBA Outline Plan of Work 2007, copyright Royal Institute of British Architects (RIBA), are reproduced here with permission from the RIBA.

It is not just contractors that require such information: relevant pre-construction information must also be provided to designers (see *Future maintenance* below).

A major failing in the past has been the lack of a proper client brief and it is anticipated that there is an opportunity under CDM 2007 to improve procedures such that the briefing process better informs the design team/project team as to the client's particular needs and requirements, especially those relating to the building in use and aspects such as future cleaning and maintenance.

THE CLIENT BRIEF

Although not specifically mentioned in the Regulations or the ACOP, a proper client brief is a key factor in establishing at the outset what it is the client actually wants: the ability to provide a clear brief, or perhaps more importantly, the ability to elicit such a brief from the client, demands a particular skill set that has not always been in evidence.

The case for an adequate client brief applies for all projects, whether notifiable or not, and it should be regarded as part of the normal process for clients providing information to the project team.

The consequences of not providing an adequate client brief will normally be (but are not confined to) a lack of understanding, inadequate co-ordination, design changes throughout later stages of the project and delays, overruns and additional costs.

The failure of the client to provide an adequate brief was a major contributory factor in the case of the Port Ramsgate walkway collapse, where fatalities involving members of the public occurred: the failure led to the prosecution of the client as well as members of the project team.

Case study – Port Ramsgate

The summary to the investigation into the Port Ramsgate collapse[29] emphasises the fact that the failure by the client 'to provide vital information to the designer, e.g. a design brief, specification for the project and environmental data' was a major contributory factor leading to the collapse.

This failure was further compounded by the designers producing design calculations which were 'based upon inadequate assumptions, were inaccurate and failed to provide a safe design'.

In this case the client was prosecuted along with the designers, contractors and a third party accreditation organisation (who failed to adequately check the design).

Establishing the client brief early on in the project does allow the design team and the CDM-C to ask the right questions, and should, at least in theory, allow the design to reach a stage where it can be fixed and signed off by the client far earlier than would otherwise be the case.

There are a number of issues that should also be raised by the CDM-C at any initial meeting with the client – including such issues as 'mobilisation', requirements for documentation and information flows. (A useful aid for both the client and the CDM-C at the initial meeting is provided in Appendix A.)

Future maintenance

There are very real issues relating to both the cost and safety of those undertaking future cleaning, maintenance and repairs which are often overlooked at the design stage because other matters such as initial build cost are given greater priority.

Where safety issues are addressed at the design stage these tend to concentrate on safety during construction; designing out risks during the actual build and again overlooking safety issues that might occur whilst the building is being cleaned, maintained or repaired in the future.

Sometimes a slightly higher risk should be tolerated during construction in order to achieve a reduction in risk during maintenance: the construction risk only occurs once – the maintenance risks may occur literally thousands of times throughout the lifetime of the building.

The reduction of risks during maintenance can therefore be shown to have a far greater impact on safety, especially where the management arrangements and controls on those carrying out routine maintenance are relaxed over time.

Various studies have highlighted the 'headline cases' where the cost of changing a light bulb was several thousand pounds and the cost of replacing a section of external cladding has cost £40,000 and required a road closure.

It is important that clients understand the implications of design decisions where a low initial capital cost is gained at the expense of future operating costs. The initial capital costs may be concentrated into a period of 6 to 18 months but the recurring costs of maintaining the structure will extend throughout the lifetime of the building or structure. The cost of ownership can vary greatly and in future the assessment of these costs will have a far greater role in determining the value of real estate than has previously been the case.

Life cycle costs

Much work has been undertaken in recent years to gain an understanding of the concept of life cycle costing and the Royal Institution of Chartered Surveyors (RICS) and the Building Costs Information Service (BCIS) have both been at the forefront in developing techniques and methodology to allow accurate forecasts to be made.

This work has included the development of ISO 15686 Part 5 on life cycle costing and it is anticipated that UK guidance will be developed and brought into use during 2007[30].

Key points

Achieving an early fix on design (i.e. the design is agreed and frozen) should provide the following benefits:

- reduction in non-productive time due to abortive work;
- significant savings to both client and design team in terms of time and money;
- significant reduction in risks to programme; and
- improve safety throughout construction and post-construction by allowing more focus on safety issues during design.

It should also allow better co-ordination between the various parties involved in design – with all working to the same brief rather than producing design solutions based upon invalid assumptions.

A further benefit can be that later design can be brought forward, again to the benefit of the programme.

Business objectives

It is also important at this early stage to review the business objectives and ask the following questions:

- Is a project the right answer?
- Does the project deliver tangible benefits to the business?
- Would it be more beneficial to look at an alternative scheme?

Initial design – design for planning

We have already seen in the case study 'town centre development team' that even in the initial phases of the design process there is often a need to appoint a sizeable team of consultants in order to get to the stage where a planning application can be lodged with some degree of certainty that all relevant issues have been addressed in the submission accompanying the design scheme drawings.

An additional benefit is that it avoids additional delays and the extra costs of subsequent changes to the planning consent, or any conditions attached thereto.

Where the designer has been the initial point of contact then the additional expertise required to progress the planning application will often come from colleagues of the appointed designer, with the client accepting them onto the team at the recommendation of the designer.

This has the advantage, especially where they have previously worked together on a number of schemes, that the team are familiar with each other's work and that co-operation (regulation 5) and co-ordination (regulation 6) between the various consultants is much easier to achieve.

However, this will not always be the case, and, where the CDM co-ordinator is appointed in sufficient time, this is one of the issues that he or she needs to discuss with the client.

The client's initial exposure to the construction industry will be dependent upon the size and nature of the project and the circle of business contacts.

The HSE report on SMEs[6] (see Chapter 1) notes that in many cases such contacts are often limited to a fairly close circle of business colleagues (these could be based on the local Chamber of Commerce, networking groups, or even on the local golf club).

Some clients will already be in contact with professional advisors and will more than likely turn to them, at least for initial advice as to how to proceed with a construction project.

With smaller projects, clients will no doubt be able to rely entirely upon their existing professional advisors and local contacts for the procurement of the entire project.

For larger or more complex schemes then it may

well be necessary for a client to appoint a project team and CDM co-ordinator and bring in additional expertise from elsewhere.

As regards competence, which is dealt with in greater detail in Chapter 7, again, where the client is working with a familiar team, then less checking will be required (although the client will need to be satisfied that the levels of competence as set out in the ACOP are met).

Note: Transitional provisions are covered later in this chapter.

Advice rather than design

In the initial design stages, a number of consultants brought in to provide particular expertise in respect of planning matters will not necessarily be cited as duty holders (i.e. they are not designers) and will not be expected to have expertise or knowledge in health and safety matters.

Where, for example, an expert in respect of rights of light is engaged to report upon how the scheme might affect adjoining properties and comment upon how the building should be designed in order not to interfere with the levels of light enjoyed by the adjoining properties then that person's competence should be in respect of his or her particular expertise and not in respect of the core criteria as set out in the ACOP.

On the other hand, someone commenting on fire engineering issues may have a far greater involvement in the actual design process and will therefore need to be measured against the core criteria for competence as set out in Appendix 4 of the ACOP.

Case study – CHP installation

A project to install a combined heat power plant (CHP) in existing premises comprising TV studios and an office complex was initiated by the building services engineer (manager) who brought in a mechanical services consultant and a risk management consultant.

The client had in-house teams dealing with general health and safety and fire issues. This team was sufficient to deal with the complexities of installing the new plant in an existing basement car park, connections to the existing gas supplies, an electrical shutdown (required to make connections to the main electrical control panels) and the builders' work (required in connection with fire compartmentation and associated works).

The client was able to rely upon an existing team that he had worked with before on various mechanical and electrical projects and he knew would be able to deliver, on the evidence of past performance.

As the scheme evolved it became clear that the project would come within the criteria for a notifiable project and the risk management consultant also took on the role of planning supervisor (as was under CDM 1994).

Notification of construction project

The CDM co-ordinator is required at a fairly early stage to notify the HSE (or relevant enforcing authority) of the client's intention to carry out a construction project.

The initial notification should be made by the CDM co-ordinator 'as soon as is practicable after his appointment' (regulation 21(1)).

Additional information relating to the F10 and requirements relating to notification is provided in Chapter 9 *Provision of information*, but it is worth noting that there are significant changes to these requirements including:

- the client is now required to sign the F10 instead of the planning supervisor and principal contractor (as previously required under CDM 1994);
- contact details for designers are now required; and
- details of the period of time allowed for mobilisation by the principal contractor are now required.

By signing the F10 the client is affirming that he or she is aware of his or her duties under CDM 2007.

Application of CDM to non-notifiable projects

It is perhaps worthwhile reiterating at this point that CDM 2007 applies to all construction projects and that for non-notifiable projects it is only Part 3 of the Regulations that does not apply.

The following sections apply to **all** projects:

- **Part 1 – Introduction** – Citation and commencement, Interpretation and Application
- **Part 2 – The general management duties applying to construction projects** – Refer to Chapter 3 for the duties covered under this section.
- **Part 5 – General** – Civil liability, Enforcement in respect of fire, Transitional provisions, and Revocations and amendments.

The following sections apply to all projects when construction works are being carried out:

- **Part 4 – Duties relating to health and safety on construction sites**. These duties are basically a re-enactment of CHSW 1996 which has now been incorporated into CDM 2007 (subject to amendments).

Client's duties in respect of regulation 9

The client's duties in respect of regulation 9 (Arrangements for managing projects) equally apply to smaller projects (i.e non-notifiable projects) and without the advice and assistance of a CDM co-ordinator it is important for the client to have access to suitable advice (especially for the one-off client without any previous knowledge or experience of dealing with construction work).

It may well be the case that the client can obtain some advice from the designer but this is not part of the designer duties and arguably a designer should not offer such advice where not qualified to do so.

In other words, designers should beware of taking on the role of the CDM co-ordinator where such a role is not required under the Regulations.

In larger organisations a health and safety advisor may be employed, and this employee may take on the role of 'competent person' as defined under regulation 7 of the *Management Regulations* 1999.

Clients should, however, be aware that even where such advice is available in respect of the normal operations of the business it may be necessary to bring in additional expertise for construction-related projects. Where the competent person has previous experience of construction work, he or she may well be able to provide suitable and sufficient advice; but, where such knowledge is outside of their normal scope of experience, additional expertise should be brought in.

(See the 'Fatty Arbuckle' case in Chapter 12 *Enforcement and lessons to be learned*.)

Early involvement of HSE and other enforcing authorities

The issue of the F10 to the HSE may, especially in the case of large, complex, high profile projects, trigger an interest on the part of the Principal Inspector for Construction for the area in which the project is located.

There is a policy for early involvement in these types of project. Such involvement on the part of the HSE is likely to lead to greater numbers of those involved in both the design and construction process being exposed to the intervention process.

The HSE involvement can commence at the design stages, follow the project through onto site, and establish a dialogue with the client and the design team as well as the contractors.

The process can be beneficial to both sides, with the design team gaining a better understanding of the issues that HSE considers to have most influence on safety during construction and for future maintenance. The HSE is able to bring considerable experience to the table from its knowledge of where, why, and when things go wrong. At the same time, HSE inspectors are likely to gain from the insight afforded by the design team into the design process.

Case study – bus stop

The early involvement of the HSE on a scheme to build a new hotel in a busy part of central London helped to identify the need for a bus stop and bus shelter to be removed and temporarily relocated during the construction phase. Transport for London (TfL) readily agreed to the client's proposals upon learning of the HSE's involvement.

On another project, the early involvement of the local Environmental Health Officer (EHO) overcame a number of problems relating to noise and dust arising from the site and secured a longer period during which noisy works could be carried out each day than would otherwise have been the case.

THE TEAM STRUCTURE

In order for the client to get the structure needed to support its business, it will usually be necessary to appoint a team of professionals to define the structure.

Known as the 'design team' or 'project team', it usually includes the following members:

- the client;
- project lead;
- design lead; and
- designers.

Client: Usually considered to be a part of the project team, the client's role is to provide the rest of the team, through the person fulfilling the project lead function, with all the information that they need to define the 'structure' (see CDM 2007 regulation 2 for a definition of structure).

A high percentage of construction projects emanate from the small business sector – often from individual traders, small partnerships or limited companies, and in these cases there will be direct contact with the client. However, in the case of larger companies or public bodies there might be no direct contact with the client, and some form of intermediary will be required in order to interface with the project team (the project lead or client's project manager or sponsor).

Project lead: The project lead forms the conduit between the client and the rest of the project team: clients do not usually instruct the project team directly about their business needs.

Problems can arise from lack of clarity where the client organisation does not provide a **single** person within the organisation (to project manage the project) with the authority to take decisions on behalf of the organisation.

An external consultant is often appointed to take on the project manager role but those taking on this function often suffer from a lack of authority – i.e. it is not a true project management role if the holder is not empowered to make decisions.

The scope of the role and the authority afforded to the person or organisation (either internally from the client organisation or from external consultancy undertaking the project management role) needs to be agreed from the outset.

It is also important that the client organisation obtains input throughout the design process from the facilities management (FM) side of the business. The input provided by the FM team can be invaluable; providing advice and guidance on lessons learned from previous projects. It can also enable significant savings to be made in the costs of future repairs and maintenance.

Design lead: Ensures that the designers work together to deliver the definition of the structure that the client needs to support its business and ensures that the definition information is co-ordinated.

Designers: Designers appointed directly by the client produce the definition information which will allow a contractor to build the structure. The different types of designers that are engaged on a project depends on the nature of the project but often includes those listed below.

It should also be noted that during the construction phase there is likely to be ongoing design input from those involved with temporary works such as false work, formwork and scaffolds. These all come within the definition of design under CDM 2007 and the designers will need to be aware of, and comply with, the requirements placed upon designers (regulations 11 and 18).

Contractors undertaking works packages with a design element will also be deemed to be designers for the purpose of these Regulations.

The project team can also include a number of specialist consultants and other professionals who all play an integral part in getting the project off the ground. Depending on the type and size of the project these could include:

- planning specialists;
- fire engineering consultants;
- land remediation consultants/specialists; and
- civil engineers dealing with tunnelling, highways, bridges, etc.

What do designers do?
Designers are given different names and what they actually do depends on what the client contracts them to do, but the most common definitions are:
- **Architectural designer:** Plans the form and layout of the structure to meet the client's needs

and decides what the finished structure will look like.
- **Civil or structural designer:** Provides the definition information required to ensure that the structure can support the activities that will take place in or on it, that it can resist natural elemental forces and that it can support cladding and services that are required to meet the client's performance requirements.
- **Services designer:** Provides definition information about the services that will be required for the structure to function and meet the needs of the users in terms of mechanical, electrical, heating and ventilation and public health services. Often the completion of the services design will fall to designers appointed by the installation contractors.
- **Cost consultancy:** Provides information about what the structure defined by the designers will cost to construct and usually monitors expenditure.
- **CDM co-ordination consultancy:** Supports the client as it discharges its duties under CDM, ensures that information relating to health and safety risk is passed to those parties that need it, ensures that designers perform their duties under CDM and ensures that the health and safety aspects of the design are co-ordinated.

Alphabet soup – What do the letters mean?
Designers usually use designatory letters to indicate which professional institutions they are members of. The majority of the professional institutions are members of the Construction Industry Council (CIC), which has around 30 full members and around 20 associate members. Use their website www.cic.org.uk to unscramble the soup and remember that sometimes you have to add an M on the front for Member or an F for Fellow:
- ACA: Association of Consultant Architects;
- APS: Association for Project Safety;
- CIBSE: Chartered Institution of Building Services Engineers;
- ICE: Institution of Civil Engineers;
- IStructE: Institution of Structural Engineers;
- RIBA: Royal Institute of British Architects;
- RICS: Royal Institution of Chartered Surveyors.
There are also a couple of sets of other letters that are related to professional recognition but not institutions, e.g. ARB (Architects Registration Board) and CEng (Chartered Engineer).

Others

In addition to those involved in the construction process there may be also be other professionals involved in different aspects of the development, such as a legal team or a party wall surveyor.

The **legal team** may be involved in land assembly:

- sorting out lettings and sales (it is important to ensure that the legal team understand the issues relating to the health and safety file and make it a requirement of leases, etc. to retain file information/provide information, etc.); and/or
- looking at access agreements, oversailing rights for cranes, etc.

In addition, most developments, especially in urban areas will be built close to existing properties and will require the services of **party wall surveyors**:

- It is important that procedures under the *Party Wall etc Act* 1996 are allowed for, and implemented, in good time otherwise there is a real risk that failure to do so can delay the project.
- This applies where the requisite notices required under the Act have either been served late or missed altogether.
- In the former case there may be a delay of a month or so but in the latter may result in an injunction with serious consequences for the whole project.

Contractor involvement

It is suggested in the ACOP that the services of a contractor be engaged by the client to support the team with buildability, the programme and cost advice as the team prepare the definition information.

A decision also needs to be made about which route will be taken in respect of building control: either employing the services of the local authority building control or engaging the services of an 'approved inspector'.

In the case of procurement routes where early involvement of a contractor is the norm, e.g. PFI projects, or where procurement is by way of a negotiated price with a single contractor, then it may be possible to obtain early advice on aspects of the build.

In practice and especially under traditional routes where several builders are involved by way of competitive tender, it is unlikely that early involvement is achievable.

Continuing design

Although this chapter is primarily concerned with getting the project started, it should be recognised that design can, and does, continue well into the construction phase, with elements such as fit-out of bathrooms, domestic and commercial kitchens, etc. often being undertaken by fit-out specialists.

Traditionally, speculative office developments have been fitted out to a Cat 2 standard, only for incoming tenants to rip out ceilings, light fittings and partition walls and replace them to their own bespoke design. This has initiated a debate as to sustainability issues, with the suggestion that a developer should only complete a shell and core elements of the scheme leaving the rest to incoming tenants.

How the initial client brief and design will implement the requirements for the design to take account of the *Workplace Regulations* 1992 (regulations 9(1)(c) and 11(5) of CDM 2007) are also relevant to this discussion.

Some decisions may have to be made by the developer that dictate how the final end user deals with issues such as:

- mechanical and electrical design;
- size, location and number of riser ducts; and
- the zone(s) provided for raised floors or for plant and equipment in the ceiling zone.

Both the client and the lead designer need to retain some control over the overall design and allocate the design responsibilities for building services in order to ensure that there are no gaps in the end product, or that late design changes do not introduce problems that are difficult to resolve or involve substantial additional costs.

Useful information and guidance can be found in *A Design Framework for Building Services – design activities and drawing definitions*[31]. The guide provides a framework for allocating design activities to different members of the project team.

Case study – refurbishment

Late decisions by the client relating to the siting of plant rooms in a major refurbishment of a club, bar and restaurant led to a major redesign of the scheme at a stage where the subcontractor installing suspended ceilings was ready to commence work.

The requirement to install ductwork in the ceiling void required additional support and strengthening of the roof trusses in order to take the additional weight of gantries now required to provide safe access to the ductwork. Additional penetrations had to be made through newly constructed masonry walls, and major problems were encountered because the original design had not allowed for ventilated pipework routes for the gas pipes (which now had to be relocated from their original positions).

Apart from the fact that late design decisions were partly responsible, little thought had been given to the mechanical and electrical requirements by the architect who was more concerned with the concept design.

It is important that the design responsibilities for these elements are carefully thought through and allocated at an early stage.

INTEGRATED RISK MANAGEMENT

Having appointed the team there is a need to identify and track the risks pertaining to the project.

Even where the client and lead designer are clear as to the allocation of design responsibilities, there is still a likelihood that the risks arising from design may be overlooked unless adequate procedures are put in place.

The HSE has stressed that the use of Designer Risk Assessments (DRAs) as experienced under CDM 1994 has no place under the new Regulations.

What is required is a risk register that identifies and addresses the risks to the project.

Tasmanian Project Issues Register

This is a project management tool developed by the Tasmanian Government to aid the development of a project risk register and, more importantly, to track the actions taken in order to reduce or eliminate the risk.

Once the risk has been identified, action must be taken in order to mitigate the risk, tasks should be allocated to stakeholders to deal with these actions, the status of the risk should be monitored, and the actions closed out.

The distinguishing feature of this particular model is that the risks must be dealt with and actions implemented, and then closed out as a result of successful actions, rather than simply being recorded.

The usefulness of many risk registers is negated by the fact that the risks are simply identified and no further action is taken to reduce or mitigate the risk.

The Tasmanian Project Issues Register provides a mechanism for seeking and acting on feedback regarding project issues to encourage the involvement of key stakeholders.

The Register should be maintained throughout the project.

It will change regularly as existing risks are dealt with and new risks identified.

Part of the usefulness of this management tool is that it enables the users to look at the consequences associated with a risk and consider a range of actions including:

- **preventative actions** – planned actions to reduce the likelihood that a risk will occur and/or reduce the seriousness should it occur;
- **contingency actions** – planned actions to reduce the immediate seriousness of the risk if/when it does occur; and
- **recovery actions** – planned actions taken once a risk has occurred to allow matters to be dealt with. This allows a much quicker recovery period and reduces further risks that might arise from an unplanned response.

This particular tool is freely available and can be adapted for use on most types of project.

Prince 2

There are other management tools such as Prince 2:

- Prince 2 is recognised as the standard method for project management across many fields including finance, IT and construction. It is a generic but simple to follow project management tool.
- Prince 2 has a range of standard documentation and templates that cover all aspects of the life cycle of a project and provide a valuable audit tool.
- Further information can be found on the Office for Government Commerce (OGC) website: www.ogc.gov.uk/methods_prince_2.asp

Project risk register for:					Project ref:				
Ref. no	Risk description	Risk owner	When risk occurs		Life cycle cost implications		Risk review	Date	Risk resolution
	Brief description including references to documents/ drawings	Name of source, e.g. client, designer (who has created the risk)	During construction	During use	During construction	Lifetime use	Review risk controls and life cycle costings	Date risk first identified	Risk accepted including all implications
1.0									
2.0									
3.0									

Design sourced outside Great Britain

In recent history there has been a trend to have some of the definition information prepared outside Great Britain and there was some confusion under CDM 1994 about how CDM should be applied. Regulation 12 of CDM 2007 is very clear that a designer in Great Britain who has design(s) prepared outside Great Britain is the person responsible for ensuring that the designers address the duties on designers in CDM. Where a client arranges for design to be prepared outside Great Britain this duty falls to the client.

In the Port Ramsgate case[29] (referred to earlier in this chapter) both the designer and the contractor were based in Sweden, and it is believed that regulation 12 was introduced in response to this type of situation.

> *CDM 2007 regulation 12 – Design prepared or modified outside Great Britain*
> 'Where a design is prepared or modified outside Great Britain for use in construction work to which these Regulations apply:
>
> (a) the person who commissions it, if he is established within Great Britain; or
> (b) if that person is not so established, any client for the project,
>
> shall ensure that regulation 11 [Duties of designers] is complied with.'

Current trends towards globalisation have enabled design practices to make use of capacity available overseas, where preparation of drawings for building control purposes and/or construction detailing can be carried out either at cheaper rates or overnight.

Where such work is commissioned by a design practice then it is up to the designer to ensure that the work meets the requirements of CDM: where the work is commissioned directly by the client then it is up to the client to ensure that compliance is achieved.

One of the key elements of CDM is that those engaged in preparation of the definition information are competent.

Clients are required to assess that the designers and the CDM co-ordinator they propose to appoint are competent to carry out their duties under CDM **before** they make the appointments (regulation 4). (In reality this duty extends to anyone who is appointing a designer, CDM-C or principal contractor (PC)).

Whilst the Approved Code of Practice for CDM 2007 has provided clearer information on the subject, it is the duty of the CDM-C to assist the client in making this assessment.

For this reason, if no other, it is beneficial to appoint the CDM co-ordinator before any others. It must be remembered that, for projects that are not notifiable, clients are not obliged to appoint a CDM-C and so do not have this source of support available to them. However, they should be able to get help from their competent advisor (regulation 7 of the *Management of Health and Safety at Work Regulations* 1999).

To simplify the process (and reduce the amount of bureaucracy that the Health and Safety Executive thought that this process created) CDM 2007 requires people to only accept appointments if they are competent to discharge them.

The ACOP confirms that clients can accept the information that is provided to them about competence in good faith.

Transitional provisions

Although the transitional provisions allowed under regulation 47 provide for the CDM co-ordinator and principal contractor to attain the levels of competence now required under regulation 4 and Appendices 4 and 5 of the ACOP which set out the core criteria, this does not mean that clients (or others) will be able to appoint persons (or companies) to undertake work on their behalf if they do not meet the levels of competence already required under existing legislation.

In the event that these duty holders are not able to demonstrate their competence to meet the levels that would previously be required under CDM 1994, the client would not be able to hide behind the cloak of the transitional provisions if matters go wrong.

Design and build (novated team appointments)

Sometimes clients want the contractor to take responsibility for the design as well as the construction using 'design and build' or 'design and construct' routes to their finished structure.

In some instances clients will want the contractor to use the designers that the client originally engaged to prepare the design, so called 'novation'.

Whilst this is generally not liked, from a CDM perspective it is important to note that in these circumstances contractors are effectively engaging the designers and should therefore satisfy themselves about the designers' competence.

It might be assumed that, if the client appointed these designers in the first place, their competence had been adequately assessed and the principal contractor could take them on without any further assessment. However, it could not be guaranteed that the contractor would come to the same conclusion.

In addition to assessing the competence of those that they are thinking of appointing before they appoint them, clients also need to satisfy themselves that their appointees will make, maintain and review, adequate arrangements for managing the delivery of their duties (including the provision of sufficient time and resources) in compliance with CDM (regulation 9).

Again, the CDM-C (or competent advisor on non-notifiable projects) will provide support in this assessment. This duty also extends to ensuring that the client, similarly, has adequate arrangements for managing the discharging of its own duties.

Client's performance

A client's level of ability to discharge its CDM duties will depend on its experience. CDM 2007 sets a much higher standard of performance for clients than was previously the case, or than is common for the industry.

If clients cannot perform to the required standard they need to get professional help. The CDM-C is required by the Regulations to support the client to a certain extent and to help to ensure that they perform, but clients may need some abilities above and beyond the support duties placed on the CDM-C by the Regulations.

A CDM-C will be able to help a client assess its ability and performance against the standard set in the Regulations and some can also provide the support that clients require, albeit that this is beyond the statutory role.

Whilst the role of the CDM-C is much broader than its predecessor (the planning supervisor), i.e. to advise and assist the client, the client cannot pass its obligations on to the CDM-C. As with regulation 7 of the *Management of Health and Safety at Work Regulations* 1999 and despite the ruling in the *Fatty Arbuckle* case, a client who does not perform will be held responsible. (See Chapter 12 *Enforcement and lessons to be learned*.)

If a client tries to maintain that it was badly advised by a CDM-C whose performance fell significantly below that which was required, it is likely that the client would be deemed to have failed in its duty to assess competence, albeit that the client is at liberty to rely on its reasonable enquiries and the CDM co-ordinator is obliged not to take a commission for which he or she is not competent (see Chapter 7 on competence assessment).

Clients undertaking design

Unless they are competent to do so, clients need to ensure that they do not carry out design. The Regulations do not assign design duties to clients who are arranging for designers to undertake design on their project but are clear that where clients make decisions about the form of the structure or detailed decisions about the materials to be used they will be considered by the enforcing authorities to be undertaking design and therefore to have the same duties as designers under the Regulations.

With the new two-way burdens on competence, they may also need to prove that they are competent to design. With the help of their professionals, clients should be able to clearly express their desires for the project in the strategic brief and then leave it to the designers to deliver a structure that meets the requirements of the brief.

SCOPE OF SERVICES

For clients to get best value out of the consultants that they appoint they need to be very clear about what they want them to do. Whilst it should be clear to a competent consultant what is required of them by CDM, it is invariably not the case that clients and their consultants are clear about what each other wants and intends to provide for the fee.

These mutual expectations are laid out in the various consultants' contracts and associated scopes of services that are available. The form produced by the Construction Industry Council (CIC) in the spring of 2007 is particularly clear and as this book goes to press the RICS are working on their own form.

CIC Scope of Services

The Scope of Services that accompanies the CIC Consultant's Contract is very explicit about what is required to provide adequate definition information for the structure to be built and the support services that the client will need during the execution phase of the project.

It does not matter who the client engages to deliver what services, what is important about the CIC form is that clients will need someone to deliver each of the services if the structure is to be defined in such a manner that it can be built.

The CIC is also clear about the interrelationship of the delivery of the services, e.g. you cannot expect the architectural designer to finish the definition of the plant rooms until there has been input from the services designers about the size and location of the pieces of plant to be housed in the plant room.

Some clients instruct solicitors to prepare bespoke forms of appointment for their consultants. This route usually results in debate between the client's and consultant's solicitors about what is acceptable to each party. The CIC form attempts to resolve this as acceptability to clients was part of the brief to the authors.

RICS Scope of Services

RICS has recently been completely revamping its *Scope of Services* documentation. This covers all of the services provided by surveyors in the construction faculty and includes an updated section covering provision of services under CDM 2007.

General

Whichever form of appointment is used, the important point is that any request for a fee proposal should be accompanied by **form of appointment** and **scope of services** so that the consultant can be clear about the deliverables that the client wants from the consultant and the risk that the client wants the consultant to bear.

Whichever form of appointment and scope of services are selected, it is important that performance of statutory duties is mentioned.

A consultant who fails to perform his or her statutory duty may be prosecuted by the enforcing authorities. However, there are significant exclusions of civil liability and therefore the client will not be able to take a civil case on the back of the criminal case.

With the right clause in the contract any failure to comply with statue that results in material loss to the client could be remedied under contract law.

Rather than appointing consultants on a project-by-project basis it may be more convenient and more beneficial to appoint consultants to a framework where there is an arrangement between a client and one or more consultants to work together for a period of time, e.g. three years. In addition, following on from the work done by Sir Michael Latham, Sir John Egan and the Strategic Forum for Construction, some clients formed partnerships with their project team. Whilst these arrangements have their supporters and detractors, as far as CDM is concerned the general principles apply – there should be competent people with adequate management arrangements in place and adequate time and resources to discharge their duties under CDM.

6 Buying the construction work

This chapter looks at the different procurement options available to the client, the information that has to be provided to contractors as part of the procurement process, evaluation of tenders, and the impact of CDM on this process.

The production of specifications and bills of quantities has been well documented over a number of centuries and requirements relating to health, safety and provision of welfare facilities preceded the introduction of CDM in 1995.

CDM has to accommodate a wide variety of procurement routes and allows clients, funders and others to be creative in the way in which they fund and procure construction projects.

In general CDM does not interfere with the contractual arrangements. It allows both clients and contractors a certain degree of flexibility, but does impose requirements relating to competence, co-ordination and communication, flows of information, provision of welfare facilities and the period to be allowed to contractors for mobilisation.

The requirements relating to provision of information should, at least in theory, ensure that all contractors bidding for the works are provided with the same information, that there is better information from which to price and that, with less surprises emerging during the construction phase, programmes are more predictable.

SMALL WORKS AND MINOR PROJECTS

Many smaller projects are still sourced directly by a client without recourse to professional advice or other intermediaries: in some cases the client will have employed a designer (who is engaged solely for the purpose of obtaining any necessary planning and building consents) but does not seek, or use, the services of a professional to supervise the construction works.

There are also instances where the client feels that he or she can self-manage the project, dispensing with the 'main' or 'principal' contractor and letting the works out as a series of packages, thereby making some savings on contractors' overheads and profits.

In both cases, as long as the works come within the definition of 'construction works' as set out in regulation 2 of the CDM Regulations then the client will be a 'client' for the purposes of the Regulations and is obliged to comply with the Part 2 duties.

A client who also controls the way in which the construction work is carried out would also have to comply with the Part 4 duties relating to health and safety on construction sites (i.e. compliance with regulations 26 to 44) and would also take on the contractor's role and duties.

If the works last longer than 30 days (or involve more than 500 person days) then the works become notifiable and all of the additional duties under Part 3 apply.

In theory any contractor taking on work in these circumstances should only do so if he or she is satisfied that the client is aware of its duties. In practice, these are the type of projects where there is likely to be a lack of awareness of the CDM Regulations, and the HSE finds it difficult to raise awareness of health and safety requirements. These are also the type of projects where most minor accidents and incidents are likely to occur and where there is room for substantial improvement in safety culture.

PROFESSIONAL ASSISTANCE

Where professional assistance is provided in either the procurement or supervision of the work then improved compliance must be anticipated.

CDM 2007 demands significant changes from the situation that prevailed under the old CDM Regulations, inasmuch as the Regulations apply to **all** construction work.

Where smaller projects are handled by managing agents or firms of building surveyors, it is important that all relevant regulations are applied, but their application should be proportionate to the type of work undertaken.

If the works are tendered in the traditional manner with a written specification under a small works contract then the client should ensure that health and safety issues are addressed.

DEFINITIONS

CDM 2007 applies to all construction work and regulation 2 (Interpretation) provides definitions in respect of:

- construction site;
- construction work; and
- structure.

The work and structures covered is wide ranging and the definitions are noted below as a reminder as to the diversity of the construction industry and the need for the Regulations to provide a sufficient degree of flexibility to enable them to be applied across such a broad range of activities.

Construction site

A ' "construction site" includes any place where construction work is being carried out or to which the workers have access, but does not include a workplace within it which is set aside for purposes other than construction work;'.

Construction work

' "Construction work" means the carrying out of any building, civil engineering or engineering construction work and includes:

(a) the construction, alteration, conversion, fitting out, commissioning, renovation, repair, upkeep, redecoration or other maintenance (including cleaning which involves the use of water or an abrasive at high pressure or the use of corrosive or toxic substances), decommissioning, demolition or dismantling of a structure;

(b) the preparation for an intended structure, including site clearance, exploration, investigation (but not site survey) and excavation, and the clearance or preparation of the site or structure for use or occupation at its conclusion;

(c) the assembly on site of prefabricated elements to form a structure or the disassembly on site of prefabricated elements which, immediately before such disassembly, formed a structure;

(d) the removal of a structure or of any product or waste resulting from demolition or dismantling of a structure or from disassembly of prefabricated elements which immediately before such disassembly formed such a structure; and

(e) the installation, commissioning, maintenance, repair or removal of mechanical, electrical, gas, compressed air, hydraulic, telecommunications, computer or similar services which are normally fixed within or to a structure,

but does not include the exploration for or extraction of mineral resources or activities preparatory thereto carried out at a place where such exploration or extraction is carried out;'.

Structure

' "Structure" means:

(a) any building, timber, masonry, metal or reinforced concrete structure, railway line or siding, tramway line, dock, harbour, inland navigation, tunnel, shaft, bridge, viaduct, waterworks, reservoir, pipe or pipe-line, cable, aqueduct, sewer, sewage works, gasholder, road, airfield, sea defence works, river works, drainage works, earthworks, lagoon, dam, wall, caisson, mast, tower, pylon, underground tank, earth retaining structure, or structure designed to preserve or alter any natural feature, fixed plant and any structure similar to the foregoing; or

(b) any formwork, falsework, scaffold or other structure designed or used to provide support or means of access during construction work,

and any reference to a structure includes a part of a structure.'

Case study – block of flats

A firm of managing agents of a block of 12 flats was asked to arrange for external works of repair including:

- renewal of tiling to the sloped roofs and asphalt to several areas of flat roofing;
- renewal of flashings to chimney stacks;
- general areas of repointing of brickwork;
- redecoration of exterior; and
- internal redecoration of common parts by the freeholders (each leaseholder having a share in the freehold).

The managing agents prepared a written specification of work and tender documentation which was sent out to three local contractors specialising in this type of work.

They also discussed the extent of the works and the requirements of the CDM Regulations with their client and it was agreed that, as the works were likely to last at least 12 to 14 weeks and it would be necessary to provide a scaffold, CDM would apply to the works (as defined by regulation 2) and the works would also be notifiable (regulation 2(3)).

The managing agents took on the role of CDM-C and, as it was some time since they had routinely checked the competence of any of the contractors, prepared a health and safety questionnaire for completion by the contractors.

The tendering contractors were also asked to attend an interview in order to answer their concerns relating to security and health and safety and also to indicate how they would meet their obligations under CDM.

The managing agents were able to undertake the CDM-C role and the whole approach was proportionate to the risks associated with the type of works being undertaken.

STRATEGIES FOR RISKS

Clients adopt many strategies to get their structures built.

The strategies adopted depend on what the risks are perceived to be on each project and how prepared they are to take such risks (or whether they wish to pass a particular risk on to someone else).

These risks are mainly financial but also include risks of delay to the project due to uncertainty over planning, or party wall and access issues where these have not been resolved at the start of the construction phase.

Clients cannot take such an approach with matters relating to health and safety and cannot contract out of their legal liabilities. One of the central planks of CDM is that health and safety risks are clear to people who are assessing the resources and they are required to manage those risks safely.

Designers are required to eliminate hazards and reduce risks and the CDM-C is then required to pass information about the remaining significant design risks along with the site's contextual risks (e.g. presence of contaminated ground, presence of asbestos, continued use of the site, neighbouring activities like schools, etc.) to people who are assessing the resources that are required to manage those risks safely.

Cost consultants

As the complexity of the project increases additional resources will be required to deal with the necessary tender documentation: a role normally undertaken by cost consultants (the traditional quantity surveyor role).

Cost consultants will be able to provide advice on the available procurement options and the most appropriate form of contract for the client.

Procurement decisions

Procurement decisions have a profound effect on balance of risk and reward on projects, and the roles of each party in that project.

The UK construction industry has never had the best reputation for meeting its clients' expectations.

Evidence of this poor performance comes from the National Audit Office (NAO) report *Improving public services through better construction,* which concludes that failure to fully implement best practice procurement and project management in central and local government currently costs £2.6 billion a year in terms of avoidable capital and operating costs.

As demands on projects become more complex and multifaceted, incorporating such elements as sustainability and whole life value, the problems associated with defining and achieving the criteria for success become greater.

However, there are few projects, particularly in the private sector, that are subject to regular structured project reviews that enable these issues to be tackled at an early stage.

As a result, project success may be achieved more by accident than design – albeit that the client and the project team will be working hard to achieve the best possible result.

The text of Procurement decisions is copyright Davis Langdon. It is from an article that was originally written by Simon Rawlinson of Davis Langdon, first published in Building magazine on 10 February 2006, and is reproduced here with permission.

Procurement options

There are a large range of procurement options available to clients including traditional single stage tenders, two stage tenders, construction management, and design and build, as well as such innovations as PPP, PFI and other forms of procurement which extend over a period of years and include the management of the facility for an agreed period.

However, what is becoming increasingly clear is that whatever procurement option is adopted clients need to ensure that projects are subjected to regular structured project reviews.

CDM provides a basic model upon which management of health and safety issues is based, but also provides the opportunity to introduce greater discipline into the whole project risk management process.

The concept of gateways, based upon key stages in the management of CDM should facilitate the introduction of regular structured project reviews. This concept is equally valid for both small and large projects and can be applied across the whole range of procurement options.

Contract documentation

Consideration needs to be given as to how contract documentation information is passed on to those who need it.

Clearly, the CDM-C has a duty to pass on information under regulation 20, but this is a statutory requirement and consideration also needs to be given as to how contractual issues will be dealt with.

Although changes and amendments have been made to most standard forms of appointment and JCT and NEC contracts, clients and their cost consultants (or other advisors involved in the provision of advice relating to contract documentation) will need to ensure that other documentation, including their own bespoke contracts, have been updated and amended to take account of the requirements of CDM 2007.

Similarly, with NBS and other standard specifications care should be taken to ensure that the requirements of CDM 2007 have been taken into account.

The CDM-C will need to discuss with other members of the project team how these issues will be addressed and how contractual liabilities are allocated in addition to the statutory requirements placed upon the duty holders under CDM.

Mobilisation period

CDM 2007 requires clients to provide potential principal contractors with information about the minimum amount of time that has been allowed for the principal contractor to plan and prepare construction work before starting work on site. The appropriate amount of time can be determined by the client, based upon the knowledge and advice supplied by the client's designers and the CDM-C.

The requirement, as set out in regulation 10(2)(c) is for the client to provide, as part of the pre-construction information:

'the minimum amount of time before the construction phase which will be allowed to the contractors appointed by the client for planning and preparation for construction work;'.

It should be noted that this requirement applies to both notifiable and non-notifiable projects.

The ACOP makes quite clear that contractors should be provided with adequate time in which to mobilise their workforce and equipment, and make arrangements for welfare facilities to be provided.

For notifiable projects there is a requirement for the time allowed to be noted on the *F10 Notification of construction project*. Item 9 in Schedule 1 of CDM 2007 refers to:

'The time allowed by the client to the principal contractor referred to in regulation 15(b) for planning and preparation for construction work.'

The provision of this information to contractors may influence their decision as to whether they wish to tender for the work – the timescale allowed may fit in neatly with their own work requirement and availability of resources and lead to a competitive bid or, on the other hand, the information may lead them to decide that resources would not be available and thus to decline to bid.

Key points
Non-notifiable projects

- Client advises contractors of the minimum time allowed for planning and preparation.

Notifiable projects

- Client agrees period to be allowed.
- CDM-C passes on information to principal contractor and any other contractors that might be appointed by the client.
- CDM-C includes details of mobilisation period on the F10.

Decisions made about the time allowed should be part of the discussions between the client and the CDM-C – made well in advance of contractors being invited to tender.

Where the CDM-C has made an initial notification immediately upon his or her appointment then details of the 'mobilisation period' should be provided to HSE as soon as the decision as to the time allowed has been reached.

Paragraph 19 of the ACOP states:

'… Any missing information must be notified once it becomes available, and the notifier should make clear that it relates to an earlier notification. …'

ASSESSMENT OF COMPETENCE

As with designers there is an obligation on clients to assess the competence of principal contractors and contractors (for non-notifiable projects) **before** appointing them and a reverse obligation on principal contractors and contractors not to accept commissions unless they are competent to deliver them.

This also applies to any other contractors directly appointed by the client on notifiable projects.

CDM 1994 stipulated that a contractor had to be someone who undertakes, carries out or manages construction work.

Under CDM 2007 there is no longer an explicit requirement for them to be experienced in undertaking or managing construction work, although it is logical to assume that this is a fundamental point of competence.

Assessing competence is covered in Chapter 7 but the following key points should be noted:

- the client has duty to assess competence (regulation 4);
- the client can take advantage of pre-qualification to limit the tender list to competent contractors;
- formal schemes such as CHAS and Achilles Link-

up can be used as long as a Stage 2 assessment of competence is also undertaken, i.e. ability to undertake the type of project involved;

- competence standards and 'core criteria' are set out in Appendix 4 of the ACOP;
- the duty to assess competence rests with the client; and
- the client should be able to rely upon the CDM-C to provide suitable advice and assistance.

Under CDM 2007, clients are also now required to ensure that principal contractors and contractors make, maintain and review suitable arrangements for the delivery of their duties.

In other words, clients should satisfy themselves that not only have they appointed a competent contractor but, in turn, the contractor will also make appointments of competent people.

A number of contractors have already put in place a process to ensure that competence and the assessment of subcontractors is extended down the supply chain.

CHOICE OF CONTRACTOR – EVALUATION OF TENDERS

Tender protocols

Where a formal tender process has been followed there are protocols designed to ensure fair play to all contractors participating in the process, with tenders being opened all at the same time and compared against each other.

The aim is to ensure that the tenders are being compared like for like, that any anomalies are noted and that checks are made for errors and omissions, additions and conditions/conditional pricing, etc.

The cost consultant will then prepare a tender report which may include relevant information about competing contractors' responses to health and safety issues.

It should be noted that tender costs are now significantly higher than in the past as the level of information required to evaluate tenders is much greater.

This is especially true of tenders that have been notified in the Official Journal of the European Union (OJEU) following a ruling in the Dutch Courts that requires a transparent process: all contractors must receive the same treatment – if one contractor is called for interview then all contractors (remaining in the tender pool) should be provided with the opportunity to attend an interview.

The whole of the process must be seen to be fair and equitable.

Choosing the contractor

What are key points for measuring the value of a tender?
The key points for measuring the value of a tender include:

- best value considerations – not lowest price;
- contractors meet all the criteria set by client including availability of resources and ability to meet timeframe, site logistics, etc.;
- competence – contractors are able to meet standards of competence as set out in the ACOP; and
- past performance – contractors are able to demonstrate past performance in respect of similar projects.

Tender interviews

A tender interview provides an opportunity for both client and contractor to gain a better understanding of each other's expectations and for the contractor to present its case.

The client is able to probe for explanations that are not apparent in the tender documents and meet at first hand the team that will deliver the project on site.

A client should ascertain whether the team that is at the meeting is the team that will be closely involved with the client's own particular project or (as is often the case) the 'team in suits' that specialises in such presentations.

The site manager is often the key to a good project, and from the contractor's point of view, the tender interview meeting is a good opportunity to put forward a first class candidate for the project.

The CDM-C does not have a formal role in the selection process (other than to advise whether each of the contractors tendering for the project is competent or not) but can play a useful role at such interviews in prising additional information in respect of health and safety issues from the contractor's team.

Key questions
The contractor's accident record might appear good on paper but a question about the company's insurance claims record might reveal a different story. The question should include figures for pending claims as well as active ones already with insurers.

Figures for near misses and incidents involving damage to property can also indicate poor performance on site.

It should be noted that with respect to accidents it is not necessarily the number of accidents that a potential contractor has had that is important (albeit that the incident rate or frequency rate provides a better indicator of performance) but what the potential contractor has done as a consequence (through post accident learning) to prevent reoccurrence – this may provide a better indicator of competence.

The knowledgeable CDM-C will also have a further range of questions to be asked depending upon the type of site and project. Additional questions might include:

- Who within the contractor's organisation will take on responsibility for producing the health and safety file (or obtaining information for the file)?

- What part will the site manager have in the assembly and compilation of file information?
- Who within the contractor's organisation will take on responsibility for producing the building manuals and ensuring that all relevant certificates, guarantees and warranties are obtained and included in either the file or the manuals as appropriate?
- Who within the contractor's organisation will be responsible for producing risk assessments and method statements?
- What procedures will be in place for ensuring that relevant health and safety information is passed on to other contractors and for obtaining and reviewing method statements produced by subcontractors?
- Who will be responsible for preparing the construction phase plan and how will it be updated on site?
- Who will provide site inductions?
- What arrangements are in place for carrying out statutory inspections on the site?

Some of this information may already have been provided in the written documentation provided by the contractor as part of the original tender submission but such questions at tender interview probably provide a better insight as to how these matters will be dealt with once the contract has been awarded.

Value engineering

Whilst the CDM co-ordinator should, in accordance with regulation 20(2)(d):

> 'take all reasonable steps to ensure co-operation between designers and the principal contractor during the construction phase in relation to any design or change to a design'

the CDM-C has no role to play in any value engineering exercise unless there is any significant change affecting health and safety, either during construction or subsequently during cleaning or maintenance.

Again, the CDM-C can perform a useful function by attending a value engineering exercise, but equally can fulfil his or her duties under regulation 20(2)(d) by obtaining relevant information from designers.

Procurement under framework agreements – call-offs

With framework agreements all of the contractors have already undergone a process of scrutiny and vetting prior to being placed upon the list of approved contractors (the same applies to professional consultants).

The type of work and the value of contracts has already been placed into categories and bands so, in

theory, when a project comes up the client is able to call off a contractor to either bid for the work or to accept an assignment.

It should be noted that the assessment of competence has been carried out by the client organisation without any involvement of the CDM-C.

The vetting procedures are normally fairly stringent but clients are advised to review the original vetting process in order to ensure that the standards align with the core competencies as set out in Appendix 4 of the ACOP.

In any event regulation 47 (Transitional provisions) requires that, where the client has already appointed contractors under regulation 6 of CDM 1994, within 12 months of the new Regulations coming into force the client shall 'take reasonable steps to ensure that any CDM co-ordinator or principal contractor so appointed is competent within the meaning of regulation 4(2)' of CDM 2007.

'Don't get something for nothing'

As with appointing designers, best value is obtained by being clear about what the contractor is required to do in addition to the risks that are to be managed.

One of the key issues that the client needs to be clear about in this respect is who is to prepare the health and safety file because, whether it be the CDM-C or the principal contractor, someone needs to allocate resources to prepare it.

Whilst senior figures in the industry do not think that tendering is an appropriate way to select the contractor that the client needs to carry out the work, there will always be a point at which it is necessary for a client to make a choice between two or more offers received from contractors.

At this point it is important for clients to be clear about the criteria that they are using to differentiate between the competing contractors. There are many criteria that clients can use to carry out this differentiation activity.

Actually being satisfied that the potential contractor is competent is an important prerequisite and CDM 2007 requires clients to be satisfied that any potential contractor can provide from day one, and maintain for the duration of the project, adequate welfare facilities. The welfare facilities that are expected on site are listed in Schedule 2 of CDM 2007. (See Chapter 8 for additional information relating to provision of welfare facilities.)

Whatever other criteria clients are using, if they are using price to differentiate it is important that they select the contractor whose price is right rather than just the cheapest.

As John Ruskin said back in 1860:

> 'It is unwise to pay too much, but it's worse to pay too little. When you pay too much, you lose a little money – that is all. When you pay too little, you

sometimes lose everything, because the thing you bought was incapable of doing the thing it was bought to do. The common law of business balance prohibits paying a little and getting a lot – it can't be done. If you deal with the lowest bidder, it is well to add something for the risk you run. And if you do that, you will have enough to pay for something better.'

It is generally considered beneficial to make the package of health and safety risk information that is provided to the contractor when assessing the resources required to manage the risks part of the contract documentation.

This gives the client redress under contract law if the principal contractor is not managing one of the key health and safety risks that has been identified, e.g. keeping escape routes clear, positioning fire watchers whilst smoke detectors in a live building are hooded, etc

Similarly, whilst a client should not need leverage over competent contractors to make them address obligations set in health and safety statutes, it can be beneficial to stipulate compliance with statutory obligations in the contract to give a basis for dialogue.

A client may also choose to build rights to exercise a strategic health and safety function into the building contract.

Both the EC Directive 92/57/EEC of 24 June 1992, *Temporary or mobile construction sites*, and CDM Regulations make it quite clear that it is the contractors' duty to manage health and safety on site, but clients inevitably visit site.

Whilst not wishing to intervene in the management of the site (and risk assuming obligations under regulations 26–44, see regulation 25(2)) the client might wish, in pursuance of health and safety performance goals, to be able to stop work where he or she feels that health and safety performance does not meet the required standard.

Without a suitable clause in the building contract, the client will be liable for the consequences of this action, but with the requisite clause, where stops are

justified, the contractor will be liable for the consequences.

The role of the CDM-C

The stated duties of the CDM-C are to 'give suitable and sufficient advice and assistance to the client ...' (regulation 20(1)(a)) in helping him or her perform the client's duties.

A competent CDM-C will have the knowledge and expertise to do this.

It should be clear that the role of the CDM-C is restricted to giving such advice and does not extend to making a choice between equally competent contractors.

The CDM-C should be able to provide advice on the competence of contractors, the management arrangements of the principal contractor (and the sufficiency of the construction phase plan at the start of the construction phase) but beyond that does not have a statutory role to play in the selection of the contractor.

That decision rests entirely with the client – and it will be based upon a range of issues including financial issues, the availability of the chosen contractor to meet the programme set by the client, the ability to perform and deliver the project, possession of adequate insurances and tax status (CIS scheme), as well as issues relating to compliance with CDM.

The next step

This chapter has taken us through the tender process and to a stage where the client can now be satisfied that he or she has both a project and a budget available to allow him or her to proceed with one or other of the contractors that has cleared each of the hurdles in the tender process.

Chapter 7 examines in greater detail how each of the duty holders should be assessed on issues of competence. Chapter 8 then deals with getting construction projects on site and underway.

7 Competence and resources

INTRODUCTION

The concept of requiring 'competent persons' to undertake specific tasks has long been recognised, particularly in respect of the requirements for those undertaking statutory inspections.

The opening section of this chapter, which looks at the legal definition of 'competence', is mainly concerned with the difficulties of ascertaining what qualities are required by a 'competent person'.

It is accepted that those undertaking statutory inspections of lifts, cranes, scaffolds, excavations, gas appliances, pressure vessels, etc. should be able to demonstrate adequate levels of competence in order to carry out the task.

The difficulty arises when clients are expected to extend the concept of competence to all those that they appoint, be they designers, contractors or whatever – how can it be measured, do qualifications equate to competence, what levels are required?

CDM 2007 addresses these issues to a certain extent: the ACOP introduces the concept of core criteria and sets out how this should be applied to both individuals and companies throughout the supply chain, and this is explored further in the rest of this chapter.

LEGAL DEFINITION OF COMPETENCE

The statutory requirement for the appointment of a 'competent person' stretches back for 100 years or more and has its origins in legislation relating to factories, docks and quarries.

The legislation did not define competent and it was left to the courts to provide a definition.

For example, in *Brazier v Skipton Rock Co Ltd* [1962] 1 All ER 955, which concerned a personal injury claim, the head note of the law report says:

'a competent person within the meaning of reg. 2(1)(b) and reg. 41 of the *Quarries (General) Regulations* 1956 was one who, on a fair assessment of the requirements of the task, the factors involved, the problems to be studied and the degree of danger implicit, could fairly, as well as reasonably, be regarded by the manager, and in fact was regarded at the time by the manager, as competent to perform such an inspection: on the facts, the plaintiff was competent in that sense and accordingly there had not been any breach of regulations'.

In the case of *Gibson v Skibs A/S Marina* [1966] 2 All ER 476, Cantley J. commented:

'Who is 'a competent person' for the purpose of such an inspection [of lifting gear under *Docks Regulations* 1934]? This phrase is not defined.

I think that it is obviously to be taken to have its ordinary meaning of a person who is competent for the task. I think that a competent person for this task is a person who is a practical and reasonable man, who knows what to look out for and knows how to recognise it when he sees it.'

Of a more general nature (but this really concerns negligence) is the Bolam test which comes from a medical negligence case. The direction McNair J. gave to the jury in *Bolam v Friern Hospital Management Committee* [1957] 1 WLR 583 at page 587 was:

'... that he is not guilty of negligence if he has acted in accordance with a practice accepted as proper by a responsible body of medical men skilled in that particular art. Putting it the other way round, a man is not negligent, if he is acting in accordance with such practice, merely because there is a body of opinion who take a contrary view.'

COMPETENCE AND RESOURCES – THE BUSINESS CASE

Although clients are now required to consider competence for all those involved in the construction process (the requirements relating to competence now apply to **all** construction projects – regulation 4), it is the business case that is more compelling.

Projects that complete on time and budget are not left to chance: they are achieved by getting the right people for the job and managing risks.

Definitions of competence tend to include both inputs (such as knowledge or ability) and outputs (such as completion or performance), and Jessup[32] stresses that 'it is performance which essentially characterises competence'. So competence must be a worthwhile attribute for members of the project team.

Where clients understand the assessment process and are able to appoint companies (contractors and other duty holders) that are both competent and adequately resourced, then tangible benefits will normally be realised.

This approach has been embraced by the HSE in the Approved Code of Practice (ACOP) and will be a key factor for clients undertaking projects in the future. This chapter looks at the duties of the various duty holders in respect of competence, how competence should be assessed, formal assessment schemes, and the requirements relating to individuals.

Whilst much of the ACOP concentrates on companies and organisations, the requirements relating to competence also apply to individuals. The formal assessment schemes apply mainly to companies (compliance with *Management Regulations* 1999 and adequacy of documentation). Assessment of individuals (membership of professional bodies, formal health and safety qualifications, CPD, etc.) is considered later in this chapter.

Carpenter report

Although CDM 1994 required the appointment of competent persons, the actual requirements were far from specific.

For CDM 2007 the HSE commissioned John Carpenter[33] to undertake research into the issues related to competence of both individuals and organisations and to develop guidelines for the selection of competent co-ordinators, designers and contractors.

Initially the report was tasked with researching and making recommendations into the competence of designers and contractors but this was later widened into looking at the experience and competence of CDM co-ordinators and some of the recommendations were transposed into the draft ACOP.

Carpenter broadly identified how competence should be measured both at a corporate level and on an individual level and made the following recommendations:

- 'Competence should be demonstrated at a corporate level and at an individual level within the corporate framework if it is applicable. This applies to all contractor and design organisations (and those offering to discharge the functions of Co-ordinator) of whatever size.'
- **Corporate competency**
  Competency should be assessed by a two-stage process:
  – Stage 1 – the use of core criteria.
  – Stage 2 – 'a review of track record to establish the ability to identify the hazards and manage the anticipated risks'.
    Evidence '… should reflect the size of the organisation and its exposure to risk'.

'The importance of corporate competency should be recognised by insisting that applications and statements be signed by the Managing Director or equivalent.'

- **Individual competency**
  Carpenter recommends that:
  – 'all Contractors and Designers involved in a project should be competent to undertake the assigned tasks unless they are undergoing training and under the supervision of a competent person;
  – there should be a sufficient number of persons with the requisite competence to perform tasks assigned to them; and
  – all those discharging the functions of a Co-ordinator should be competent.'

© *Crown copyright material is reproduced with the permission of the Controller of HMSO and Queen's Printer for Scotland.*

Carpenter recognises that by assessing duty holders to a higher standard of competence there will be significant numbers unable to achieve the requisite standards straight away.

The CDM Regulations recognise this by means of a transition period (see regulation 47, Transitional provisions, which allows a 12 month period for both principal contractors and CDM co-ordinators to take such steps as are necessary to ensure that they are competent within the meaning of regulation 4(2)).

The HSE has taken on most of the Carpenter recommendations (albeit with some changes) and included them in the ACOP – *Managing health and safety in construction*[4].

Best practice

Carpenter also suggests that clients seek demonstration of best practice from those organisations that they employ.

As examples of best practice he quotes adoption of the 'respect for people agenda', the regular use of the Considerate Contractors Scheme, Key Performance Indicators (KPI's) and the IOSH *Global Best Practices in Contractor Safety* produced by the Institute of Occupational Safety and Health (IOSH)[34].

CDM 2007 – WHAT DO CLIENTS NEED TO DO?

CDM 2007 requires the client to engage competent people to populate the project team and to undertake construction works on the client's behalf. The requirements relating to competence are found under regulation 4 (see next page).

By incorporating detailed guidance for clients and others on how to assess the competence and adequacy of resource within the ACOP the following benefits should ensue:

- the assessment process should be simplified;
- the costs to clients of ensuring contractor and designer competence should fall; and
- designers and contractors should already be competent to fulfil the functions for which they are seeking appointment.

The new guidelines place the onus on the potential appointees to gather and provide supporting evidence for the client.

The HSE (in its *Regulatory Impact Assessment*) considered that these measures would lead to a reduction in bureaucracy and paperwork and significant cost benefits. It is estimated that the time taken to carry out competency checks will be halved with potential savings to clients of £100 million.

The HSE also suggests that for designers and contractors the cost benefits of a simpler and quicker assessment process could be in the region of £220 million.

CDM 2007 regulation 4 – Competence

'4(1) No person on whom these Regulations place a duty shall:

(a) appoint or engage a CDM co-ordinator, designer, principal contractor or contractor unless he has taken reasonable steps to ensure that the person to be appointed or engaged is competent;

(b) accept such an appointment or engagement unless he is competent;

(c) arrange for or instruct a worker to carry out or manage design or construction work unless the worker is:
  (i) competent, or
  (ii) under supervision of a competent person.

(2) Any reference in this regulation to a person being competent shall extend only to his being competent to:

(a) perform any requirement; and
(b) avoid contravening any prohibition,

imposed on him by or under any of the relevant statutory provisions.'

Approved Code of Practice
Competence and training are covered in paragraphs 193–240 of the ACOP, in Appendix 4 (which sets out the core criteria against which competence can be assessed) and in Appendix 5 (which deals with larger and more complex projects).

It should be noted that these requirements (regulation 4) relate to **all** duty holders where they appoint other people to undertake construction works.

For instance, a designer letting out subcontract design work must be satisfied that the person or organisation engaged to carry out the subcontract design package is competent. This also applies where the work is undertaken abroad.

Where surveyors act as managing agents (or in a similar capacity) for a client, regulation 4 is explicit in requiring the appointment of competent persons.

Principal contractors need to ensure that all those contractors and subcontractors engaged in design work or construction works are competent and so on down the supply chain.

Assessment of competency – alternative routes

There are a number of ways in which a client can fulfil the regulation 4 duties, including:

- undertaking the assessment him- or herself using health and safety questionnaires, tender interviews, and obtaining information relating to past performance on previous projects (including seeking references from previous clients);
- obtaining relevant information from designers and contractors – organisations who are bidding for work should put together a package of information that shows how their own policy, organisation and arrangements meet the required standards;
- using formal assessment schemes for pre-qualification of contractors and designers – these schemes should provide independent accreditation to assess contractors and designers against the core criteria (as set out in Appendix 4 of the ACOP).

Clients who are not familiar with these schemes or methods for undertaking competency assessments should obtain advice from professional advisors.

For Part 3 projects, i.e. for projects that are notifiable, the CDM co-ordinator will be able to provide this advice.

In either case we would suggest that a simple test that can be applied by the client is to check whether or not the 'health and safety policy' includes in its arrangements section details of how construction projects or CDM projects will be dealt with. Alternatively, is there a separate procedures document for dealing with CDM?

Clients should also check that the organisation is adequately covered by insurances for the services offered.

The rest of this chapter looks at the various schemes and methods for assessing competence; third party accreditation, the creation by the professional and trade bodies of registers; and how these can help clients to fulfil their duties under CDM 2007.

Cross-border recognition

An issue which is likely to have an impact upon more clients in the future is that of cross-border recognition of professional qualifications and the competence of designers and contractors based elsewhere within the European Union.

Certain professional qualifications are currently recognised across borders in the EU – for arrangements relating to recognised professions see below.

Recognition of professional qualifications

Directive 2005/36/EC of the European Parliament and of the Council of 7 September 2005 on the recognition of professional qualifications (Official Journal of the European Union L 255/222 of 30 September 2005) is concerned with:

- the removal of obstacles to the free movement of persons and services;
- the right to pursue a profession, in a self-employed or employed capacity, in a Member State other than the one in which their professional qualifications were obtained; and
- cross-border recognition of qualifications throughout the Member States.

Article 63 required all Member States to bring into force the laws, regulations and administrative provisions necessary to comply with this Directive by 20 October 2007.

Contractors are also expanding their sphere of operations and operating throughout the enlarged European Union where business opportunities arise.

Contracts advertised in the Official Journal of the European Union must be open to designers or contractors based anywhere within the EU.

Clients and their advisors will need to be in a position to undertake competency assessments in these circumstances.

A further issue, initially found in London but now experienced throughout the rest of the country, is that increasing numbers of non-English speaking workers from across the EU are available to the construction industry. The language and cultural differences can lead to problems especially where contractors have no previous experience of working with non-English speaking workers.

Clients will need to be satisfied that contractors have adequate management arrangements in place to deal with such issues. HSE has translated a number of posters and guidance into a variety of languages, but both clients and contractors need to know what is available and the sources of such information.

COMPETENCE – NOT JUST HEALTH AND SAFETY

Although regulation 4(2) only requires the person appointed to be competent in respect of the relevant statutory provisions, i.e. construction health and safety, most construction projects require knowledge and experience of fire, environmental, and waste management issues and clients should not restrict their enquiries to health and safety matters.

Risk management should encompass all areas of potential risk to the project and this should include fire risks during construction, risks to the environment, and waste management.

Clearly, all contractors should already have competence in each of these areas and state in their arrangements for a project how these issues will be dealt with.

Where any of these issues are likely to be critical to a project, for example, in a refurbishment of an historic building the fire risks might be substantial, it is important that the client can identify the areas of risk in order to question and establish the contractor's competence in dealing with such issues.

Equally, CDM co-ordinators and designers should have knowledge in each of these areas and in assessing competence, clients should ensure that they check competence based upon current practice and knowledge in each of these areas.

It is reasonable to expect that CDM co-ordinators and designers have current knowledge of key legislation such as the Fire Safety Order (RRFSO), Waste Regulations, etc.

Clients should be aware that some of the formal assessment schemes (see below) only deal with an assessment of health and safety issues and that further enquiries may be necessary according to the type and scope of the project.

It is anticipated that several of these assessment bodies will amend their current schemes in order to more closely align with CDM 2007, and more schemes will come into being.

However, it should be made clear that although formal schemes will give an indication that a particular company meets the criteria set out in the scheme of assessment it does not, and cannot, replace the client's duty to only appoint competent persons or organisations to undertake work on its behalf.

Clients should also be aware of the specialist trade organisations and bodies who currently assess health and safety as part of their membership criteria. A number of schemes are now either in place, or in progress, that have been revised to take account of the ACOP requirements in respect of core criteria.

Formal assessment schemes

A number of schemes exist which profess to provide an indication as to whether or not an organisation is capable of meeting the criteria or standards of the assessing body: the emphasis varies but broadly each of these bodies is looking at the requirement for certain core criteria, e.g. possession of a signed and up-to-date health and safety policy, accident figures, organisation and arrangements, and production of supporting information.

Carpenter compiled a list of such bodies in his report[33].

The principle bodies that currently assess companies for inclusion on approved lists are:

- The **Contractors' Health and Safety Assessment Scheme** (CHAS) is administered by the London Borough of Merton. This comprises a database of those firms which have successfully completed a health and safety questionnaire and provided supporting documentation, including worked examples of risk assessments, which is assessed by an independent assessor.
- **Constructionline** is managed by Capita Business Services. This is a pre-qualification process that delves into various aspects of a company's competence, organisation and make up, including finances and insurance compliance. It recently introduced health and safety issues into the process and now works in conjunction with CHAS on the health and safety element.
- **Link-Up** is a scheme developed by Achilles Group for the rail industry that checks compliance with railway group standards. This is the only scheme that undertakes audits of members (Category A – Safety Critical) although this is to confirm compliance with railway group standards rather than an assessment of competency. Achilles Link-Up does undertake an audit (of those companies actually undertaking work on the rail infrastructure) and potentially provides a better indication of a company's compliance.

Where a formal audit is not a requirement of the assessment body (or has not yet been carried out) it is worth posing the question as to whether the organisation has undertaken its own internal audit or been audited by a third party for compliance with health and safety and CDM compliance.

What do formal assessment schemes tell you?

If clients intend to rely upon formal assessment schemes then some knowledge of the scheme (the requirements relating to the scheme, what is assessed and how the assessment is undertaken) is required by the client or the client's advisor.

Existing schemes do not necessarily test whether or not a contractor understands the requirements of the CDM Regulations or whether a contractor can manage his or her construction site safely.

Most existing schemes do not make reference to the CDM Regulations or the requirements for the construction phase plan, or assess the standard of documentation produced on a project specific basis.

They may well assess whether a contractor is capable of producing risk assessments for a range of tasks or activities, but they do not assess the performance of a contractor in running a construction project.

Formal assessment schemes – pre-qualification questionnaires

Formal assessment schemes do have a use inasmuch as they can cut out a lot of the bureaucracy associated with pre-qualification questionnaires and provide those subscribing to the scheme with a standard baseline against which contractors can be assessed.

From a contractor's point of view gaining accreditation from one of the assessing bodies does, notionally, reduce the number of pre-qualification questionnaires that contractor needs to complete.

The advantages of such schemes are somewhat lost when:

- there is now a multiplicity of such schemes;
- they lack a common standard and format; and
- clients still insist on their own pre-qualification forms being completed for financial and other aspects that they wish to assess outside of the formal assessment schemes.

It has to be understood that major clients and organisations in the public sector have to assess far more than health and safety and although they might subscribe to the principles of reduced paperwork, the procedures under which they operate preclude them from adopting a common scheme of assessment.

Moreover, they might have found from experience that although the scheme provided the contractor with pre-qualification accreditation, the performance of the contractor did not meet expectations.

To a certain extent any assessment is backwards looking, i.e. it is an indication of past performance. The assessment can provide evidence of previous training, or of the ability to produce a risk assessment for a routine task.

It does not provide any hard evidence as to whether the contractor is capable of performing in the future: this can be affected by all manner of things, such as key personnel leaving, or innovative design or construction methods being outside the scope of the contractor's experience.

Formal assessment schemes – a two-part process

The ACOP has taken on board the recommendations of Carpenter and suggests in paragraphs 202–204 that:

'Competency assessments of organisations (including principal contractors, contractors, designers and CDM co-ordinators) should be carried out as a two stage process:
Stage 1: An assessment of the company's organisation and arrangements for health and safety to

determine whether these are sufficient to enable them to carry out the work safely and without risk to health.

Stage 2: An assessment of the company's experience and track record to establish that it is capable of doing the work; it recognises its limitations and how these should be overcome and it appreciates the risks from doing the work and how these should be tackled.'

Both the industry and the HSE are seeking more consistency in the way in which competency assessments are carried out.

In order to undertake the two stage assessment it will be necessary for clients and their advisors to assess against the **core criteria** that are set out in Appendix 4 of the ACOP.

These set out:

- the criteria against which the company needs to be assessed (column 1);
- the standards to be achieved (column 2); and
- examples of the evidence that could be used to demonstrate that the required standards are met (column 3).

In assessing whether a company meets the required standard, and is able to demonstrate that it meets these standards, the ACOP is quite clear that companies only need to produce enough evidence to show that they meet the standards stipulated in column 2 of the core criteria.

Appendix 4 of the ACOP shows the main requirements of the core criteria. Those undertaking competency assessments should be in possession of the ACOP material.

Evidential-based assessments

The evidence provided needs to take account of the project and the risks which the work entails. It requires the client to make a judgement as to whether the evidence provided meets the standard to be achieved.

Again, the ACOP is quite clear in stating in paragraph 201 that:

'if your judgement is reasonable, taking into account the evidence that has been asked for and provided, you will not be criticised if the organisation you appoint subsequently proves not to have been competent to carry out the work.'

(**Note:** this does not provide the client with an excuse not to fulfil its own obligations under the Regulations: the client is still required to satisfy all of its own duties and cannot rely upon the deficiencies of the contractor in the event that the contractor has failed to provide adequate information, or allowed the construction works to commence with an inadequate mobilisation period or without a construction phase plan in place.)

The assessment should focus on the needs for the particular job and should be proportionate to the risks arising from the work. Unnecessary bureaucracy associated with competency assessment obscures the real issues and diverts efforts away from them.

The Stage 2 assessment

The Stage 2 assessment should then concentrate on previous relevant experience in the field of work: the client can undertake basic checks against previous projects in order to verify that the work was carried out with due regard to health and safety.

Clients can make use of various methods to undertake the Stage 2 assessment including formal tender interviews.

These should provide an insight into the contractor's (or consultant's) project team and their skills and attributes in managing similar projects.

Interviews provide an opportunity to probe a bit more deeply into such areas as accident statistics: a question about the organisations record and current claims status under their employees liability/public liability insurance might paint a different picture to that shown on the pre-qualification questionnaire for the last three years' accident figures.

The extent of the client's liability to assess competence is dealt with later in this chapter.

Where the client relies upon the CDM co-ordinator to carry out competency assessments the CDM-C should possess the necessary skills in order to undertake the task. This will require knowledge and understanding of 'policy' documents and other associated health and safety issues and the ability to analyse the information provided by the various duty holders.

The skills required must equate to those undertaking assessments for the recognised formal assessment schemes: the client is entitled to be able to rely upon the assessment made by the CDM-C as much as it can expect to rely upon the assessments undertaken by CHAS or similar organisations.

It should be noted that formal assessment schemes such as CHAS do rely upon qualified health and safety practitioners to undertake their vetting process.

Those putting themselves forward as CDM co-ordinators should remember that they by taking on the role of assessor they deem themselves competent for the task.

Trade bodies and organisations

A number of trade bodies and organisations already operate schemes where the membership criteria demand standards equal to those of the formal assessment schemes operated by organisations such as CHAS or Constructionline.

Some have already been prompted into bringing their schemes into line with the ACOP requirements and membership of such organisations should provide clients with the same degree of confidence as schemes which require formal assessments of companies' health and safety documentation and procedures.

A number of schemes are described below in order to provide some indication as to the membership criteria and how these align with the ACOP requirements.

ECA/HVCA

The Electrical Contractors Association (ECA) and Heating and Ventilation Contractors Association (HVCA) have promoted a joint scheme whereby the competence of members is assessed, based upon the core criteria as set out in the ACOP.

NASC

The National Access and Scaffolding Confederation (NASC) is the recognised trade organisation for the access and scaffolding industry.

The membership criteria include:
Health and safety:

- provision of signed health and safety policy statement;
- evidence that it meets current health and safety legislation;
- completion of NASC annual accident return.

Audit:

- members are subjected to rigorous third party accredited audits on a biennial basis.

Training:

- registration of site employees under the Construction Industry Scaffolders Record Scheme (CISRS) (www.cisrs.org.uk) which is affiliated to the Construction Skills Certification Scheme (CSCS) (see below);
- applicants must produce records of training and a plan for the continuation of training;
- a minimum of 75 per cent of CISRS carded scaffolding operatives is required as a condition of membership.

Code of Conduct

- Members must comply with NASC Code of Conduct and NASC Bye Laws and Rules.

The NASC publishes guidance for the access industry including SG4:05[35] and TG20:07[36].

Other organisations
When relying upon membership of trade bodies as a measure of a contractor's competence, clients should understand what the actual membership criteria really are.

Organisations such as NASC are robust in their assessment and acceptance of firms seeking membership.

Features such as requirements for a high percentage of qualified staff, regular audits and training records should be included in the scheme and the criteria set by NASC and similar organisations should be taken as a benchmark.

Competence packs – contractors, designers and CDM co-ordinators

Another route open to all of the duty holders is to produce a company profile, or statement of competence, which sets out how the individual or organisation putting itself forward for each of the roles demonstrates its competence to take on the particular role.

This can be used to demonstrate the competence of individuals or of the company to undertake the particular role (or roles) which it wishes to take on.

This has been a feature widely used under the previous Regulations and provides an alternative to clients' (or others') questionnaires. It has the advantage that it can be tailored to the specific needs of the practice and allows the company to regularly update the documentation with changes to key personnel or projects undertaken and gives control of the process to the duty holder.

The schedules contained in Appendix 4 of the ACOP provide a ready-made template.

COMPETENCE – THE INDIVIDUAL DUTY HOLDER

The earlier part of this chapter was mainly concerned with the competency of organisations (the construction company or the consultancy practice) as, by and large, it is the company that is appointed and it is therefore the company that needs to demonstrate its corporate competence to undertake the project.

For most individuals the assessment will be based upon individual professional qualifications, evidence of relevant project-related knowledge and experience. In addition, the commitment to ongoing CPD as well as knowledge of CDM 2007 and other recent legislation will be a good indicator of professionalism and competence.

Competency schemes – CSCS Cards

There are a number of schemes for individuals within the engineering and construction industries operated by either trade bodies or by professional organisations from within the industry.

The basic scheme is the Construction Skills Certification Scheme (CSCS Card) which is an industry-led scheme set up to register every competent construction operative not already in possession of a 'skills-related card', and recognises site competency which has been assessed. It also includes a multiple-choice health and safety test.

There are a number of different levels, including management levels, which are denoted by different coloured cards.

The main feature of the CSCS Card scheme is that it measures 'awareness' and is geared to persons visiting site.

It does not profess to measure knowledge, competency or compliance with CDM.

See also the Construction Industry Scaffolders Record Scheme (CISRS) at www.cisrs.org.uk

Registers

The ACOP makes mention of the use of registers for designers and CDM co-ordinators, with entry onto the registers being open to those from within the industry who are able to meet the relevant standards.

A number of schemes have either been set up, or are in the course of development and these need to be judged against the core criteria and competency standards set out in the ACOP.

ICE Register
The Institution of Civil Engineers has had a Health and Safety Register in place for several years. It is open to professionally qualified members of a relevant professional body (CEng/IEng or equivalent, e.g. through CIBSE, ICE, IStructE, RIBA, RICS, or other chartered institutions actively engaged in the construction industry).

The entry requirements include:

- a professional qualification;
- a minimum of ten years in the construction industry;
- attendance at appropriate courses;
- meets the core competencies;
- an interview by two assessors;
- sit and pass an 'open book' exam;
- commitment to keep up to date with health and safety legislation and requirements by CPD (CPD record must be submitted every two years).

This scheme sets a standard that can be used as a benchmark and is recognised by the HSE.

APS Fellowship

The award of a Fellowship by the Association for Project Safety entails a similar route of entry and again has received recognition from HSE as achieving

a standard for individuals who are capable of undertaking larger or more complex projects, or high risk projects (although it is not included in the ACOP).

CDM2007.org

A new scheme was introduced by London Borough of Bromley in May 2007 for the public sector comprising an accreditation scheme and a modular learning package linked into the CDM2007.org e-learning portal.

This scheme has been launched initially as a resource for local authorities in order to allow them to participate in an online training course with the aim of demonstrating 'competence' in order to undertake the role of CDM-C and meeting the core criteria set out in Appendix 4 of the ACOP.

Further information relating to the scheme can be found at: www.CDM2007.org

Health and safety qualifications

In fulfilling the duties relating to competence under regulation 4, it is difficult to see how any duty holder can satisfy these requirements without some understanding or awareness of construction health and safety.

It was apparent that under CDM 1994 many duty holders had only minimal knowledge of health and safety law, or of specific regulations relating to the actual projects that they were involved with (e.g. the specification of paints or adhesives containing substances that affected the human central nervous system (CNS) for use in a confined space such as a cellar or basement). Not only were the duty holders unaware of the control measures that might be required in these circumstances, they also lacked knowledge of the specific Regulations that might apply (COSHH and Confined Spaces Regulations).

CDM 2007 and the ACOP are more explicit in respect of health and safety knowledge and the qualifications that might be required in order to demonstrate competence.

The following sections consider some of the formal health and safety qualifications that are available.

Membership of IOSH
IOSH is the recognised professional body for those qualified as safety practitioners, with the following grades of membership:

- Chartered Fellow of the Institution of Occupational Safety and Health (CFIOSH) Chartered Safety and Health Practitioner
- Chartered Member of the Institution of Occupational Safety and Health (CMIOSH) Chartered Safety and Health Practitioner

All chartered members are required to undertake CPD and submit details which are subject to verification.

- Graduate member (Grad IOSH)
- Technical member (Tech IOSH).

NEBOSH qualifications

The 'Carpenter Report' and the CDM ACOP have both highlighted the relevance of NEBOSH qualifications for those working in the construction industry including those undertaking the new CDM co-ordinator role.

NEBOSH is the National Examination Board in Occupational Safety and Health and offers qualifications which have been accredited both at Level 3 (NEBOSH National General Certificate) and Level 6 (NEBOSH National Diploma) by the Qualifications and Curriculum Authority (QCA).

The Certificate syllabus, which was completely revised in May 2002, reflects the management model in the Health and Safety Executive's *Successful Health and Safety Management* (HSG65)[5], which constitutes the UK HSE's basic guide on how organisations should manage occupational safety and health. See figure 10.

The NEBOSH National Certificate in Construction Safety and Health underwent a radical change in 2003 and is now closely aligned with the General Certificate, reflects HSG65 and is a Level 3 qualification.

The system of assessment for the Construction Certificate consists of an examination (two written papers) and a practical health and safety assessment of a construction site.

In response to the perceived need for a 'Fire Risk Management' qualification, following the publication of the *Regulatory Reform (Fire Safety) Order* 2005, NEBOSH have created a new *Certificate in Fire Safety*

and Risk Management which is now available at selected centres.

SMSTS – Site Managers Safety Training Scheme

This is a five day course run and accredited by the CITB and although it is primarily aimed at construction site managers, it could provide other duty holders with a useful insight into the realities of site safety.

Other relevant courses

There are a number of universities that provide degree courses in Occupational Health and Safety at Batchelor and Masters level as well as postgraduate diplomas.

These courses are accredited by IOSH as meeting the academic requirements for graduate membership (Grad IOSH).

The NEBOSH Diploma is an NVQ Level 6 qualification and provides an understanding of health and safety issues but is not construction orientated.

There is still a need for construction knowledge and experience.

Performance standards

The concept of 'performance standards' has also been under discussion. These would be aligned to the core criteria set out in the ACOP but again are still awaiting universal acceptance by other professions and the rest of the industry.

CDM CO-ORDINATOR

The general duties of CDM co-ordinators (CDM-Cs) are set out in regulation 20 and at paragraph 200 of the ACOP:

'For notifiable projects, a key duty of the CDM co-ordinator is to advise clients about competence of designers and contractors, including the principal contractor that they engage.'

These duties are included in regulation 20(1)(a) which require the CDM-C to:

'give suitable and sufficient advice ... to the client ...'

Although CDM 1994 required that the planning supervisor (PS) should be able to provide advice on the competency of designers and contractors, if requested to do so by the client, in practice clients made key appointments before the PS was appointed and therefore did not involve the PS in the assessment process.

Larger organisations, such as public sector bodies, would often run independent checks or use formal

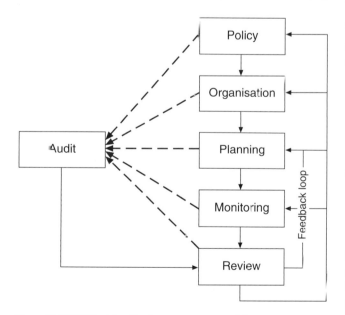

Figure 10: HSG65 health and safety management model

assessment schemes, such as CHAS or Constructionline, and would not generally involve the PS in the formal assessment process.

CDM 2007 is likely to require far greater involvement of CDM-Cs, as clients come to rely upon them to provide advice as to the competency of the design team and the construction team.

In order to provide suitable and sufficient advice, the CDM-C will require a greater degree of understanding and knowledge of the criteria against which competency is assessed, the procedures for assessing competency and knowledge of the various schemes that are available.

Clearly, those undertaking this role and offering advice to clients will require additional skills and perhaps additional training if they wish to fulfil their duties under regulation 20(1)(a), e.g. some health and safety training or qualification such as the NEBOSH Construction Certificate together with knowledge of audit systems.

As well as the formal qualifications, entry onto a recognised register (such as those discussed above) would provide clients with confirmation that the individuals concerned meet industry standards of competence.

PRINCIPAL CONTRACTOR

In assessing the competence of a principal contractor and of the resources available to him or her to undertake a particular project, some consideration needs to be given to the type and number of contractors/subcontractors that the principal contractor will be required to organise and manage, and also the extent of any ongoing design, including design undertaken by subcontractors.

Even on relatively small construction projects the number of contractors involved can easily run into dozens, with subcontractors responsible for elements of design. The whole process requires careful management, not only of the programme, but of the interface and relationship between the various contractors on site.

This is especially relevant with the prevalence of 'fast track projects' in the retail and leisure sectors – where programmes are incredibly tight and often flooded with labour in order to achieve practical completion at the appointed date.

In these cases the client needs to assess the ability of the contractor to perform, i.e. does the contractor have the right procedures in place, the ability to programme the work, and the right people with the right skills in place on site.

Consideration also needs to be given to finding the right contractor for the particular project, especially where specialist skills are required for projects such as high class retail fit-outs, or where major civil works are required.

With construction covering such a vast range of projects it is important that the contractors appointed for a particular project have a track record in the particular type of work required.

It is also important to ascertain their understanding of CDM and capabilities in producing CDM documentation such as the construction phase plan, the health and safety file and the manuals.

CDM 2007 also mentions the requirement for contractor site rules and inductions. The client should be satisfied that the contractor has the capability to produce such documentation and that this capability will be available to the construction team.

Where the contractor is otherwise knowledgeable and competent but lacks the capacity or expertise to undertake the production of this type of documentation there is no reason why these skills should not be brought in or even outsourced. In any event the CDM-C has a duty to liaise with the principal contractor over the production of the construction phase plan.

LARGER OR MORE COMPLEX PROJECTS

The ACOP differentiates between core criteria for demonstration of competence for companies, contractors, CDM co-ordinators and designers for most types of projects and the additional levels of competence required by a CDM-C for larger or more complex projects, or for projects with high or unusual risks.

Paragraph 232 of the ACOP states:

'For larger or more complex projects, or for those with unusual or high risks, the skills and knowledge of the CDM co-ordinator will need to reflect the complexity of the project and the specialist knowledge necessary to ensure that risks are properly controlled. ...'

This is supplemented by a table in Appendix 5 – *Guidance for assessing competence of a CDM co-ordinator for a larger or more complex project, or one with high or unusual risks.*

The ACOP does not provide any further guidance as to what constitutes such a project: however, this should be self-evident.

A list of high risk activities is provided in Annex II of Directive 92/57/EEC (see page 32) and in HSE construction guidance documents.

Heritage works

Historic buildings provide a special category where additional knowledge and experience is required, especially where listed buildings have fallen out of use and are in poor condition.

With some 376,000[37] listed buildings in England there is a wide variety of building types ranging from small scale domestic properties to larger commercial buildings such as mills and markets; ecclesiastical buildings such as churches, cathedrals and, more recently, listed buildings such as pre-war cinemas.

COMPETENCE – DUTY HOLDER'S ACCEPTANCE OF APPOINTMENTS

CDM 2007 requires that duty holders must ensure that they are competent before accepting an appointment.

Regulation 4(1) – 'No person on whom these regulations place a duty shall:

(a) .
(b) accept such an appointment or engagement unless he is competent.'

ACOP paragraph 119 states that designers should:

'a) make sure that they are competent and adequately resourced to address the health and safety issues likely to be involved in the design;'.

ACOP paragraph 150 states that principal contractors must:

'b) make sure that they are competent to address the health and safety issues likely to be involved in the management of the construction phase;'.

All duty holders should assess their competence against the core criteria set out in paragraphs 193–240 of the ACOP and in Appendix 4.

It is also an explicit requirement that, having declared themselves competent and accepted an appointment, all duty holders develop and maintain their competence by embarking upon a continuing professional development programme (CPD) that enables them to keep up to date with changes in legislation and professional practice.

A number of the professional organisations now set mandatory requirements for CPD, and in the case of IOSH this applies to all grades of membership – failure to undertake the required level of CPD will result in loss of the grade of membership previously attained.

EXTENT OF CLIENT'S LIABILITY TO ASSESS COMPETENCE

The ACOP clearly sets out what is expected in terms of competence and in paragraph 194 states that:

'Assessments should focus on the needs of the particular project and be proportionate to the risks, size and complexity of the work.'

The ACOP continues at paragraph 201:

'Doing an assessment requires you to make a judgement as to whether the organisation or

individual has the competence to carry out the work safely. If your judgement is reasonable, taking into account the evidence that has been asked for and provided, you will not be criticised if the organisation you appoint subsequently proves not to have been competent to carry out the work.'

Although on the face of it these words might offer some comfort to the client (or others assessing competence) the reality will always be that the judgement must be sound and backed up by sufficient evidence to demonstrate that it was **reasonable**.

It is unlikely that the client will be judged blameless without rigorous examination of the evidence – it is therefore incumbent upon the client to ensure that sufficient evidence is available to back up any assertion that the assessment that was undertaken in accordance with the guidance provided and to document the decision-making process.

The ACOP suggests that some reliance can be placed upon formal assessment schemes (such as CHAS or Achilles Link Up) but the client or the client's advisor does need to understand the requirements and limitations of any particular assessment scheme relied upon.

The questions to be asked are:

- Does the assessment scheme align with the requirements of the ACOP?
- What additional assessments does the client need to make to ascertain the competence of the contractor, designer, etc?

Conversely, those clients (or other duty holders) who fail to undertake an adequate assessment of competence will leave themselves wide open to criticism in the event that the appointed organisation subsequently proves not to have been competent.

Clients must also take into account that other legislation, especially environmental legislation, may not be so generous in discounting liability: the client's duty of care in respect of waste places strict liability upon the client for the wrongdoings of its contractors.

Conclusions

All duty holders appointing others to undertake work on their behalf must be satisfied that they have adequately assessed the competence of organisations or individuals appointed under CDM 2007 – CDM co-ordinators, designers, principal contractors and contractors.

The assessment needs to be proportional to the risks, size and complexity of the work.

Competence also needs to be assessed in respect of other statutory requirements, such as fire and the environment, and should not be restricted to health and safety requirements under CDM.

As pointed out by Dr Satish Desai in a discussion forum on CDM competence on the HSE website:

'Experience is often quoted in years, which is misleading. Breadth (of experience) is needed as much as time … as well as sound judgment.'

RICS and competence

RICS is recognised as a 'relevant professional institution' at paragraph 222 of the ACOP in respect of competence for 'individual designers' and membership of RICS is regarded 'as a strong indicator that a designer has the necessary task knowledge and an ability to recognise the health and safety implications of their design work'.

The RICS is also recognised as a 'relevant professional institution' in respect of competence for the role of CDM co-ordinator: although this is not at present noted in the ACOP, an RICS member sought and received written confirmation that this is the case subsequent to the new ACOP being published.

Individual members and companies will still need to assess their own competence against the criteria set out in Appendix 4 or Appendix 5 of the ACOP in order to demonstrate their own competence before accepting commissions as set out in regulation 4.

They will also need to be satisfied that their membership of RICS is matched by the appropriate skill sets and membership of an appropriate faculty or specialism.

At the time of publication RICS was looking at the potential for developing an accredited course for CDM co-ordinators.

RICS register

RICS is in the process of setting up a register for CDM-co-ordinators.

8 Commencing the construction phase

This chapter looks at getting the project on site, the duties and responsibilities of the client, contractor and, in the case of notifiable projects, the principal contractor and CDM co-ordinator, issues arising during construction and contractual issues.

General issues such as mobilisation (the period allowed for planning and preparation of construction works), provision of welfare facilities and the control of start on site will apply to all types of project.

The chapter also looks briefly at any specific issues related to fire in construction and different types of construction work, and deals with working in occupied or partly occupied premises (which raises additional issues to those that might arise on sites where a contractor has sole possession and control).

DUTIES AND RESPONSIBILITIES

Summary of the client's duties (notifiable projects)

Once the client has got to a point where he or she is able to select a contractor to carry out construction work on his or her behalf then the client must ensure that the following duties under CDM 2007 are complied with:

- appointment of a principal contractor – regulation 14(2);
- any such appointment is in writing – regulation 14(5);
- that the PC has prepared a construction phase plan – regulation 16(1);
- that suitable welfare facilities are in place – regulation 16(2).

The CDM co-ordinator's duties (notifiable projects)

Following the selection of the principal contractor the CDM-C has a duty to notify the HSE (or ORR – Office of Rail Regulation) of the additional particulars relating to the principal contractor.

Any additional appointments, including additional designers or contractors not already previously notified, should be included on the *F10 Notification of construction project*.

Notifiable projects – getting the project started

CDM 2007 is quite clear in respect of what is required in order for a contractor to be able to commence construction work.

For a notifiable project the client must fulfil his or her duties under Part 2 (which apply to all projects whether notifiable or not) and also comply with the additional duties under Part 3.

Matters relating to procurement and to competence of contractors are covered in Chapters 6 and 7.

Non-notifiable projects

For non-notifiable projects there will not be a CDM-C and all of the responsibilities of the client will be covered by its duties under Part 2 of CDM 2007, i.e. the general management duties applying to construction projects.

There may also be other requirements to be met that should not be overlooked in the eagerness to commence works on site (for example, where works involve party walls, the requirement to serve a party wall notice, or where there is a need to erect a scaffold on the pavement, an application for a scaffold or hoardings licence).

These are issues upon which either the designers or contractors should be in a position to advise the client.

Appointment of a principal contractor

The requirements relating to the appointment of a principal contractor are contained within regulation 14(2):

14(2) 'After appointing a CDM co-ordinator under paragraph (1), the client shall appoint a person ("the principal contractor") as soon as is practicable after the client knows enough about the project to be able to select a suitable person for such appointment, to perform the duties specified in regulations 22 to 24.'

Clients should also take note that once a project commences on site there is a requirement for a principal contractor (PC) to be in place:

14(3) 'The client shall ensure that appointments under paragraphs (1) and (2) are changed or renewed as necessary to ensure that there is at all times until the end of the construction phase a CDM co-ordinator and principal contractor.'

This does allow for the role to be taken over by another contractor at various stages through the life of a project, for example:

- demolition and site clearance – demolition contractor appointed as principal contractor;
- ground works package – civil engineering group called in to undertake the principal contractor role during the piling and ground works package;
- shell and core – a further contractor took over as principal contractor for the main construction works;
- fit-out – a specialist fit-out contractor took over the final phase of the works in order to complete the fit-out package.

Clients are quite free to choose whether they only appoint a single contractor to undertake the principal contractor role for the whole of the project or to split it up into packages with a different principal contractor for each stage of the project.

Circumstances may arise where, either due to contractual difficulties or through the whim of the client, there are periods where no appointment is in place.

This could occur, for example, through a principal contractor running into financial difficulty (this is explored later in this chapter), or through a falling out between the two parties.

In these circumstances the client is deemed to take on the role of principal contractor and all of the duties that apply.

Regulation 14(4) will then apply:
'The client shall:

(a) be deemed for the purposes of these Regulations, save paragraphs (1) and (2) and regulations 18(1) and 19(1)(a) to have been appointed as the CDM co-ordinator or principal contractor, or both, for any period for which no person (including himself) has been so appointed; and

(b) accordingly be subject to the duties imposed by regulations 20 and 21 on a CDM co-ordinator or, as the case may be, the duties imposed by regulations 22 to 24 on a principal contractor, or both sets of duties.'

Regulation 14(5) requires that any such appointment is in writing (the definition of which 'includes writing which is kept in electronic form and which can be printed' – regulation 2).

This is a statutory requirement and should not be confused with any contractual arrangements that may be entered into between the two parties.

In many cases a project will commence on site without a formal written agreement or contract in place at the time of commencement. In practice the two parties may prefer for there to be some written confirmation before allowing the contractor to commence works on site comprising either an exchange of letters or a 'letter of intent'. It may well be many months before such an exchange of letters is followed up by the formal contract.

However, it should be noted that the lack of any formal contract documentation does not reduce the requirements placed upon contractors by health and safety legislation and the need for contractors to implement and comply with the requirements placed upon them as duty holders under CDM 2007.

In addition, general health and safety legislation, including HASAW 1974 and the *Management Regulations* 1999, applies to all of their activities.

Early appointment of principal contractor

CDM 2007 requires (under regulation 14 (2)) that the client **appoints** a principal contractor as soon as practicable: basically once in a position to do so.

In practical terms this is unlikely to take place as early as the Regulations imply because of the difficulties concerned with the contractual arrangements.

However, where the opportunity arises to bring the expertise of a contractor on board as a consultant at an early stage, tangible benefits are certainly achievable. The expertise of contractors can make a significant contribution to the build aspects – if the best solutions are identified early in the design then savings can be achieved not only at the construction stage but also during design.

Although the impetus will be placed quite clearly on achieving a design that offers the best technical solutions, the benefits should translate into more efficient (and thus cheaper) build. There is also the prospect that the design will have been thought through with safety issues being taken into account at this stage.

Although the general principles of prevention should be taken into account throughout the design process (see regulation 7), it is the unplanned changes that take place during construction (when it is found that the design does not work) that provide the highest degree of risk. This is because, in the haste to make changes, safety considerations can be left out, or because components already installed have to be adapted or rebuilt.

Case study – hotel design changes

Late changes to the mechanical design for a new hotel well into construction meant that the location and size of a number of riser ducts running up through several floors of the building required formation of new openings through existing concrete slabs.

This work required the use of diamond drilling to cut through the existing slabs and for existing openings to be altered. In addition, the resited risers meant that additional works had to be carried out on each floor to ductwork with new penetrations through walls and partitions and with openings which now needed to be filled in.

In this particular case the contractor failed to provide adequate temporary edge protection or coverings to the openings formed in the floor slab in sufficient time to prevent a worker plunging through the unprotected opening.

When the original risers were formed all necessary precautions had been taken but in the rush to implement the changes the protective measures were overlooked.

(Apart from the structural works, the integrity of the passive fire precautions may be compromised if attention is not paid to the design of fire stopping.)

The client's duty in relation to the start of the construction phase where a project is notifiable

The client's duties are clearly stated in regulation 16.

CDM 2007 regulation 16 – The client's duty in relation to the start of construction phase where a project is notifiable
'Where the project is notifiable, the client shall ensure that the construction phase does not start unless:

(a) the principal contractor has prepared a construction phase plan which complies with regulations 23(1)(a) and 23(2); and
(b) he is satisfied that the requirements of regulation 22(1)(c) (provision of welfare facilities) will be complied with during the construction phase.'

This is an important gateway in the life of the project and the client should ensure that adequate time is allowed in its own programme for these key stages to be dealt with properly.

The CDM co-ordinator has a key role to play at this stage including liaison with the principal contractor, advising the client and ensuring that the HSE is notified of additional appointments including that of the principal contractor. The duties of the CDM-C are dealt with in greater detail later in this chapter.

However, the CDM-C is required to give suitable and sufficient advice and assistance to the client in performing its duties under regulation 16.

This does mean that the CDM co-ordinator requires sufficient knowledge and expertise to provide this advice to the client and to identify any deficiencies that might exist in any plan presented to the client by the principal contractor.

The construction phase plan

The content of the construction phase plan (the 'plan') will depend upon the type of project and type of structure but as a general guide will include most of the elements included in Appendix 3 of the ACOP.

Further information on the content of the construction phase plan is provided in Chapters 9 and 10.

The requirement is for the principal contractor to have prepared a plan which complies with regulations 23(1) and 23(2).

CDM 2007 regulation 23 – The principal contractor's duty in relation to the construction phase plan
'(1) The principal contractor shall:

(a) before the start of the construction phase, prepare a construction phase plan which is sufficient to ensure that the construction phase is planned, managed and monitored in a way which enables the construction work to be started so far as is reasonably practicable without risk to health or safety, paying adequate regard to the information provided by the designer under regulations 11(6) and 18(2) and the pre-construction information provided under regulation 20(2)(b);
(b) from time to time and as often as may be appropriate throughout the project update, review, revise and refine the construction phase plan so that it continues to be sufficient to ensure that the construction phase is planned, managed and monitored in a way which enables the construction work to be carried out so far as is reasonably practicable without risk to health or safety; and
(c) arrange for the construction phase plan to be implemented in a way which will ensure so far as is reasonably practicable the health and safety of all persons carrying out the construction work and all persons who may be affected by the work.

(2) The principal contractor shall take all reasonable steps to ensure that the construction phase plan identifies the risks to health and safety arising from the construction work (including the risks specific to the particular type of construction work concerned) and includes suitable and sufficient measures to address such risks, including any site rules.'

PROVISION OF WELFARE FACILITIES

This is an area that might have been ignored by clients in the past, but CDM 2007 places clear responsibilities upon the client to ensure that adequate welfare facilities are provided and available throughout the course of the construction phase (regulation 16(b)), i.e. that:

> 'he is satisfied that the requirements of regulation 22(1)(c) (provision of welfare facilities) will be complied with during the construction phase.'

CDM 2007 applies to all construction projects and, therefore, welfare facilities are required for **all** construction projects regardless of their size or duration. The requirement applies to fixed sites and also to works on transient construction sites, for example, works being carried out along a section of highway.

The full requirements in relation to provision of welfare facilities are set out in Schedule 2 to the Regulations covering the requirements of regulations 9(1)(b), 13(7) and 22(1)(c).

Key points

- Adequate welfare facilities should be provided and available throughout the course of the construction phase.
- The client needs to be satisfied that they will be available.
- Contractors need to make sure that they make adequate allowance in their pricing so that they can provide adequate facilities throughout the construction phase.
- The provision of these facilities may vary during the course of the construction phase dependent upon the physical conditions and requirements on site.
- Additional facilities may be required for operations such as asbestos removal, removal of contaminated land or hazardous materials – a decontamination unit might be provided in these circumstances.
- Use can be made of existing client facilities where appropriate.
- Advance planning for provision of welfare facilities may be required where new service connections (water, drainage and electrical connections) are needed.
- A fire risk assessment should be prepared in respect of the site accommodation.

Provision of these facilities should be a contractual requirement and therefore liaison will be required between the client, the CDM-C (for notifiable projects) and the contract administrator and/or cost consultant in order to ensure that these requirements are properly documented and adequate sums allowed for in the budget.

Various options are set out below and further information can be found in HSE Information Sheets Nos. 18[38] and 46[39].

FIRE RISK ASSESSMENT

It should be noted that fire certificates are no longer issued by the HSE in respect of site accommodation, as previously required under the provisions of the *Fire Certificate (Special Premises) Regulations* 1976.

Instead, there is now a requirement to carry out a '**suitable and sufficient**' risk assessment in accordance with the requirements of article 9(1) of the *Regulatory Reform (Fire Safety) Order* 2005.

The responsibility for carrying out the fire risk assessment will normally rest with the contractor where he or she has control of the construction site.

However, in those cases where the welfare facilities are shared with the client (e.g. where the works are being carried out in occupied premises or otherwise being shared) then the client may also be involved in the fire risk assessment process.

Provision of welfare facilities – options

Decontamination units will be required if any of the following contaminants are present:

- asbestos;
- lead (in a process or form where fumes may be given off or otherwise ingested);
- bird droppings or other animal excreta;
- chemical or biological contamination;
- contaminated ground.

A decontamination unit should provide:

- an undressing area, with facilities for safe disposal of contaminated clothing and PPE – disposable items should be securely bagged and disposed of as hazardous waste, other items should be laundered by a specialist laundry and PPE should be cleaned according to the manufacturer's instructions in a separate area to prevent contamination of other items;
- a shower with a water collection unit to ensure all contaminated water is collected and either passed through a filtering/cleaning process and then recycled or stored for safe disposal;
- a dressing area with clean clothes and a separate used towel disposal area, towels should be laundered by a specialist laundry;
- staff dealing with cleaning and maintenance of the decontamination unit and the cleaning of contaminated items should wear full protective clothing and go through the decontamination process themselves when they have finished work.

Welfare units – types now available:
- Self-powered, self-contained units in various sizes that contain a generator (usually LPG fuel) for provision of light, heat and hot water, a manually filled cold water tank, a waste water tank (requiring regular pump-out), toilet(s), wash basin(s), restroom and clothes storage.

Build temporary facilities:
- For a long term project with large numbers of workers to cater for, this can be the most effective option (e.g. a two-year project to build a large hotel in London used this option very successfully; temporary facilities were constructed in the basement, which is now the hotel car park).

Use existing client site facilities:
- This option is feasible if the client site has adequate capacity to cater for the increased numbers of people requiring toilet, washroom, changing room and restroom facilities. Ideally construction workers should have welfare facilities specifically dedicated to their use. Responsibility for cleaning and restocking the facilities should be agreed between the client and contractor prior to construction commencing on site.

Use public facilities:
- If the construction site is close to the public conveniences, i.e. within five minutes walk, this is a viable option provided the local authority gives its consent. The usual arrangement is for the contractor to stock and clean the public facilities on a daily basis for the duration of the project.

Mobile site facilities:
- Mobile units providing facilities similar to those described under 'welfare units' for a small number of workers are available for hire or purchase.

The Regulations require **all** welfare facilities to be:

- regularly restocked with toilet paper, soap and clean dry towels;
- kept in a clean, usable and hygienic condition at all times; and
- of sufficient size and capacity to cater for the number of workers expecting to use the facilities.

It is the contractor's responsibility to provide, stock and maintain adequate welfare facilities, however, the client is responsible for ensuring that the provision of adequate welfare facilities is allowed for throughout the construction phase of the project.

NOTIFICATION OF PROJECT – DISPLAY OF F10 PARTICULARS

The requirements relating to the issue of the *F10 Notification of construction project* have been dealt with earlier but it should be noted that the principal contractor (PC) has to:

'ensure that the particulars required to be in the notice given under regulation 21 are displayed in a readable condition in a position where they can be read by any worker engaged in the construction work;' (regulation 22(1)(k)).

Whilst the Regulations only require the CDM-C to ensure that notification is made to the HSE, it is accepted practice that the CDM-C makes copies available to the PC, in order to enable the PC to comply with his or her duties to display the particulars on site.

DUTIES OF THE CDM CO-ORDINATOR

The general duties of the CDM co-ordinator prior to and during the construction phase are set out in regulation 20 of CDM 2007 and generally require liaison and co-operation between the CDM-C and the PC.

CDM 2007 regulation 20(1) – General duties of CDM co-ordinators
'(1) The CDM co-ordinator shall:
(a) give suitable and sufficient advice and assistance to the client on undertaking the measures he needs to take to comply with these Regulations during the project (including, in particular, assisting the client in complying with regulations 9 and 16);
(b) ensure that suitable arrangements are made and implemented for the co-ordination of health and safety measures during planning and preparation for the construction phase, including facilitating:
(i) co-operation and co-ordination between persons concerned in the project in pursuance of regulations 5 and 6, and
(ii) the application of the general principles of prevention in pursuance of regulation 7; and
(c) liaise with the principal contractor regarding:
(i) the contents of the health and safety file,
(ii) the information which the principal contractor needs to prepare the construction phase plan, and
(iii) any design development which may affect planning and management of the construction work.'

PROVISION OF INFORMATION

A point for clients to bear in mind is the fact that the construction phase plan is compiled by the principal contractor on the basis of information supplied by the client (via the CDM-C). In the event of a construction phase plan being deficient due to inadequate or missing information then the client may find him- or herself in some difficulty when confronted with such a plan.

In circumstances where the client either knows about the inadequacies of the information or would be deemed responsible for the provision of information that is missing (after making suitable enquiries) then the client would find it difficult to approve such a plan.

The type of information that tended to be missing in the past was that relating to items such as:

- fragile surfaces – roof lights and roofing materials or roof structures;
- asbestos;
- underground services – pipes, cables, sewers;
- overhead electrical supplies;
- confined spaces;
- plant and equipment that could start up unannounced – flood sluices, fans, etc.

The CDM-C has a duty to liaise with the PC regarding the information which the PC needs to prepare the construction plan but there will be circumstances where inadequate or inaccurate information has been provided by the client to the CDM-C.

Whilst the CDM-C has a duty to identify what information might be required and take appropriate steps to obtain such information, the CDM-C is not required to check the accuracy or veracity of such information and should be able to rely upon the information provided, as and when it is passed on by the CDM-C to others who might require it.

Information flows

There are a number of information flows that need to be maintained throughout the course of the construction phase including those between client and designers and the CDM-C and also those between the CDM-C and the PC.

For the construction team there are additional flows involving the contractor (in the case of non-notifiable projects) or the principal contractor (in the case of notifiable projects) and all of those persons present on the construction site including contractors, their employees and others involved in the supply chain.

Most construction projects are defined by the ever changing nature of the workforce: apart from the main contractor's permanent team who will remain on site for the life of the project, the majority of the workforce will be transient in nature and on site for varying periods of time ranging from a couple of hours, to a couple of days or to several weeks or months.

It is notoriously difficult to engage with such an ebb and flow of people and, especially where the workforce remains on site for a matter of days, to instil a safety culture into the workforce.

That is why CDM 2007 places such emphasis on the importance of provision of information to the workforce and on worker engagement and communication.

Starting off with basic information such as site induction, information and training, there will be a continuing requirement for information flows throughout the life of the project on site.

> **ACOP paragraph 243**
>
> 'All those in control of construction work are required to provide workers (including the self-employed) under their control with any information that worker needs to carry out the construction work safely and without risk to health.'

Site induction, information and training

Contractors must not start on a construction site until they have been provided with basic information. This should include information from the client about any particular risks associated with the project (including information about existing structures where these are to be demolished or structurally altered), and from designers about any associated risks associated with the design.

Site inductions should be provided to all workers who will be working or entering the site and also to consultants and other regular visitors to the site.

Worker engagement and communication

ACOP paragraph 241 states:

> 'Involving the workforce in identifying and controlling risks is crucial to reducing the high incident rate associated with construction work. …'

Information for the health and safety file

It is important right from the start of the project that adequate arrangements and procedures are set up to facilitate the flow of information back up through the supply chain of information required for the health and safety file.

Similar procedures need to be in place for provision of information for building and other manuals.

Some system needs to be in place to check the status of relevant information throughout the course of the project with regular reviews by the client or (in the case of notifiable projects) the CDM-C.

It is far easier to identify and capture information for the file early in the project rather than leave everything until the final stages of the project.

Mobilisation – the period allowed for planning and preparation

The requirements relating to the period allowed for planning and preparation were touched upon in Chapter 6 *Buying the construction work*.

As part of the information provided to contractors, the client is obliged to provide information about the period allowed for planning and preparation in accordance with regulation 10(2)(c):

'the minimum amount of time before the construction phase which will be allowed to the contractors appointed by the client for planning and preparation for construction work;'.

Regulation 10(2)(c) applies to all construction projects regardless of their type, size or duration and applies to both notifiable and non-notifiable construction projects.

The clear intention of this regulation is that by asking the client to consider the amount of time that is made available to plan and prepare for the construction work contractors will be less likely to make an immediate start on site with no preparation whatsoever.

It should be noted that neither the ACOP nor the Regulations specify the amount of time that should be allowed.

The period of time allowed is within the judgement of the client: who is able to take advice from other members of the team including the CDM-C.

Whilst intended as a measure to secure safer working by ensuring that enough time is allowed to prepare the necessary documentation, evaluate risks and ensure that adequate control measures are in place, positive benefits should also arise for principal contractors by providing adequate time to their subcontractors to plan matters further down the supply chain.

Certainly at the lower end of the market the industry is beset by problems relating to the failure of contractors to turn up on site, more often than not because they are unable to schedule work in with unrealistic lead in times.

The opportunity afforded by the requirement for a 'mobilisation' period should, at least in theory, lead to more reliable and thus more efficient working in the industry.

Case study – brownfield redevelopment

On a recent brownfield development involving a 15 acre city centre site the contractor's site manager and safety advisor were able to spend time over a period of six months working up detailed proposals for the construction phase including project safety documentation and the construction programme.

At the commencement of works:

- the construction phase plan;
- a detailed overall methodology for the scheme which involved diversion of major utility services and change to the local road layout;
- method statements for all major subcontracts;
- induction programmes; and
- a detailed week-by-week programme accompanied by drawings showing the work programmed for each week of the eight month enabling works programme;

were all available.

The meticulous planning enabled the health and safety issues to be properly identified and control measures adequately planned. The detailed development of the programme enabled the supply chain to perform in accordance with the programme demands.

Another benefit was that the detailed transport management plan enabled the contractor to meet and satisfy the requirements of the Highways Authority in respect of vehicle movements in a highly congested part of the city.

The high volume of vehicle movements and the traffic routing provided potential conflicts with a bus lane during the peak morning period which could have led to major reductions in the permitted lorry movements and would have had a significant impact on the programme.

Some temporary road closures were required and planned for and these were easily accommodated within the mobilisation period allowed.

Control of start on site

As stated previously this is an important gateway in the life of the project and it is suggested that some form of QA procedure is adopted by the client to ensure that all necessary issues are properly addressed before allowing the construction phase to commence.

The Regulations refer to the construction phase plan and provision of welfare facilities but there are a number of issues that also need to be in place that could be included as part of the checking procedure.

The following could provide the basis for a checklist. Has the client:

- assessed the competence of contractors, including the principal contractor, that have been appointed by him or her?
- taken reasonable steps to ensure that the arrangements made for managing the project are suitable to ensure that:
  (a) the construction work can be carried out so far as is reasonably practicable without risk to the health and safety of any person;
  (b) the requirements of Schedule 2 are complied with in respect of any person carrying out construction work; and
  (c) any structure designed for use as a workplace has been designed taking account of the provisions of the *Workplace Regulations* 1992 which relate to the design of, and materials used in, the structure?
- provided any relevant information to both designers and contractors to allow them to plan how to carry out the work safely and implement any necessary measures to do so?
- ensured that an F10 has been issued to the HSE (or other relevant enforcing authority) with a declaration signed by the client that he or she is aware of his or her duties?
- satisfied him- or herself with the proposals in relation to provision of welfare facilities by the contractor?
- satisfied him – or herself that a construction phase plan has been prepared in accordance with the requirements of CDM 2007?

Monitoring

This section looks at the requirements of clients to monitor performance of the contractors appointed by them to undertake construction work on their behalf.

The client's duty in relation to arrangements for managing projects are set out in regulation 9, whereby the client is required to ensure that there are suitable arrangements for:

(a) 'the construction work to be carried out so far as is reasonably practicable without risk to the health and safety of any person;'
(b) 'the requirements of Schedule 2 [provision of welfare facilities] are complied with …'.

Once the works have commenced on site, regulation 9(2) requires that:

'the client shall take reasonable steps to ensure that the arrangements referred to in paragraph (1) are maintained and reviewed throughout the project.'

The ACOP states at paragraph 53 that:

'**Most clients on non-notifiable projects should be able to carry out these checks [i.e. contained in paragraph 52] for themselves.**'

If help is needed it is suggested that the competent person appointed under regulation 7 of the *Management Regulations* 1999 should be able to provide advice.

For larger projects advice would be available from the CDM-C.

ROLE OF PRINCIPAL CONTRACTOR

It is quite clear that it is the principal contractor (or contractor in the case of non-notifiable projects) who controls the site throughout the contract.

This remains the duty of the principal contractor from site set-up on day one right through to handover at practical completion.

Does the client have a role in monitoring performance of contractors?

As noted above, it is up to the contractor running the site to ensure that the arrangements he or she has stated will be in place remain in force for the duration of the construction phase.

The ACOP at paragraph 54 suggests that a client who has made a reasonable judgement as to the adequacy of the contractor's arrangements based upon the information and evidence provided:

'… will not be criticised if the arrangements subsequently prove to be inadequate, or if the company who has made the arrangements fails to implement them properly without the client's knowledge'.

The client is not required to undertake site inspections or to employ third party assurance advisors to monitor health and safety standards on site. Neither is the CDM-C required to supervise the principal contractor's implementation of the construction phase plan or supervise or monitor construction work.

Thus it is quite clear from the ACOP that under CDM 2007 as long as the client has made a reasonable judgement of the contractor's arrangements before allowing the contractor to commence construction works then no liability will attach to the client under CDM 2007 in the event that the contractor fails to perform.

However, there are a number of cases brought before the courts where the expectation under health and safety law is that employers will attract liability for the actions of their contractors.

For example, in the case of *HSE v Barnet LB* (Hendon Magistrates' Court) the HSE brought a prosecution because Barnet Council failed to adequately monitor the performance of their contractors who had been contracted to handle refuse collection within the Borough.

Although no case was brought against the client, the remarks of the Judge in the 'Bethell' case below highlight the importance of ensuring that adequate risk assessments and method statements are prepared prior to works commencing on site.

In some cases it will become obvious to the client that the contractor is failing to perform and that health and safety standards are woefully inadequate. Once it becomes apparent that this is the case, the client will not be able to ignore the failings of the contractor and will need to review what course of action is required.

The client's response will need to consider both the contractual implications and the criminal liability that may attach to the parties involved if no action is taken at all, or if the response is inadequate taking the circumstances into account.

The course of action taken by the client must be appropriate and in some circumstances (e.g. where it is quite clear that the contractor is not able to demonstrate that he or she would be able to continue the work in a safe manner) the client may have no option but to terminate the contract.

The 'Bethell' case

A case at Liverpool Crown Court highlighted the issues relating to the management of subcontractors and the necessity for the main contractor to carry out its own risk assessments.

Bethell Construction Limited, of Preston, had been hired to perform maintenance work in a large underground structure forming part of the local sewerage system and subcontracted the work out to another contractor, who in turn took on additional subcontracted labour.

The prosecution arose following the death of a subcontracted labourer who fell five metres onto a concrete platform.

Both contractors were found guilty of breaches of section 3 of the HASAW 1974 and regulation 3(1) of the *Management Regulations* 1999.

The Judge commented:

'the subcontracting arrangements had been very loose and should have been properly managed so that each party had understood its roles and responsibilities'.

Concerns were also raised that:

'Method statements were crossing in the post with the contract ... and that method statements and risk assessments' were rushed to and fro 'without an opportunity for paused reflection'.

Under CDM 2007 clients will have to give more thought as to whether such arrangements are adequate.

FIRE IN CONSTRUCTION

Clients do need to understand the impact that fires (and other incidents such as flooding, explosions, etc.) might have on their projects, or on third parties.

It is quite clear from the incidents at King's Cross and Colindale in 2006 that the fires on each of these sites had significant impact, not only on the construction project but also on the adjoining owners.

The case of King's Cross concerned a building site adjacent to the main signal box controlling the King's Cross area, which had to be closed for over 24 hours because acetylene cylinders were present at the site and had become unstable during the fire.

The fire on a construction site at Beaufort Park in Colindale, in a new residential development of six-storey timber framed flats, not only resulted in a devastating fire destroying the flats in course of construction but also caused significant heat damage to several adjoining premises.

The fire destroyed the first six-storey block in less than ten minutes and then ripped through the adjoining block which was also subsequently destroyed. It affected adjoining premises including halls of residence at the local university. Hendon Police College also suffered damage, 30 cars were destroyed and 2500 people were evacuated during the course of the fire.

In terms of risk to the project and third parties, the above examples highlight the fact that the effects of fire can be far greater than most accidents on site (apart from collapses of structures or cranes).

These are matters that should be taken into account both during design and construction.

Fire risk management

Issues to be considered include:

- What is the risk of fire occurring during construction?
- What are the consequences to the client/contractor, i.e. risk of injury, risk of loss, impact on programme, financial consequences?
- What are the consequences to others, i.e. risk to property or persons – risk of damage to adjoining premises, adjoining owners (risk of injury or loss of life), passers by, or vehicles?

There is a history of fires happening during works of renovation in stately homes (such as Uppark, Windsor Castle) and other premises caused by sources of ignition such as halogen lights or naked flames used for stripping paint or used in plumbing.

There is often an increase in the fire load in the form of combustible materials including timber products, saw dust, and cardboard packaging.

In the case of works being carried out in occupied premises there is an additional risk to those in occupation of other parts of the building, especially where fire detection systems have been disabled thus delaying detection and alarm, and where walls, ceilings and partitions have been removed or penetrated thus allowing a more rapid spread of fire.

Risk assessment

The client and the project team need to consider potential risk during both design and construction, and to explore ways in which such risks can be mitigated.

The Colindale fire highlighted risks now apparent during new build and designers must now indicate what measures might be required in order to close out potential fire risks as early in construction as possible.

It is also necessary to consider the risks to construction workers who might be exposed to risk of fire whilst working in various situations, including existing buildings being refurbished, new build, high buildings, etc.

Consideration must be given as to the adequacy of the means of escape from such buildings, especially where staircases are incomplete.

Case study – temporary fire precautions

During the construction of a new hotel comprising seven floors and with two staircases (one at either end of the building), the decision was taken during design that, due to the size and the height of the building, provision for internal means of escape would be required as early as possible once the shell and core were complete.

One of the staircases was provided with temporary fire doors, signage and emergency lighting to provide the primary means of escape throughout the fit-out stage, with the doors being replaced at the end of the project with the permanent fire doors.

Although there was a cost implication in providing a temporary set of fire doors, this was partly set off by the fact that the permanent doors were able to be fixed late in the fit-out stage and as a consequence were not damaged by the ongoing construction activities. The contractor was able to make use of them on subsequent projects.

Without the internal escape route it would have been necessary to provide an external temporary staircase as an alternative to ladder access on the scaffold.

The design team were aware that a contractor in Glasgow had been prosecuted following a fire on a construction site where the provision for means of escape had been deemed inadequate. In this case the only provision for access and egress via the scaffold had been a single point of access comprising ladders between the scaffold lifts. In an emergency situation this was completely incapable of providing a satisfactory escape route for the number of workers on the site.

Fire plan

Contractors should be required to produce a 'fire plan' which sets out the arrangements for dealing with fire risks throughout the construction phase.

The fire plan needs to take account of the changing nature of the site during the various stages of construction: there will be significant changes to both the fire load and the potential sources of ignition as the project progresses. Such risks as naked flames, the use of abrasive wheels during construction, and the introduction of live gas and electrical services in the latter part of the project during testing and commissioning need to be considered.

Clients should pay particular attention to the final fit-out period, especially where their own carpets, furniture and IT and telecommunications hubs are being installed or brought into the premises. They should also be clear as to the timing of insurances and ensure that there are no gaps between cessation of contractor's insurance and their premises insurance coming into effect.

For larger sites, where road layouts or access to the site or adjoining premises change during the course of the programme then close liaison with the Fire Service and other emergency services is required: changes should always be notified in advance of the changes taking place.

Case study – road layout

On a major city centre development several changes to the road layout were planned, including road closures on a primary traffic route (which affected access to the main railway station and several town centre car parks as well as local schools and businesses).

A site location and traffic access plan was drawn up indicating the changes in the road layout and access routes into the train station and car parks, and copies were provided to the local fire station and the ambulance service.

CDM Regulations – Part 4

The provisions relating to fire covered in Part 4 of CDM relate to the duties of contractors on construction sites but the client and CDM-C also need to understand the issues involved and ensure that the matters have been adequately considered during the design stage.

Regulation 40 deals with the means of escape issues (discussed above).

Regulation 41 deals with issues relating to fire detection and fire fighting which is explored in greater detail in the later section dealing with occupied premises.

Fire Prevention on Construction Sites – 6th edition

Clients should make provision in the tender documentation for contractors to comply with the requirements of the *Joint Code of Practice on the Protection from Fire of Construction Sites and Buildings Undergoing Renovation*, published by the Fire Protection Association 6th edition, 2006)[40].

This code sets out various requirements relating to fire during design and construction and measures to reduce the likelihood of fire occurring.

CDM 2007 regulations 40 and 41

40 Emergency routes and exits

'(1) Where necessary in the interests of the health and safety of any person on a construction site, a sufficient number of suitable emergency routes and exits shall be provided to enable any person to reach a place of safety quickly in the event of danger.

(2) An emergency route or exit provided pursuant to paragraph (1) shall lead as directly as possible to an identified safe area.

(3) Any emergency route or exit provided in accordance with paragraph (1), and any traffic route giving access thereto, shall be kept clear and free from obstruction and, where necessary, provided with emergency lighting so that such emergency route or exit may be used at any time.

(4) In making provision under paragraph (1), account shall be taken of the matters in regulation 39(2).

(5) All emergency routes or exits shall be indicated by suitable signs.'

41 Fire detection and fire-fighting

'(1) Where necessary in the interests of the health and safety of any person at work on a construction site there shall be provided suitable and sufficient:

(a) fire-fighting equipment; and
(b) fire detection and alarm systems,

which shall be suitably located.

(2) In making provision under paragraph (1), account shall be taken of the matters in regulation 39(2).

(3) Any fire-fighting equipment and any fire detection and alarm system provided under paragraph (1) shall be examined and tested at suitable intervals and properly maintained.

(4) Any fire-fighting equipment which is not designed to come into use automatically shall be easily accessible.

(5) Every person at work on a construction site shall, so far as is reasonably practicable, be instructed in the correct use of any fire-fighting equipment which it may be necessary for him to use.

(6) Where a work activity may give rise to a particular risk of fire, a person shall not carry out such work unless he is suitably instructed.

(7) Fire-fighting equipment shall be indicated by suitable signs.'

Fire enforcement on construction sites

The recent changes to both CDM and fire legislation have altered the way in which the enforcement of fire on construction sites is dealt with.

The HSE is responsible for enforcement in respect of the general fire precautions within the curtilage of the site, including site accommodation, and where provided, any sleeping accommodation.

Where such facilities, i.e. welfare facilities, site accommodation (and where provided, any sleeping accommodation) is outside the confines of the site or separated from the site (for example, by a road) then enforcement falls within the jurisdiction of the Fire and Rescue Service.

If a site is contained within, or forms part of another premises (i.e. the works are being undertaken in occupied premises) then the enforcing body for the premises would be responsible for the construction site as well.

CDM 2007 regulation 46 – Enforcement in respect of fire

'46(1) Subject to paragraphs (2) and (3):

(a) in England and Wales [a fire and rescue] authority within the meaning of article 25 of the Regulatory Reform (Fire Safety) Order 2005; or

(b) in Scotland [a relevant] authority within the meaning of section 61 of the Fire (Scotland) Act 2005,

[for the area in which the construction site is or is to be situated] shall be the enforcing authority in respect of a construction site which is contained within, or forms part of, premises which are occupied by persons other than those carrying out the construction work or any activity arising from such work as regards regulations 39 and 40, in so far as those regulations relate to fire, and regulation 41.

(2) In England and Wales paragraph (1) only applies in respect of premises to which the *Regulatory Reform (Fire Safety) Order* 2005 applies.

(3) In Scotland paragraph (1) only applies in respect of premises to which Part 3 of the *Fire (Scotland) Act* 2005 applies.'

Note: It should be noted that regulation 46 only applies to non-domestic premises.

Fire investigations

In the event of a fire on a construction site any fire investigation would normally be carried out by the Fire Service.

Where it appears that the cause of the fire is due to an uncontrolled work process, for example, hot works not carried out in a controlled manner (with inadequate procedures and control measures, or without a hot works permit system in place) then the investigation would be passed over to the HSE (or, as appropriate, the local authority) for further investigation.

The Regulatory Reform (Fire Safety) Order 2005

The *Regulatory Reform (Fire Safety) Order* 2005 reforms the law relating to fire safety in non-domestic premises and replaces the requirement for fire certification under the *Fire Precautions Act* 1971 with a regime of risk assessment for all classes of premises.

During the construction phase the contractor will be responsible for ensuring that fire risks are reduced to a minimum throughout the construction phase and that the fire risk assessment is changed in accordance with the changing circumstances on the site.

This is especially relevant as the fire load increases with the introduction of furnishings, etc. during the end phase of the project and where works are being carried out in occupied premises.

It should also be noted that fire certificates are no longer issued by the HSE in respect of site accommodation, as previously required under the provisions of the *Fire Certificate (Special Premises) Regulations* 1976.

'CONSTRUCTION WORK'

'Construction work' covers a wide range of activities and it should be stressed that the Regulations apply to all construction work.

A full definition of 'construction work' is included in regulation 2 (Interpretation). This is covered in more detail in Chapter 6.

For the sake of simplicity we have broken down the range of construction activities into the following broad categories:

- demolition – including stripping out and dismantling;
- repairs and maintenance;
- refurbishment – including alterations, additions, repairs, redecoration and testing and commissioning; and
- new build – including all types of structures and premises, fitting out and testing and commissioning.

We also deal with working in occupied or partly occupied premises, which raises additional issues to those that might arise on sites where a contractor has sole possession and control.

The preparation of schedules of dilapidations also raises a number of issues in respect of how CDM might apply and the circumstances in which the lessor could become a 'client'.

SCHEDULES OF DILAPIDATIONS

The preparation of schedules of dilapidations raises a number of issues as to when CDM should be applied.

When the process is broken down the individual stages can be tested to ascertain whether CDM should apply.

- Stage 1: Undertaking survey of premises to ascertain their condition against the lease covenants.
- Stage 2: Preparation and pricing of schedule and service of notice on lessee.
- Stage 3: Negotiations with lessee as to the accuracy of the schedule and validity of the claim.
- Stage 4:
  (a) Negotiated settlement of claim; or
  (b) disputed claim to be dealt with by legal action – arbitration, court, etc.
- Stage 5: Works undertaken in order to comply with the schedule.

It is perhaps worth noting that the preparation of a schedule of dilapidations arises from the failure of a lessee to comply with the repairing covenants contained within the lease, that the scope and extent of the works may be disputed and that, in the event of the matter going to court, the lessee may seek to limit the extent of any damages to the extent of any damage to the value of the reversionary interest.

The schedule can only include those works which the lessee is under an obligation to carry out in order to comply with the repairing covenants and in many cases the works contained within the schedule may never be carried out.

At the expiry of a long lease the freeholder may well decide to undertake a complete upgrade and refurbishment of the premises, for which a totally new specification will be required. This may include:

- stripping out and replacement of toilet fittings, cubicles and tiling;
- renewal of ceilings and light fittings;
- upgrades to cabling for IT provision; and
- upgrades to ventilation, heating and air conditioning.

Where the demised premises comprise a complete building then planned enhancements may include replacement of plant, lifts, external cladding, upgrades to fire detection and alarm systems, and to security and CCTV installations.

Application of CDM – testing the various stages

If we now consider each of these stages then some assumptions can be made.

Stage 1 – Survey

The ACOP (in paragraph 13(e)) states quite clearly that surveying is not construction work and:

'this includes taking levels, making measurements and examining structures for faults;'.

It can therefore be assumed that the actual inspection to record the dilapidations and wants of repair comes outside the scope of CDM and there is no requirement for the client to appoint a CDM co-ordinator. It should also be noted that, at this stage, the lessor is not a client duty holder under CDM.

It can also be assumed that the inspection is restricted to a visual inspection only. Where the scope of the inspection is extended to include investigation and excavation (refer to the definition of 'construction work' in regulation 2 – Interpretation) then this will be deemed to be 'construction work' and CDM will apply.

Stage 2 – Preparation and pricing of the schedule

Stage 2 would appear to meet two of the tests, namely:

- the works to be carried out fall within the definition of construction, i.e. renovation, repair, upkeep, redecoration or other maintenance; and
- the preparation of the schedule appears to fall within the definition of design, i.e. preparation of specifications or bills of quantities.

In other words, both the preparation and pricing of the schedule would appear to come within the definition of:

- construction work, and
- design.

and the person drawing up the schedule may attract duties as a designer within the strict interpretation and application of the CDM Regulations.

However, there are a number of caveats which will be explored later.

Stages 3 and 4 – Negotiations, arbitration or court action

Both of these stages appear to be completely outside the scope of CDM: these are negotiations or legal argument about the merit of the individual claims.

Stage 5 – Undertaking the works

As soon as the works are put out to tender and there is an intention for the works to be undertaken then the situation changes and CDM will apply because there is a project and there is a 'client':

'a person who in the course or furtherance of a business:

(a) seeks or accepts the services of another which may be used in the carrying out of a project for him; or
(b) carries out a project himself;' (regulation 2).

The issue then becomes one of who will undertake the work and take on the role of client: the client will have duties under Part 2 of CDM, i.e. to check the competence of contractors and to provide information.

Where the works contained within the schedule of dilapidations are likely to last for more than 30 days then Part 3 will apply: both a CDM-C and a principal contractor will need to be appointed and a construction phase plan and health and safety file will be required.

Lessor or lessee as client?

The final question to be answered is who would take on the client role and at what stage would the client duties come into effect?

- In the normal course of events it is the lessee who is required to undertake the works and take on the role of client.
- The only situation where the freeholder becomes involved is where the lessor takes possession of the premises on the expiry of the lease and undertakes the work him- or herself. In these circumstances the lessor would take on the role of client.
- In most cases there will not be a client until such time as negotiations have been concluded and a decision made as to whether the works will be carried out.
- Once the works are put out to tender then CDM applies and a CDM-C and principal contractor should be appointed where the works are notifiable.

Stage 2

If we now consider the situation at Stage 2, then the freeholder has no role: the freeholder has only instructed his or her surveyor to look at the premises and prepare and price a schedule for the purpose of making a claim against the outgoing lessee. At this stage the freeholder has no intention of instructing anyone to undertake construction works on his or her behalf and cannot be considered a client for the purpose of the Regulations.

Although Stage 2 would appear to meet the criteria for both 'construction work' and 'design', the lessor is only entitled to have the premises put into good repair (or whatever the wording of the repairing covenant requires).

Apart from the other arguments that might be applied, it is arguable as to whether reinstatement and repair in order to meet the repairing covenants of the lease comprises 'design' as there is no scope for varying the extent or the scope of the works – these are predetermined by the wants of repair found by the surveyor during the course of the inspection.

Again, depending upon the wording of the lease clauses relating to the repairing covenants, the surveyor can only ask for the premises to be put back into repair: the surveyor is not undertaking design – he or she is merely preparing a schedule in accordance with well established principles of property law.

However, if at this stage the lessor/freeholder recognises that the schedule may become the basis of a project for him or her, then that lessor/freeholder is likely to be a client as defined by CDM (see the definition of client above).

Although at this stage there would be few duties on the client, the client would need to comply with regulation 4 (i.e. the appointment of a competent surveyor) and possibly regulations 5, 6, 7, 9 and 10 – but only so far as was necessary.

In reality there would be very little for the client to do at this stage – although there may well be information required under regulation 10 that should be passed on to the surveyor at the time of instruction (see below for more detail).

Application of CDM – principles of prevention

The other area of concern to the surveyor preparing the schedule is in relation to the application of CDM and the principles of prevention.

The role of the surveyor is to apply the well established principles of property law, as noted earlier, and the surveyor cannot ask for something:

- to be done that is not covered by the repairing covenants; or
- to be provided that was not originally provided at the commencement of the lease.

For these reasons, the surveyor preparing a schedule of dilapidations is not in a position to apply the principles of prevention required under CDM (**these principles apply to design work**).

However, that is not to say that the surveyor would, or should, ignore health and safety issues. In pricing up the schedule a surveyor should have regard to whether a scaffold is required in order to undertake works to roofs or external elevations and build these requirements into the overall claim figure.

It should also be noted that the original design of the premises or structure may incorporate features that are no longer considered to be 'safe design'. Such features may also have been added at a later stage in the life of the building or added by the lessee, either with permission by way of a licence to carry out alterations or without the knowledge of the freeholder.

This raises a number of issues for the surveyor preparing the schedule. Should the surveyor:

- include works in the schedule that cannot be undertaken safely;
- ask the lessee to reinstate features in the premises or structure that should be 'designed out'; or
- require additional works to be undertaken to improve the safety of the structure or premises?

However, once the schedule strays into areas where design decisions are required, or the stage is reached where there is a clear intention for the works to be carried out, then the principles of prevention **must** be applied.

This will have implications for surveyors dealing with the claim, as, no doubt, any variance to the schedule brought about by the requirements of regulation 7 (General principles of prevention) will lead to discussion between the surveyors as to the inclusion or otherwise of such items in the schedule and the claim.

It will then be necessary to refer to the relevant clause in order to ascertain whether or not the lessee is obliged to undertake works of improvement in order to comply with any statutory requirements.

Provision of information

Any client instructing a surveyor to prepare a schedule of dilapidations (which requires an inspection to be undertaken) has a duty of care to pass on information as well as statutory duties under CDM and other regulations.

The general duty of care requires the client to provide persons who may be affected thereby with information relating to the condition of the premises and information relating to any hazardous substances that may be present (e.g. asbestos or lead), and also information relating to plant or equipment that may also affect the health or safety of persons undertaking inspections (e.g. defective cooling towers that may contain legionella bacteria, or high voltage electrical apparatus).

Specific legislation requiring provision of information includes the *Control of Asbestos Regulations* 2006 and the *Control of Lead at Work Regulations* 2002.

Regulation 10 of CDM 2007 requires clients to provide information and it is appropriate for clients to pass such information to their appointed surveyor at the initial appointment.

These requirements in respect of provision of information do, however, raise a number of issues. It may well be the case that it is the lessee who is in possession of the information, not the instructing client, i.e. the freeholder of the premises or structure. Where the lessee is in occupation of the whole premises or structure, it may be the lessee who is obliged to pass on the information (e.g. details from the asbestos register).

Once there is an intention to undertake the works, i.e. stage 5 has been reached, then all of these requirements for the provision of information must be incorporated into the procedures for dealing with the project and made available to contractors tendering for the work.

Application of CDM regulations 11 and 18

The preparation of the schedule may stray into the definition of 'design' and therefore the person drawing up the schedule may have duties as a designer in accordance with regulations 11 and 18. The extent of these duties will depend directly upon the nature of the work identified in the schedule.

This means that the person preparing the schedule may be required to comply with regulations 4, 5, 6, 7 and 11.

Because at this stage it may not be certain who the client may be (lessee, lessor, freeholder), it is very unlikely that the duties in regulation 18 would apply at this stage - because if it is not certain if there will be a project, it is not possible to determine if the project will be notifiable.

The surveyor undertaking the preparation of the schedule of dilapidations and the claim therefore needs to be aware of the strict interpretation of design and whether these requirements apply.

Application of CDM to the dilapidations claim

The other issue that arises is whether or not the actual claim against the lessee should allow for the application of CDM.

This is probably a lot more straightforward if the works included in the claim are likely to last for more than 30 days (or more than 500 person days), where the works become notifiable and a CDM-C will be required: there will also be a requirement for a principal contractor, a construction phase plan and a health and safety file and all of these requirements can be built into the pricing of the schedule.

It should be noted that the requirement for a file will apply even where there is no contractual obligation for the lessee to produce one within the terms of the lease.

Note: Claims in respect of residential premises where the lessee is in occupation of premises deemed to be domestic are slightly different inasmuch that domestic occupiers are not clients under CDM. If the freeholder is a company then the normal rules will apply if the works are undertaken by the freeholder.

DEMOLITION

Demolition is often carried out well in advance of the main construction works and under a separate contract. With modern methods and use of mechanical

plant it is often the case that the work can be undertaken within the 30 day threshold and would therefore not be liable to notification under regulation 21.

Demolition is recognised as a high risk activity and clients should ensure that adequate management arrangements are in place to enable the works to be carried out safely. There are numerous methods of demolition that have evolved as the technology and availability of machines has developed and clients should be aware of the various options that are now available.

However, whatever method is used it is essential that demolition work is properly planned and adequate measures taken to safeguard the health and safety of all those who might be affected by the demolition works.

> *CDM 2007 regulation 29 – Demolition or dismantling*
> '(1) The demolition or dismantling of a structure, or part of a structure, shall be planned and carried out in such a manner as to prevent danger or, where it is not practicable to prevent it, to reduce danger to as low a level as is reasonably practicable.
>
> (2) The arrangements for carrying out such demolition or dismantling shall be recorded in writing before the demolition or dismantling work begins.'

Key points

For demolition works clients should ensure that the following points are considered and dealt with:

- appointment of competent demolition contractors;
- provide adequate information especially in relation to services (both underground and overhead), hidden voids such as cellars, vaults, shafts and tunnels both under the property and below the adjoining pavement and highways;
- provide information about the nature and condition of the premises especially in respect of defective structures;
- notifications to HSE in respect of asbestos removal;
- notifications under section 80 of the *Building Act 1984* in respect of intention to demolish a structure;
- arrangements for shutting down services, making safe and disconnecting supplies;
- provision of hoardings, fencing and scaffolds and appropriate licence applications where placed upon the public highway;
- arrangements for temporary closure of pavements or the highway where considered necessary to ensure the safety of the public;

- provision of welfare facilities;
- environmental issues – mitigation measures required in respect of noise, dust and fumes;
- party wall issues – where demolition is carried out and there are adjacent premises then notices should be served in accordance with the requirements of the *Party Wall etc. Act* 1996; and
- temporary propping or support and provision of weathering to exposed walls to adjacent premises following demolition.

There will be other issues that need to be taken into account depending upon the nature of the works and type of structure to be demolished.

Where these works are undertaken as part of the main contract then the principal contractor will normally be in technical possession of the site and will need to ensure that proper measures are in place.

The CDM-C will be responsible for ensuring that all necessary information has been handed over to the principal contractor in those cases where the work is part of the main contract or the demolition works are scheduled to exceed 30 days.

REPAIRS AND MAINTENANCE

The definition of construction work (regulation 2) includes works of renovation, repair, upkeep, redecoration or other maintenance (including cleaning which involves the use of water or an abrasive at high pressure or the use of corrosive or toxic substances).

The inclusion of the former CHSW Regulations within CDM 2007 means that all types of repair and maintenance work are now covered by the Regulations, which place duties upon the client irrespective of the size or duration of the works. Thus, minor roofing repairs or works of external decoration will come within the scope of CDM 2007 and clients should consider what changes they need to make to their existing procedures for dealing with works of repair and maintenance.

For many, the changes will not be significant because their policies and procedures already included and allowed for works being undertaken by contractors within their premises.

These arrangements were required, in any case, under the *Management Regulations* 1999 and may already have included permit systems to enter confined spaces or gain access to roofs, or included hot work permits for use of naked flames or abrasive wheels.

Clients who do not already have such procedures in place will need to ensure that they do so in future.

Advice on the formulation and implementation of such policies and procedures should be readily available from the person undertaking the role of 'competent person' in accordance with the requirements of regulation 7 of the *Management Regulations* 1999.

Where this falls outside a client's expertise then advice should be brought in to ensure that these issues are adequately dealt with.

Key points

For repair and maintenance works clients should ensure that the following points are considered and dealt with:

- appointment of competent contractors;
- provide adequate information regarding any asbestos present in the buildings or structure;
- provide information about the nature and condition of the premises especially in respect of defective structures;
- work at height – issues relating to working at height on both pitched and flat roofs, fragile surfaces including roofing materials and skylights, unprotected edges;
- work in confined spaces – working conditions in unventilated or poorly ventilated areas including roof voids, cellars and vaults, especially where working with hazardous substances;
- use of hazardous substances including adhesives, solvents, paints and varnishes;
- interface with occupiers (also see the later section on working within occupied premises);
- provision of adequate access – especially important where access is restricted or difficult where makeshift solutions need to be avoided;
- use of ladders, scaffold towers and scaffolds;
- use of cradles;
- use of man-safe systems, harnesses;
- use of abseiling techniques; and
- issues related to lone working or vacant premises.

This type of work accounts for a disproportionate number of accidents and incidents, often down to inadequate planning and procedures.

REFURBISHMENT

Refurbishment includes alterations, additions, repairs, redecoration, and testing and commissioning.

This category of work accounts for a disproportionate number of accidents and incidents, sometimes down to lack of information about the condition and nature of the structure, inherent problems related to the age of the building and type of construction, difficulties related to access, narrow doors and corridors and the need for manual handling of plant, equipment and materials.

This category of work also has the highest incidence of unplanned collapses of the structure.

Key points

For refurbishment works clients should ensure that the following points are considered and dealt with:

- appointment of competent contractors conversant with this type of work and the associated problems;
- provide adequate information especially in relation to services (both underground and overhead), hidden voids such as cellars, vaults, shafts and tunnels both under the property and below the adjoining pavement and highways;
- provide information about the nature and condition of the premises especially in respect of defective structures/structural stability;
- issues relating to imposed loadings on floors or other parts of the structure;
- temporary propping or support where internal walls, columns or other supporting structure is removed;
- notifications to HSE in respect of asbestos removal;
- arrangements for shutting down services, making safe, and disconnection and reconnection of supplies;
- provision of hoardings, fencing and scaffolds and appropriate licence applications where placed upon the public highway;
- provision of welfare facilities;
- environmental issues – mitigation measures required in respect of noise, dust and fumes;
- party wall issues – where any works are planned to the party wall including underpinning, raising of walls or roofs, removal of chimney stacks, etc. then notices should be served in accordance with the requirements of the *Party Wall etc. Act* 1996;
- materials – asbestos, old plaster, lead paint, etc.

NEW BUILD

Although considered to be more straightforward than refurbishment work, new build does bring about its own set of problems and requires different skill sets from both designers and contractors.

Depending upon the scale of the project new build is likely to involve a far greater amount of plant and machinery than the preceding categories and could involve ground works contractors, including specialist piling contractors, retaining walls, special foundations, deep excavations and sewers, and diversions to existing utilities and highways.

Above ground there are various types of superstructure to be considered including precast concrete, in situ concrete, steel framed and composite structures, various types of roof and roofing systems, cladding, and windows.

Internally there will be issues relating to internal walls, staircases, lifts, use of pre-assembled bathroom pods or traditional methods, mechanical and electrical plant, fittings, and risers and ductwork.

It is assumed that most projects involving the construction of new buildings or structures will be on site for more than 30 days so will be notifiable and command the services of a CDM co-ordinator.

The client needs to ensure that the appointed CDM-C has sufficient knowledge and experience in respect of the type of project the client is involved in.

WORKING IN OCCUPIED PREMISES

This section examines the issues relating to construction works taking place in occupied premises, including control of access and the employer's duties and obligations in respect of his or her employees whilst works are being carried out.

Controlling access onto construction sites

Where there is clear demarcation it is quite clear from the Regulations where the responsibility for controlling access onto the site lies. Regulation 22(1)(l) states that the principal contractor shall 'take reasonable steps to prevent access by unauthorised persons to the construction site'.

In most cases the nature and layout of the site will allow the contractor to control access to the actual area where construction works are taking place but problems can arise where works are undertaken in premises or sites that remain in occupation or partly in use.

For example, where works are carried out on the rail infrastructure or on the highway there is often a requirement to keep part of the track or highway operational for other traffic. In some cases, especially on a rail track or in a motorway environment, strict segregation can be provided through the use of barriers.

In other cases, where, for example, the works are being undertaken in a busy station environment or the highways works involve renewal of pavings, or build outs in a busy town centre, separation from the public becomes a much greater problem.

The client will need to decide, in conjunction with the contractor, how control of these areas will be achieved. In some cases, complete separation with Heras fencing will be required, but for works of a more temporary nature simple barriers may suffice.

Where the works are being carried out within part of an office building, retail unit or a factory it may not always be possible to achieve complete separation, especially where separate access for contractors cannot be provided.

Also, during the initial set up and the final shut down of the site the interface between the two becomes more difficult to control.

Client liability

In these situations the client clearly has to take on some of the liability for controlling the actions of its own employees, or in the case of the railway or highways works those third parties (i.e. members of the public) who are on the client's premises.

The client will need to ensure that contractors have prepared their own risk assessments and method statements and introduced controls aimed at safeguarding the safety of their own employees and subcontractors, as well as third parties (i.e. employees of the client organisation and members of the public who might be affected by the works).

At the same time the client organisation will be required to undertake its own risk assessments in respect of its own employees and others who might be affected by the works whilst on their premises or land.

Clients owe a duty of care to persons coming onto their premises under the *Occupiers Liability Act* 1957 and 1984, as well as having general duties under sections 2 and 3 of the *Health and Safety at Work etc. Act 1974*.

The liability to undertake risk assessments stems from regulation 3(1) of the *Management of Health and Safety at Work Regulations* 1999.

Phased handovers

Similar problems will arise in the case of phased handovers, where access to the premises is shared and the client is unable to provide separate access dedicated to the needs of contractors still working on the site.

Where the client premises include private access roads and parking areas, it is the client who will be solely liable for control of movement of vehicles in these areas unless a separate traffic entrance and traffic routes solely for the use of contractors can be provided.

All of these issues need to be addressed at the planning stage and phased handovers should only be permitted where the client is satisfied that safety issues can be adequately resolved.

LIQUIDATIONS AND RECEIVERSHIPS

A problem that is increasingly encountered on construction sites is where one of the companies carrying out the works goes out of business.

Announcements concerning companies going into administration and/or any confirmed report that any organisation involved in the on site operations has financial difficulty (sufficient to reduce or destroy the resources or disrupt the procurement process on the site during the course of a construction project) generally concentrate on the impact on the programme and the financial losses – with little mention being made of issues connected with health and safety or with CDM.

Client can assume duties of principal contractor

Under CDM 2007 the rule is clear – if the client fails to appoint a principal contractor then the client is assumed to discharge such duties.

Thus it can be construed the client must act as the principal contractor during the period of liquidation or financial collapse of the existing principal contractor until such time as the client is able to appoint another principal contractor.

There are two distinctly different situations to consider immediately following collapse of the principal contractor:

- Has all site operation ceased?
- Are subcontractors continuing to remain on site?

The client should discuss a strategy with the CDM-C as to how best to deal with both types of situation in order to minimise potential exposure to risks created by the failure of the principal contractor.

There are a number of issues that will need to be addressed in the immediate aftermath by both the client and the CDM-C.

The first relates to the continued security of the site: the principal contractor has a duty to maintain safety of the site but, where a principal contractor goes out of existence or pulls off site, there are very real issues that the client will need to address until such time as another contractor can be appointed. Under regulation 14(4) the client takes on the responsibilities of the principal contractor and takes on liability for maintaining the security and safety of the site.

The second relates to how, or, whether it is possible to maintain the operations on site in the absence of a principal contractor. As noted above, regulation 14(4) passes liability onto the client (although there may be a short period where the site is 'locked out' by the liquidator). It is in the interest of both the client and the subcontractors to maintain the flow of work, otherwise there is an additional risk that the subcontractors will walk off site and not return until such time as new financial arrangements are put in place.

In some cases the client may be able to undertake and fulfil the role of principal contractor, but quite clearly there will a necessity to bring in another contractor or arrange for one of the subcontractors to undertake the role.

Whatever route is taken it is likely to involve both the client and the CDM-C in a period of intense activity whilst matters are resolved.

Effect of financial failure of subcontractors

If the financial difficulty occurs in an organisation under the direct control of the principal contractor then the principal contractor still retains the duty to assess the construction phase plan and adapt as necessary.

The principal contractor may seek additional financial resource from the client under certain circumstances, e.g. where the contractor was a nominated subcontractor or organisation named by the client.

Documentation for the file

A further issue is that of documentation and information for the health and safety file.

Whilst the principal contractor remains on site there is a possibility of pulling together any information that has been collected on site, but the chance of getting sufficient information from elsewhere, even if the project is close to practical completion, is remote.

Where the principal contractor owes money to its subcontractors, there is little likelihood of them wishing to provide any information while this is outstanding.

Once the liquidator has been appointed or the organisation has simply financially collapsed then the CDM-C should attempt to obtain whatever information might be available. Of course, the duties of the liquidator lie elsewhere and, in the event that information is not forthcoming, there are few options available.

One option that the CDM-C can explore is to secure additional funding from the client to obtain the required information him- or herself or, alternatively, where subcontractors are in a position to provide information then the CDM-C may agree with the client to make arrangements direct with the subcontractor for the production of the 'missing' information.

For more information on liquidation issues see Appendix B, by David Jones.

9 Provision of information

INFORMATION FLOWS

One of the significant changes in CDM 2007 is the way in which information flows are managed throughout the construction project – from inception through to completion and then throughout the life cycle of the structure or premises until demolition.

The emphasis is now on provision of information to those who need it, with clients being required to provide information for all projects, whether they are notifiable or not.

The pre-construction phase plan (formerly produced for contractors at tender stage) is now replaced by 'pre-construction information'.

The requirements for information can be summarised as follows:

- pre-construction information:
  - provided by the client for non-notifiable projects;
  - handled by the CDM co-ordinator for notifiable projects (includes details of mobilisation period).
- *F10 Notification of construction project*:
  - declaration signed by the client for notifiable projects;
  - issued by the CDM co-ordinator for notifiable projects (includes details of mobilisation period;
  - issued to HSE for construction sites;
  - issued to Office of the Rail Regulator for rail infrastructure projects.
- construction phase plan:
  - prepared by principal contractor for notifiable projects;
  - relevant details provided to contractors (includes details of mobilisation period);
  - site induction and site rules.
- health and safety file.

This chapter has been split into three sections which provide further information on each of these (apart from the file), setting out the legal requirements and how clients and their advisors can ensure that these requirements are met.

The requirements relating to the production of the file, production of manuals and how these can be used by facilities managers and others involved in the

future operational requirements are dealt with in Chapter 10 *The health and safety file*.

Phase	Information	CDM-C
Initial phase	Gather information Agree H&S file format	Advise client F10 submission
Design phase	Share information	Advise design team
Tender phase	Contractor information Mobilisation period Issue H&S file info.format	Contractor competency Revised F10 submission
Construction phase	Construction phase plan Collect H&S file information	Welfare facilities Design changes
Handover phase	Prepare and hand over H&S file	Project review

Figure 11: Project information structure

SECTION 1: PRE-CONSTRUCTION INFORMATION

This section looks at the requirements for provision of information in the initial stages of a project, the type of information required, and the additional guidance contained within the ACOP.

The significant change from the old Regulations is that information must be provided to designers and all those involved in the construction process who require information and that the process flows throughout the whole of the project: the process does not end once construction commences (where further design takes place) or with the production of a single document.

The concept of a continuous flow of information is illustrated in figure 12.

The former pre-construction health and safety plan is no longer a statutory requirement instead CDM 2007 refers to **pre-construction information**.

The client's duties in respect of provision of information

The client's duties in respect of provision of information are made clear under regulations 10 and 15 of CDM 2007 and by virtue of regulation 10 must be provided to every person involved in the design and

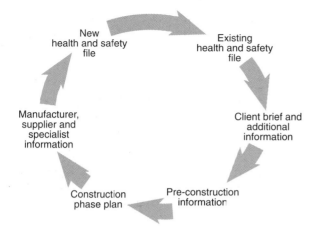

Figure 12: Information flows are a continuing cycle

also to the contractor undertaking the construction work.

Regulation 10 requires the client to provide information for all projects, whether they are notifiable or not.

Regulation 15 relates to notifiable projects and requires that the client provide the CDM co-ordinator appointed in respect of the project with all of the information that he or she is required to provide under regulation 10.

It should also be noted that designers are also required to provide clients, other designers and contractors with information for all projects, and to provide the CDM co-ordinator with information for notifiable projects.

> **CDM 2007 regulation 2 – Interpretation**
> ' "pre-construction information" means the information described in regulation 10 and, where the project is notifiable, regulation 15.'

Pre-construction information

Appendix 2 of the ACOP sets out the range of information that needs to be considered for inclusion in the pre-construction information (PCI).

This is information that needs to be made available both to the client's project team or advisors (in order that they can better understand the issues that they need to deal with during the design stages) and to contractors undertaking construction work (in order that they can better understand the issues that they need to deal with during the construction works).

As part of the initial process it will be necessary to obtain basic information about the structure, premises or site including the following site information:

- Surveys and investigations:
  - historical information (desk top study) into former uses of the site, topographical features, etc.;
  - geological survey;

  - site investigations, ground conditions and contamination reports;
  - structural information including condition surveys.
- Asbestos register
  - information required, etc.;
  - Type 3 survey.
  Note: See the section on Asbestos later in this chapter for further information relating to asbestos and construction projects.
- Hazardous materials
  Note: See the section on Hazardous materials later in this chapter for further information relating to hazardous materials and construction projects.
- Lead
  Restoration and refurbishment projects, especially those involving historic properties and old structures such as bridges and viaducts, should include information relating to lead. This includes lead used in paintwork and in plumbing.
- Information contained within any existing health and safety file.

Desk top study

A desk top study can provide an effective means of gathering a lot of information relating to the past history of the site and also current information such as flood levels, with a lot of this information being freely available and accessible via the internet.

In most areas Ordnance Survey information is available from the end of the 19th century and provides a good starting point for tracing the past history of the area and former land uses.

See also *Historical perspective* on the next page.

Information available for desk top studies includes:

- **Ordnance sheets** – Historic maps are available (depending upon location) from the 1870s, 1890s, the early 1900s, 1930s and late 1940s, and into the era of post-war mapping.
- **Geology** – The geology of the site can be ascertained from British Geological Survey (BGS) 1:50,000 scale maps.
- **Hydrology and hydrogeology** – Information relating to flood risks and aquifers can be obtained from the Environment Agency (www.environment-agency.gov.uk).
- **Legal documents** – Legal documents such as leases and title deeds can provide useful information relating to site boundaries, easements, rights of access and other issues that might affect the manner in which the works have to be carried out.
- **Planning status** – The status of the premises and surrounding areas can be ascertained from existing planning documents and by making enquiries at the local planning authority in which the premises are located.

  Tree Preservation Orders (TPOs), Conservation Areas, Listed Buildings status, and locations within

Areas of Outstanding Natural Beauty (AONB) or Sites of Special Scientific Interest (SSSI) may all influence or dictate the manner in which works are undertaken.

Historical perspective

Records have probably been kept for as long as drawings, specifications and schedules have been in existence and there is certainly evidence available of schedules and detailed costings dating back to the Middle Ages.

In the case of ecclesiastical buildings, royal palaces and other buildings of prominence the archives will probably contain building information going back 300 years or more.

The great urban and industrial expansion witnessed in the Victorian era, together with the coming of the railways, the installation of sewers, mains water, electrical and gas supplies was accompanied by the Municipal Corporations and the requirement for more extensive record keeping brought about by various public health acts and model building by-laws – all of which required the provision of accurate drawings and records.

The Victorian era also saw the founding of the great professional institutions, including the RICS which gained its Royal Charter in August 1881, which together with the Mechanical and Civil Engineers are still clustered around Parliament and the seat of government.

Most of the larger organisations of the day would have had a 'premises department' or 'estates department' with whom these records were lodged and maintained, and where details of future changes and alterations were recorded.

The image of the 'plan room', often deep in the bowels of the basement, survived in many cases well into the 1960s and provided those organisations with a unique source of information.

Regrettably, in many instances a lot of this information has been lost over the last 30 years or so as businesses have merged or been taken over and financial and space restraints have resulted in much valuable information being discarded.

Desk top studies often rely upon information gleaned from the Ordnance Survey in order to trace the history of the site: former uses (such as coal yards, tanneries or the local town gas works) might indicate potential ground contamination.

Additional sources of information

For clients with existing property portfolios, managing agents and premises or facilities managers there is often a considerable amount of data that can be collected and fed into the design process. Data that should be available includes:

- accident reports and statistics relating to incidents including slips and trips arising from slippery or uneven surfaces – floors and access routes; and
- maintenance data – historic and ongoing data relating to costs for maintenance activities: high life cycle costs arising from inadequate access arrangements to plant areas or specification of poor performance plant and equipment.

This type of information can prove invaluable but is often not captured by the design team and repetition of previous mistakes may cost a client vast sums of money over the life cycle of a building.

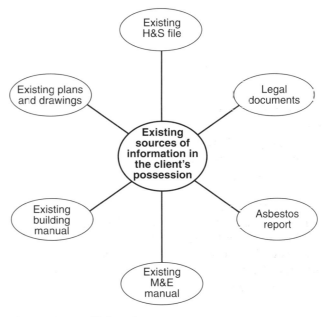

Figure 13: Sources of information

Asbestos and hazardous materials

It is important that information is provided to contractors regarding the presence of hazardous materials in existing structures.

Apart from the obvious materials, such as lead and asbestos, there are a number of both hazardous and deleterious materials that need to be identified (hazardous because of the potential effect on people and the environment; deleterious because of the potential effect on the structure itself).

Where information is not readily available (e.g. from a previous health and safety file) then measures must be put in place to obtain any necessary information (as required under CDM regulation 10 – *Client's duty in relation to information* and under regulation 15 – *Client's duty in relation to information where a project is notifiable*).

The client is required to provide all of the information in its possession or which is reasonably obtainable, including any information about or affecting the site or the construction work.

This requirement to provide information does mean that it is up to the client to make all the necessary enquiries and commission surveys where necessary (both of the site and of any buildings or structures where works are to be undertaken).

For new structures it is common practice to commission soil and ground investigations and also to undertake desk top surveys into the historical background of the site and surrounding areas.

An old Ordnance Survey sheet may well reveal the presence of previous industrial activity (e.g. old gas works or coking plants; chemical works; petrol stations; coal yards) or all manner of activities which might give rise to hazardous materials or residues remaining in situ, thus posing a potential risk to those undertaking works or others who might be affected.

It may also be necessary to commission a full condition survey of buildings and structures in order to identify what materials may be present, their condition and the potential hazards that have been identified. Old plasters may contain horse hair; old buildings may contain lead paint, may be contaminated by rats urine or a build up of bird droppings, or may have housed old industrial type activities such as chromium plating with traces of chemicals, or may even have high build up of radioactive contamination.

In undertaking these surveys it may be necessary to employ invasive techniques in order to ascertain the type and condition of materials that may be covered up, built into the structure or otherwise concealed (e.g. asbestos laggings or other asbestos containing materials that have been subsequently covered over; galvanised metal wall ties that have suffered corrosion; or coatings to steel beams that are covered up with plasterboard or other sheet materials).

Although some of the problems associated with hazardous materials have been well documented in the past (and, for example, in the case of lead have been subject to regulation for over 70 years), as time goes by and the common usage of such materials becomes a thing of the past, the problems associated with the use of such materials also becomes less well known or understood.

Clients, designers and others working with older properties do require some understanding of the nature of hazardous materials commonly used in the past and how they can best be dealt with when encountered on a project.

Hazardous materials
Further information can be found in *Investigating Hazardous and Deleterious Building Materials*, published by RICS Books[41].

The following list indicates some of the hazardous materials that might need to be addressed.

- asbestos;
- chlorofluorocarbons (CFCs);
- crystalline silica;
- formaldehyde;

- lead;
- polychlorinated biphenyls (PCBs);
- man-made mineral fibre;
- vermiculite;
- volatile organic compounds (VOCs);
- wood preservatives. *

* It should be noted that materials such as creosote, which were once widely used to preserve external timbers (especially fencing) are now prohibited. Further information relating to hazardous substances can also be found in EH40[42], *Workplace Exposure Limits: Containing the list of workplace exposure limits for use with the Control of Substances Hazardous to Health Regulations 2002 (as amended)*.

The above list is not exhaustive and surveyors dealing with older properties should produce their own checklists derived from their own experience.

Contaminated land

Checks can also be made with the local authority for entries in the Contaminated Land Register and with the local water authority for discharge consents (which are required under the *Water Resources Act* 1991 as amended by the *Environment Act* 1995).

Where it is considered from the desk top study and after making enquiries that there is a potential for land contamination, further surveys and investigations should be commissioned and appropriate measures put in place.

Further advice can be obtained from the Environment Agency (www.environment-agency.gov.uk).

Professional advisors

The client will more often than not rely upon existing professional advisors or one of the project team (where appointed) to commission or undertake the various surveys and investigations outlined above.

It should be stressed that such investigations will normally be required (depending upon the nature of the project) for both notifiable and non-notifiable projects.

Where the project is notifiable the client will have access to the CDM co-ordinator for advice (see below).

What is the CDM co-ordinator required to do?

The ACOP (at paragraph 93) suggests that where 'there are any significant gaps or defects … [in the information] these are filled by commissioning surveys or by making other reasonable enquiries'.

Regulation 20(2)(a) requires that the CDM-C 'take all reasonable steps to identify and collect the pre-construction information'.

Contractually the CDM-C would not normally be in a position to commission surveys or investigations and there are obvious issues relating to payment and contract. The CDM-C is acting as an advisor to the client, not as the client's agent.

It is clear that where the CDM-C identifies deficiencies in the information provided and further surveys or investigations are required he or she should advise the client in writing of what further actions are required.

Furthermore, the other members of the design or project team should also be advised because such information may influence design decisions.

As there is no longer a single 'gateway' for the provision of this information it is suggested that the CDM-C keeps track of the information required and provided and that all duty holders are provided with a copy of the schedule.

Professional advisors should ensure that where they are provided with information by the client the information is passed on to those that require it, be they other members of the professional team or contractors carrying out the work. This also applies to dissemination of information within their own organisations: duty holders need to ensure that their own employees are kept within the information loop.

A number of prosecutions have been taken against professional advisors who failed to pass such information on.

Case study – failure to pass on information

A number of prosecutions have taken place where consultants have either commissioned surveys or been provided with survey reports by the client, but then failed to pass the information on to contractors who were tendering for the work.

A typical case has been where information has been obtained (such as services information or condition surveys) in the initial stages of a project that has then been put on hold for a period of time.

When the project has been resurrected the information has either been mislaid or forgotten altogether and not passed on, with the result that contractors have cut through live cables or pipes, or buildings have collapsed.

Where workers have been injured prosecutions have resulted.

Several of these cases have involved the failure to pass on information relating to asbestos, with construction workers subsequently being exposed to asbestos fibres.

Asbestos

Clients should be especially aware of the requirements relating to asbestos, both in respect of their role as controller of premises under the *Control of Asbestos*

Regulations 2006 which requires that they properly manage any asbestos present in their properties and also the requirements of regulations 5 and 9 (see below).

Asbestos

The *Control of Asbestos Regulations* 2006 came into effect on 13 November 2006. These Regulations consolidate and replace all of the previously existing legislation in respect of asbestos. Although similar provisions applied under the old legislation, these Regulations provide clarity on the requirements relating to construction works in existing premises.

Regulations 5 and 9 are of especial importance to those involved with construction projects:

Regulation 5 – Identification of the presence of asbestos

'An employer shall not undertake work in demolition, maintenance, or any other work which exposes or is liable to expose his employees to asbestos in respect of any premises unless either:

(a) he has carried out a suitable and sufficient assessment as to whether asbestos, what type of asbestos, contained in what material and in what condition is present or is liable to be present in those premises; or
(b) if there is doubt as to whether asbestos is present in those premises he:
(i) assumes that asbestos is present, and that it is not chrysotile alone, and
(ii) observes the applicable provisions of these Regulations.'

Regulation 9 – Notification of work with asbestos

'(1) Subject to regulation 3(2), an employer shall not undertake any work with asbestos unless he has notified the appropriate office of the enforcing authority in writing of the particulars specified in Schedule 1 at least 14 days before commencing that work or such shorter time before as the enforcing authority may agree.'

Investigations during construction

There may well be circumstances where it is not possible to undertake all the necessary investigations prior to construction commencing.

There will be times when the necessary opening up, exposure of existing structural elements, or breaking out of slabs or foundations can only take place once contractors are on site with all the necessary plant and equipment and the premises have been vacated, thus allowing such works to be undertaken in comparative safety.

In these circumstances the client must ensure that:

- adequate time is allowed in the programme for further investigations to take place;
- budget allocation is made for such investigations; and
- the results are fed back to the design team where this may affect their design, especially as to the sequence of works, requirements for temporary support and the removal of hazardous materials.

Where possible such works should be dealt with as a separate works package under the control of the contractor (on the assumption that the contractor has already taken possession of the site).

Personal safety

In undertaking these surveys the client or employer should not overlook the fact that surveyors, engineers and others completing such surveys may also be exposed to risks of which they might not be aware.

It is important that suitable and sufficient risk assessments are undertaken by employers in accordance with regulation 3(1) of the *Management Regulations* 1999 before such surveys are undertaken. Further guidance on the potential hazards and pitfalls of surveyors and others undertaking surveys is available in the RICS publication *Surveying Safely*[43].

Environmental issues – provision of information

Clients should not overlook the necessity to obtain and provide information relating to other issues, including environmental issues and the requirement for an environmental impact assessment.

The impact of environmental issues can provide as many headaches to the developer (including delays in the construction programme) as health and safety related issues.

The presence of newts or slow worms on a construction site can be very disruptive and lead to long delays in the construction process because of the short windows of opportunity for their removal and relocation to a new home.

The timing of such events is crucial and requires sufficient advance planning to enable the project to run on time: relocation may need to be planned some six to nine months in advance – failure to do so may result in a project being delayed by a complete season, especially if the presence of fauna had not been noticed prior to works commencing.

Increasingly client organisations now have environmental strategies in place that the project may need to take into account, both in design and in the selection of materials.

Also, especially for larger projects, the planning authority is likely to impose conditions relating to environmental issues in the conditions attached to the

consent or in a separate Section 106 Agreement made between the authority and the developer.

Clients need to ensure that this information is passed on to both designers and contractors, and, although strictly speaking not covered by the requirements under CDM 2007 (which only relate to health and safety issues), may wish the CDM-C to deal with such issues as part of the overall management arrangements for the project.

Case study – badgers

Works were due to commence on a development site which contained badgers but a local group of residents formed a protest group in order to prevent the badger setts being disturbed and the badgers relocated to an alternative location.

Despite the developer having obtained a licence from the Department for the Environment and Rural Affairs (Defra) for the destruction of the setts and the removal of the badgers, the protestors managed to get the licence suspended for over 18 months and involved the developer in considerable additional costs fighting the case through the courts.

Where badgers or other protected species are disturbed without a licence in place then prosecutions are likely to follow as well as considerable delays to the project.

Where adequate surveys are taken out in the initial stages of the project and the information provided to the designers then it may be possible to come up with a design solution that can avoid disturbance of the protected species or, where this is not possible, to optimise the timescales for the construction works by moving the protected species out of the breeding season, and containing the site to prevent recolonisation.

INFORMATION FLOWS: PRE-CONSTRUCTION INFORMATION

Appendix 2 to the Approved Code of Practice contains a list of the type of information that might be required to be passed on to those preparing designs or bidding for construction work.

As mentioned earlier this information replaces the pre-construction health and safety plan and should be available to those who need it, as and when such information is required.

See Appendix C of this book for a checklist of pre-construction information.

Information – aborted projects

The information provided to designers as part of the tendering or early procurement process is referred to as the pre-construction information (PCI) and the requirements relating to the provision of such information are set out in regulation 10(2) (Clients duty in relation to information).

Regulation 10(2)(d) refers to 'any information in any existing health and safety file' and this is information that might be included in the PCI.

Situations may arise where a great deal of information has been gathered together for a project only for the project to be abandoned, either at planning or during the tender stage. This information might include, for example, asbestos surveys, condition surveys, information relating to underground services and other information as detailed elsewhere in this chapter.

In the past a lot of this information would probably have been lost because a health and safety file would not have been produced (since the project failed to proceed into the construction phase).

In such circumstances the CDM-C should discuss and agree with the client how such information will be captured and documented for use in the future.

A condition survey of the premises might, for example, reveal that there are inherent structural weaknesses and a risk of building collapse, or that timbers are affected by rot or timber infestation and that, again, this could lead to potential collapse or give rise to a risk of persons falling through weakened floors.

Similar problems could be identified in the form of fragile roofs, asbestos in boiler rooms or elsewhere in the building, vermin infestation or other hazards that have been identified and must be passed on to those who might be required to enter the building at a later date. This could include surveyors, architects, engineers and contractors who might be involved in later projects, or potential purchasers who wish to inspect the premises.

The client has a clear duty of care and needs to consider how such information should be passed on.

The client clearly has an option to retain the information in the form of individual reports, etc. but the inclusion of this information in an updated health and safety file would provide a far better solution.

SECTION 2: F10 NOTIFICATION OF CONSTRUCTION PROJECT

Summary

This section considers the significance of the apparently minor changes made both in the format of the form and the requirements relating to notification contained within the CDM 2007 Regulations and the ACOP.

There are changes to the information required to be included on the form, the signatories and also additional changes relating to the project details.

A copy of the *F10 Notification of a construction project* is included at Appendix F for ease of reference.

Notification requirements under CDM 2007

The requirement for notification under CDM 2007 now only applies to projects that are going to involve works on site for 30 days or more. This differs from the previous criteria under CDM 1994 for projects to be notified where four or more persons were going to be involved in construction work.

It should be pointed out that although the form F10 has been in existence since its introduction under the old *Factories Act* there is no longer any requirement to use this particular form.

The requirement under CDM is for the project to be notified and this could be done in letter form as long as all the information required to be provided is included in the letter.

However, for most projects the form F10 provides a convenient method for providing the required information.

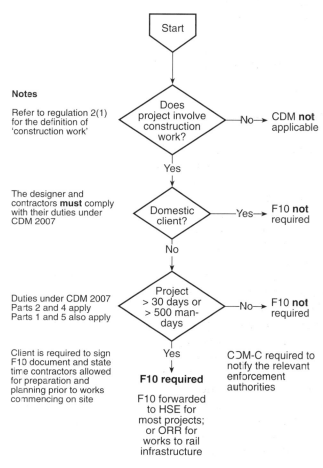

Figure 14: Decision-making process for F10

Regulation 2 – Interpretation

Under regulation 2(3) a project is notifiable if the construction phase is likely to involve more than:

(a) 30 days; or

(a) 500 person days

of construction work.

Thirty days has been interpreted as meaning six weeks, and where no construction works take place at the weekends this could well be the case. However, where works are carried out for seven days a week, or shifts are worked the actual time period reduces accordingly. Where 24-hour shift working takes place the period could theoretically be reduced down to ten days.

Where a project involves vast numbers of construction workers, for example, where say 100 workers are involved with a major civil engineering scheme, then the period could even be as short as five days.

The role of the CDM co-ordinator

The CDM co-ordinator is required at a fairly early stage after appointment to notify the HSE (or relevant enforcing authority) of the client's intention to carry out a construction project.

The initial notification should be made by the CDM co-ordinator 'as soon as is practicable after his appointment' (regulation 21(1)).

The CDM-C is also required by this regulation to include in the notice 'such of the particulars specified in Schedule 1 as are available'.

Schedule 1 (Particulars to be notified to the Executive) is included as a Schedule to the Regulations and as such becomes part of the legal requirement in respect of the notification requirements.

Schedule 1 Particulars to be notified to the Executive (or Office of Rail Regulation)

Key points

The F10 particulars are similar to the previous form but now include the following key information:

- a brief description of the project and the construction work which it includes;
- contact details required for client, CDM co-ordinator and principal contractor;
- details (name and address) required for contractors and designers already appointed;
- the time allowed by the client to the principal contractor referred to in regulation 15(b) for planning and preparation for construction work – **note:** this is the information provided to the CDM-C as part of the pre-construction information;
- a declaration signed by or on behalf of the client that he or she is aware of his or her duties under these Regulations.

Information for the F10

In practical terms the CDM-C will seek out the correct information from the client and prepare the F10 on the basis of the information provided by the client.

It is important that correct details are provided in respect of who the actual client will be for the construction works: this is not always immediately apparent as client organisations often undertake development via a separate or different vehicle to the holding company or operating company. (Reference was made earlier to Special Purpose Vehicles (SPVs) which are set up especially to undertake development work on behalf of an organisation.)

The CDM-C may also need to discuss and agree with the client the period to be allowed for preparation and planning by the principal contractor (Schedule 1 – Item 9).

It is suggested that the CDM-C allows him- or herself sufficient time in order to carry out this task correctly, making the necessary enquiries and including as much as possible of the information that should be available at this early stage in the project, including the period that will be allowed to the principal contractor for 'preparation and planning'.

Gateway – submission of initial F10

The submission of the initial F10 is a significant 'gateway' in the project documentation and the CDM-C should record when this particular 'gateway' in the life of the project has been achieved.

F10 – Additional information

It is anticipated that for most projects additional notification(s) will be required, especially where the principal contractor is concerned: notice of this additional appointment should be given as soon as is practicable after the appointment of the principal contractor.

It should, however, be noted that the ACOP at paragraph 19 suggests that 'any missing information must be notified once it becomes available' – it should also be made clear that where the HSE is updated in respect of additional information reference should be made to the earlier notification.

It is the CDM co-ordinator who is required to provide both the initial and any additional notification of the project to the enforcing authority: additional appointments must be notified but interestingly changes in duty holders need not be.

The ACOP suggests that it would be helpful to notify the HSE if a new principal contractor is appointed or if the start date changes, but this appears to be left to the discretion of the CDM co-ordinator.

It should be noted that where a succession of principal contractors are appointed to undertake separate scheduled phases of the project these appointments would normally be notified to the HSE.

The information that needs to be provided by the principal contractor on site will need to be accurate and updated as necessary where there are changes in the key duty holders.

The principal contractor is required under regulation 22(1)(k) to:

'ensure that the particulars required to be in the notice given under regulation 21 are displayed in a readable condition in a position where they can be read by any worker engaged in the construction work;'.

This information must include the particulars that are given on the F10 but can be provided in any suitable format provided that it contains the information included in Schedule 1.

In practice the principal contractor will normally display a copy of the F10 provided by the CDM-C.

There is no explicit duty on the part of the CDM-C to provide copies of the F10 to anyone other than the HSE and the client: in practice copies should be made available to all duty holders as this is a method by which they can be satisfied that the client is aware of their duties and that a CDM-C has been appointed.

Notification of project – declaration by the client

Previously (under CDM 1994) the F10 was signed by the planning supervisor and the principal contractor but under CDM 2007 the only required signatory is that of the client.

Under Schedule 1 the client is now required to sign a declaration that he or she is aware of the client's duties under these Regulations.

The question must arise as to who within the client organisation is authorised to sign the *F10 Notification of construction project* on behalf of the client organisation.

The signatory will require authorisation to sign what amounts to a statutory declaration that the client organisation is aware of its duties and it is assumed that in most organisations some reappraisal of their procedures will be required in order to ensure that the signatory is at an adequate level of authority to sign such a declaration.

There are a number of significant changes in the format and content of the *F10 Notification of construction project* including the requirement under regulation 21(3) for the notice to be signed by or on behalf of the client (or, if sent by electronic means, shall otherwise show that the client has approved it) and, under item 15, for a declaration signed by or on behalf of the client that he or she is aware of the client's duties under these Regulations.

The declaration by the client that he or she is aware of the client's duties is a significant change from the position under CDM 1994 and is no doubt intended to reinforce to the client that the client organisation takes on considerable duties and responsibilities under these Regulations.

In smaller companies it will usually be the Managing Director (MD) or the Company Secretary as they will normally be involved in the day-to-day affairs of the company or organisation.

As the size of the company or organisation becomes larger or more complex, it may become more difficult to identify the appropriate level within the organisation to which responsibility for signing the declaration on behalf of the organisation can be devolved.

There are obvious issues relating to liability within the company or organisation for identifying those persons within the organisation who are able to deal with such matters.

It is probably worthwhile to refer back to some of the earlier chapters and remind ourselves as to whom clients might be.

The ACOP at paragraph 28 states:

'A client is an organisation or individual for whom a construction project is carried out. Clients only have duties when a project is associated with a business or other undertaking (whether for profit or not). This can include, for example, local authorities, school governors, insurance companies and project originators on [PFI] projects. ....'

For most companies or organisations the Health and Safety Policy (the section outlining the organisation and arrangements) should provide some assistance in confirming who might be in a position of authority to sign the *F10 Notification of construction project*.

For larger projects, or those involving Special Purpose Vehicles (SPVs) set up to finance and manage the project there may be a number of clients involved in the project; there may be changes in the identity of the company or organisation as the funding arrangements and responsibility for the project progress; and there may be a need for the F10 to be amended and reissued to cover these changes.

Where the F10 is signed on behalf of the client, by a person from within the client organisation, then procedures should be in place to ensure that the signatory is aware of his or her duties.

It is no longer possible for a third party, such as the client's agent or the CDM-C to undertake the role of the client and sign the declaration made by the client that he or she is aware of the client's duties.

Clients can still appoint a client's agent to carry out work on their behalf but can no longer pass on their duties or responsibilities under CDM 2007 (for more detail on this see Chapter 4).

Mobilisation period

The client will need to agree with the CDM-C the information to be included on the F10 in respect of the time allowed to the principal contractor for planning and preparation.

This is covered in some detail in Chapter 6 *Buying the construction work*.

NOTIFICATION REQUIREMENTS UNDER CDM 2007 – CONTRACTORS

A significant change from the previous situation is that contractors are no longer required to notify projects where a CDM co-ordinator is not appointed (i.e. non-notifiable projects or works for a domestic client). Previously a contractor was required to notify projects, even for domestic clients, if the project met the 30 days/more than four persons rule.

These notification requirements dated back to requirements placed upon contractors under the *Factories Act* 1961 but were repealed by the CHSW Regulations 1996.

NOTIFICATION REQUIREMENTS UNDER CDM 2007 – DEMOLITION

An area of considerable contention and debate has been the issue of demolition works (which are often by the very nature of the work short-lived) and the requirements relating to notification: notification only being required where the timescale criteria come into play.

Most demolition work is relatively high risk, both to those undertaking the works and to persons who are in the vicinity (including passers by and those occupying adjacent properties or working in the vicinity).

There has been much concern that such high risk activities are not automatically notifiable to HSE regardless of the extent or duration of the works. There are, in fact, a number of safeguards which should go some way to allaying such fears.

- Firstly, under regulation 29 (Demolition or dismantling) there is a requirement for all demolition work to be planned and carried out in such a manner as to prevent danger (or to reduce it where it is not possible to prevent it) and for the arrangements to be recorded in writing.
- Secondly, most demolition works will require notification under other legislation (including *Control of Asbestos Regulations* 2006 and the *Building Act* 1984).

Demolition

Most demolition work will require notification to the relevant authorities including:

- Section 80 – *Building Act* 1984 – Notice of intention to demolish a structure
  Notification is to Building Control at the Local Authority in which the demolition works are to be carried out. The required notice is at least 30 days, being the period of advance warning required by the Utility Companies in order that any apparatus or supplies can be disconnected or protected. Where sewers are taken out of commission the end of the sewer or drain must be blocked to prevent entry by vermin.
- The *Control of Asbestos Regulations* 2006 Regulation 9 – Notification of work with asbestos
  '9(1) Subject to regulation 3(2), an employer shall not undertake any work with asbestos unless he has notified the appropriate office of the enforcing authority in writing of the particulars specified in Schedule 1 at least 14 days before commencing work or such shorter time before as the enforcing authority may agree.'
  Notification under regulation 9 is to the HSE, who deal with asbestos licensing.

It should be noted that where the demolition works are likely to last for 30 days or more, or involve more than 500 person days, or they comprise part of the main contract then they will automatically fall within the notification criteria and a CDM co-ordinator will have to be appointed and an F10 submitted to the HSE or other relevant enforcing authority.

F10 Notification of construction project

Although it will now be possible to file the form online, copies will still be required by the client and the contractor and, as an important legal document, some may prefer to maintain hard copies for future reference. The F10 form can be found at: www.hse.gov.uk/forms/notification/f10.pdf

For an example of an F10 form, see Appendix F.

SECTION 3: THE CONSTRUCTION PHASE PLAN

This section looks at the content of the construction phase plan and how this relates to the concept of information flows throughout the project; how the pre-construction information is dealt with; what action is required by the client; and what advice should be provided by the CDM-C to enable the client to fulfil his or her obligations under regulation 16 (the client's duties in relation to the start of construction phase where a project is notifiable).

It is important that the construction phase plan is developed on the basis of the information provided at tender stage: the document should reflect the specific site and project issues identified by the project team rather than contain generic information that does not truly represent the issues that will be encountered on site.

The principal contractor's duties

We start this section by looking at the principal contractor's duties in respect of the construction phase plan because all of the other actions, including those of the client, revolve around the principal contractor (PC) producing a plan that is sufficient to allow the construction phase to commence.

The requirements placed upon the PC relating to the preparation of the construction phase plan are set out in regulation 23 – **The principal contractor's duty in relation to the construction phase plan** (see below).

Key points

- The construction phase plan should:
  - be sufficient to ensure that the construction work is planned;
  - be managed and monitored in such a way that the work is free of risk to health and safety;
  - take account of information provided by designers; and
  - take account of the pre-construction information provided by the CDM-C.
- The client should **not** allow construction works to start unless the PC has prepared a construction phase plan that complies with the Regulations.
- The construction phase plan should **not** be generic – the site specific and project specific hazards should be identified and recorded and the necessary controls and measures required in order to mitigate these hazards should be spelt out.

CDM 2007 regulation 23 – The principal contractor's duty in relation to the construction phase plan
'(1) The principal contractor shall:

(a) before the start of the construction phase, prepare a construction phase plan which is sufficient to ensure that the construction phase is planned, managed and monitored in a way which enables the construction work to be started so far as is reasonable practicable without risk to health or safety, paying adequate regard to the information provided by the designer under regulations 11(6) and 18(2) and the pre-construction information provided under regulation 20(2)(b);

(b) from time to time and as often as may be appropriate throughout the project update, review, revise and refine the construction

phase plan so that it continues to be sufficient to ensure that the construction phase is planned, managed and monitored in a way which enables the construction work to be carried out so far as reasonably practicable without risk to health or safety; and

(c) arrange for the construction phase plan to be implemented in a way which will ensure so far as is reasonably practicable the health and safety of all persons carrying out the construction work and all persons who may be affected by the work.

(2) The principal contractor shall take all reasonable steps to ensure that the construction phase plan identifies the risks to health and safety arising from the construction work (including the risks specific to the particular type of construction work concerned) and includes suitable and sufficient measures to address such risks, including any site rules.'

THE CONSTRUCTION PHASE PLAN

The plan content

The content of the construction phase plan comprises information provided by both the client and designers relating to information about health and safety risks, and information provided by the contractor relating to how the contractor intends to plan and manage the construction works.

A checklist of the information required (based on Appendix 3 of the ACOP) is provided in Appendix E of this book.

A comparison with the elements included in the pre-construction information shows that there is considerable overlap between the two, and there is therefore considerable onus placed upon the client to ensure that adequate information is forthcoming in time for the PC to prepare his or her 'plan'.

From the contractor's perspective the content of the plan will not differ greatly from those produced previously under the old CDM 1994.

However, although CDM 2007 (regulation 23(b)) allows for the plan to be updated from time to time throughout the project it will need to be more complete than was previously the case, and where there are significant gaps in the information provided by the client the PC will not be able to finalise the construction phase plan.

The production of the construction phase plan provides a significant gateway in the management process and it is essential that the client recognises the importance of this document and his or her role in effectively signing it off and allowing construction works to commence.

The client

The client's duties are set out in regulation 16, which states that the client must not allow the construction phase to start unless a suitable construction phase plan has been prepared by the principal contractor.

Under this regulation the client also has to be satisfied that adequate welfare facilities will be provided on site throughout the construction phase.

> *CDM 2007 Regulation 16 – The client's duty in relation to the start of construction phase where a project is notifiable*
>
> 'Where the project is notifiable, the client shall ensure that the construction phase does not start unless:
>
> (a) the principal contractor has prepared a construction phase plan which complies with regulations 23(1)(a) and 23(2); and
> (b) he is satisfied that the requirements of regulation 22(1)(c) (provision of welfare facilities) will be complied with during the construction phase.'

From the client's perspective:

- The client should have seen the construction phase plan.
- He or she should have read it (the client is the one who needs to be satisfied under regulation 16).
- The client should also take advice from the CDM-C.

The CDM-C is required to provide advice to the client in order to assist the client in complying with his or her duties under:

- regulation 9 (Client's duty in relation to arrangements for managing projects); and
- regulation 16 (Client's duty in relation to the start of the construction phase).

It is, however, quite clear that the decision to allow construction works to commence rests solely with the client (see ACOP paragraph 108(c)).

The Regulations are written in the negative, stating that the client should not allow the construction phase to start unless certain matters have been dealt with: they do not require affirmative action by the client, i.e. there is no suggestion that the client **must** confirm matters in writing if he or she is satisfied that construction can commence.

However, we would suggest that the client should:

- see a copy of the contractor's health and safety plan;
- seek advice from the CDM co-ordinator as to whether the plan and welfare arrangements are adequate to meet the requirements of CDM 2007;
- ensure that suitable welfare facilities are in place at

the commencement of the construction phase and that there is a suitable strategy for maintaining and developing these facilities throughout the course of the construction works;

- ensure that procedures are in place to prevent the contractor commencing work until such time as he or she has been notified by the client that construction can commence; and
- ensure that procedures are in place (both client's and contractors' procedures) for the mobilisation period to be adhered to.

In the typical rush and manoeuvrings that often take place to get the contractor on site as soon as funding has been secured for a project, it is important that that these matters are not overlooked.

Where a formal contract is not yet in place, the contractor will often have to rely upon a letter of intent (more concerned with financial issues than compliance with health and safety legislation).

However, it is important for both the client and the contractor that the statutory requirements are complied with and the client only permits works to commence on site if the above matters have been properly dealt with.

The issues relating to 'mobilisation' especially need proper consideration where contractors are required to commence construction works on the basis of a letter of intent.

The client is required by virtue of regulation 10(2)(c) to ensure that sufficient time is allowed for planning and preparation by the appointed contractor and this applies whether the start on site is instigated by the signing of the contract or on the basis of a letter of intent. The full period as previously agreed by the client and noted on the F10 must still be allowed to the contractor.

The contractor must be given sufficient time in which to prepare the necessary documentation (including the construction phase plan, initial method statements, site induction and site rules) and the CDM co-ordinator must also be provided with sufficient time in which to advise the client whether the contractor's documentation is adequate and for the client to fulfil its own duties under regulation 16.

The contractor also requires sufficient time in which to mobilise the site welfare facilities (including provision of water supplies, electrical supplies and any necessary certification where new connections are required) and obtain any necessary consents and licences for hoardings, scaffolds, etc. (where they impinge on the adjoining highway).

It is probably useful to reflect upon other issues that might need to be tied into the initial start on site, such as compliance with conditions attached to any planning consent or Section 106 Agreement, party wall awards and other consents relating to access, and any necessary insurances being in place.

A checklist of the information required under the

construction phase plan (based on Appendix 3 of the ACOP) is provided in Appendix E of this book.

Information flows – where does the construction phase plan fit in?

In practice, the construction phase plan has tended to be a fairly static document and once approved by the client at start of construction has not developed any further: it does not really provide a mechanism for dissemination of information on an ongoing basis.

The ACOP stresses the point (in paragraph 164) that the construction phase plan is to be used as 'a practical aid to the management of health and safety on site ... contractors have a particular role in both implementing and monitoring the plan to ensure that it works in practice.'

This suggests that all contractors involved with the project have a part to play in monitoring the plan: these arrangements need to be discussed by the principal contractor and subcontractors and agreed with the client.

It will be up to the principal contractor to decide what information needs to be passed onto other contractors, but the client will need to be satisfied at the outset that adequate arrangements are in place for dissemination of information to all of those involved in the construction process. This should include contractors and their workforce, as well as those involved in ongoing design (including designers of temporary works – formwork, false-works and temporary scaffolds).

Under CDM 1994 it was common practice for the main or principal contractor to pass on information from the pre-tender plan but, as the construction project progresses on site, the earlier information is likely to become out of date with little relevance to subcontractors further down the supply chain.

It is therefore important that the construction phase plan is formatted in such a way that the information contained within the document remains relevant to whoever is provided with such information: a simple structure should facilitate and allow review and update of the document and maintain its relevance for all contractors involved in the project.

The ACOP identifies the importance of the 'site rules' and 'site induction', which form part of the plan, in allowing for information to be passed on to everyone working on the site. Risk assessments (as required by regulation 13(4)(b)) and method statements are the main methods by which contractors can pass on relevant health and safety information to their workforce.

The CDM-C should have sufficient knowledge of the documentation produced by contractors to be in a position to advise the client as to whether the PC has included the elements noted above in the plan (when submitted for approval by the client) and that these elements are adequate.

Works packages

Where construction work is split up into works packages the PC must provide sufficient information to enable subcontractors to understand:

- the design principles (where the works package includes a design element);
- how co-ordination with other designers will be achieved; and
- any health and safety issues relevant to the works or other activities being undertaken at the same time.

In order to achieve compliance the following information should be included:

- information about the materials and the work – including specifications and drawings;
- information relating to hazards that might affect those carrying out the work;
- copies of relevant sections of the construction phase plan;
- information relating to the fire plan;
- information relating to the traffic management plan; and
- information relating to the waste management plan.

It should be noted that regulation 19(1)(b) requires a contractor **not** to carry out construction work unless:

'he has been given access to such part of the construction phase plan as is relevant to the work to be performed by him, ...'.

Practical completion

Many people assume that the construction phase ends at practical completion.

This is true in those cases where the project is complete, the health and safety file is handed over to the client, the site has been cleared and all of the contractors walk away from the site.

However, all too frequently the client takes possession with works either incomplete or with a whole host of snagging items and work continues on site until all outstanding issues are dealt with.

In some cases these works can continue for weeks, or even months, and the distinction between an active construction site and an area under the occupation of and under the control of the client becomes blurred.

The construction phase only finishes when the contractor completes the work and leaves site: this can be months after the contract administrator has issued the certificate giving practical completion.

Throughout the whole of this period the duties of the principal contractor, the requirements for updating the construction phase plan and all of the other issues concerned with managing a site remain.

CDM still applies and any breaches of the CDM Regulations by any of the duty holders are liable to lead to prosecution.

The client will also have duties under the *Management Regulations* once he or she takes partial or full possession of the structure or premises.

The CDM-C needs to be aware that his or her duties also remain until such time as the project is completed.

Design for the project

It is of particular importance that the design must be compliant in situ, i.e. the design must take account of the actual conditions encountered on site and in the finished structure: the information provided to the package designer must include information relating to the use, location and environment of the installed component.

With more components being manufactured off site there is a risk that the local conditions are not taken into account during the design and manufacture, with the result that a component may be difficult to bring into the building or structure because the available access routes or openings are not adequate, or, once installed the component may be difficult to maintain,

remove or replace because no thought has been given as to how this can be achieved.

CDM 2007 requires that individual design packages be co-ordinated into the main design and there is a general requirement for all parties to co-operate with one another and for design and construction to be co-ordinated.

The CDM-C has a key role to play in facilitating such co-operation.

Case study – dust and explosions

Electrical components, switchgear, etc. installed in a factory had to be replaced because the designer of the electrical works package had not been advised that the premises were to used for a manufacturing process that produced a lot of fine dust.

The dust was likely to result in an explosive atmosphere (as defined under the *Dangerous Substances and Explosive Atmospheres Regulations 2002*).

In these circumstances the design should have allowed for all electrical apparatus to be intrinsically safe, i.e. would not produce sparks that could ignite fine powder or dust.

10 The health and safety file

INTRODUCTION

The mechanism for delivery of the health and safety file (the 'file') needs to be in place at the start of the project to ensure that the file is available when construction work is complete.

The 'construction phase' ends when construction work is complete, and for many projects this coincides with 'practical completion', however, it could be later, where contractors remain on site undertaking construction work after the client has taken beneficial occupation of the structure or premises.

The CDM co-ordinator (CDM-C) must be in a position to be able to advise the client on the necessary contractual arrangements and the statutory obligations in respect of the provision of 'file information' by designers and contractors.

This is only possible if the CDM-C is appointed at the beginning of the project – ideally before any other appointments have been made – and the CDM-C has discussed the format and content of the health and safety file with the client and understands the client's needs.

For smaller, less complicated projects, a fairly basic file (encompassing the requirements of ACOP paragraph 263 – the contents of the health and safety file) will suffice.

For larger premises, with complex mechanical and electrical plant and equipment, the requirements may be far greater in terms of health and safety documentation: where the building requires the services of full time engineering staff or facilities management then the extent and scope of the file will be vastly different.

The statutory requirements (in respect of the file and provision of information by each of the duty holders) should be adequately reflected in the contractual arrangements with designers and contractors and in the pre-construction information.

It is especially important that any amendments to standard forms of contract, e.g. JCT contracts, do not alter the requirements set out in the employer's requirements and the pre-construction information.

The CDM-C will need to provide contractors with suitable documentation setting out the requirements for 'file' information as part of the pre-construction information.

Similar consideration needs to be given to the requirements for building manuals and O&M (operating and maintenance) manuals produced by contractors, including mechanical and electrical information and specialist installations.

Although CDM 1994 placed a statutory obligation upon all parties to provide information for the file, inadequate contractual arrangements often led to information not being provided in time, or not at all, resulting in disputes and delays at the end of the project.

Information for the file is also required from designers and the client should ensure that the contractual arrangements entered into by the design team allow for the provision of information for the file.

Clients and their advisors need to take on board the lessons learned from the previous regulatory regime and take the opportunity afforded by the introduction of CDM 2007 to reassess their procedures and documentation to provide information at the end of the project more suited to their specific requirements.

Key features

Irrespective of the size of the project, there are certain key features and requirements that need to be considered when preparing the file:

- the scope and format of the file;
- the structure of the file;
- the management of the file and provision for updating the file;
- the end users; and
- the production of other documentation for the project, e.g. O&M manuals, fire risk assessments, etc.

RETENTION OF INFORMATION

The clear message from both the ACOP and the HSE is that the file should only contain information that will allow future construction work to be carried out safely.

A properly written file should add considerable value by recording information that would have to be found out by survey for future work. It is acknowledged that the drafting of the Regulations cannot be prescriptive because very few files will be the same.

Those who own or occupy premises do need access to health and safety information but other legislation (such as environmental, fire and asbestos regulations) also demands that information is kept available throughout the lifetime of the building or structure.

It should also be noted that the retained information should include sufficient detail to allow future users access to original information at source (for example, information relating to plant should include the manufacturer's identification/reference number in order that further information can be obtained direct from the manufacturer if needed).

This chapter examines how these aims can be achieved but also looks at the need to retain useful information that would otherwise be discarded. It also examines issues such as whether the file should only relate to the project, or whether a file should be created that encompasses the whole of the structure or premises.

THE CLIENT'S DUTY

Clients have a duty to provide information to contractors undertaking work within their premises under several pieces of legislation including the *Control of Asbestos Regulations* 2006 and the *Management of Health and Safety at Work Regulations* 1999 (regulation 12 – Persons working in host employers' or self-employed persons' undertakings), as well as CDM 2007.

For all projects, whether they are notifiable or not, any relevant information included in any existing file must be passed on to those who are engaged in construction work, or likely to be affected by such work, or any other person(s) who might need it in order to perform their duties under the Regulations.

For notifiable projects the client must ensure that any file already in his or her possession is kept current and available for inspection by any person who may need it, and that the CDM-C is provided with all the health and safety information in the client's possession.

The client's duties in respect of provision of information are set out in regulations 10 and 15: where there is already a file it must be available to any person who might need it on any project, and made available to the CDM-C for notifiable projects.

Client's duty in relation to information

Regulation 10(1) and 10(2)(d)
'(1) Every client shall ensure that:

(a) every person designing the structure; and
(b) every contractor who has been or may be appointed by the client,

is promptly provided with pre-construction information in accordance with paragraph (2).'

'(2)(d) any information in any existing health and safety file,'.

Regulation 15 – Client's duty in relation to information where a project is notifiable
'Where the project is notifiable the client shall promptly provide the CDM co-ordinator with [the information that he is already obliged to provide to designers and contractors under regulation 10(2)].'

Although the client is already required under regulation 15 to provide the CDM-C with any existing health and safety file information, this duty is reinforced by the duties under regulation 17.

Regulation 17(1) 'The client shall ensure that the CDM co-ordinator is provided with all the health and safety information in the client's possession (or which is reasonably obtainable) relating to the project which is likely to be needed for inclusion in the health and safety file, including information specified in regulation 4(9)(c) of the *Control of Asbestos Regulations* 2006.'

It should be noted that the client also has a duty to keep the file available for inspection (after the construction phase) and keep it up to date.

Regulation 17(3) 'The client shall take reasonable steps to ensure that after the construction phase the information in the health and safety file:
(a) is kept available for inspection by any person who may need it to comply with the relevant statutory provisions; and
(b) is revised as often as may be appropriate to incorporate any relevant new information.'

Although this regulation would appear to oblige the client to keep the file up to date when future works are undertaken, this seems to be at variance with statements from the HSE to the effect that the file only needs to be updated when future works are notifiable and a CDM-C appointed.

As mentioned elsewhere in the book we would suggest that where works are undertaken at a later date and there are any health and safety implications the file should be updated and the new information recorded.

WHEN IS A FILE REQUIRED?

CDM 2007 only requires that a file is prepared for notifiable projects, so, where non-notifiable works are carried out there is no need to create a file.

For existing premises that were constructed prior to April 1995 there was no requirement under previous legislation for a file to be prepared, but, for most properties or structures there will be some information available that needs to be captured and retained for the benefit of those involved in the future occupation or use of the premises, or those involved in the cleaning, maintenance or repair of the building or structure.

Since April 1995 there has been a requirement in place for a health and safety file to be produced in accordance with the requirements of the *Construction (Design and Management) Regulations* 1994.

> *Key points – CDM 2007*
> When is a file required?
>
> - only for notifiable projects, i.e. construction projects lasting longer than 30 days (or 500 person days);
> - existing files should be amended or updated;
> - a new file should be prepared where there is no existing file;
> - no file required for non-notifiable projects, i.e. lasting less than 30 days (or 500 person days).

The file can be set up for existing buildings at any time: it is not necessary to wait until works are being undertaken. Where clients or their managing agents already have extensive archive information available there is no reason why they should not make use of the information and set up a file.

For larger estates, or even for smaller portfolios, the opportunity presents itself to create a standard file format that meets the operational requirements of the client, and is appropriate for continued use as and when individual projects are undertaken and relevant information added to the file.

The advantages of setting up a file will be illustrated when the first project is undertaken and essential information is already in place.

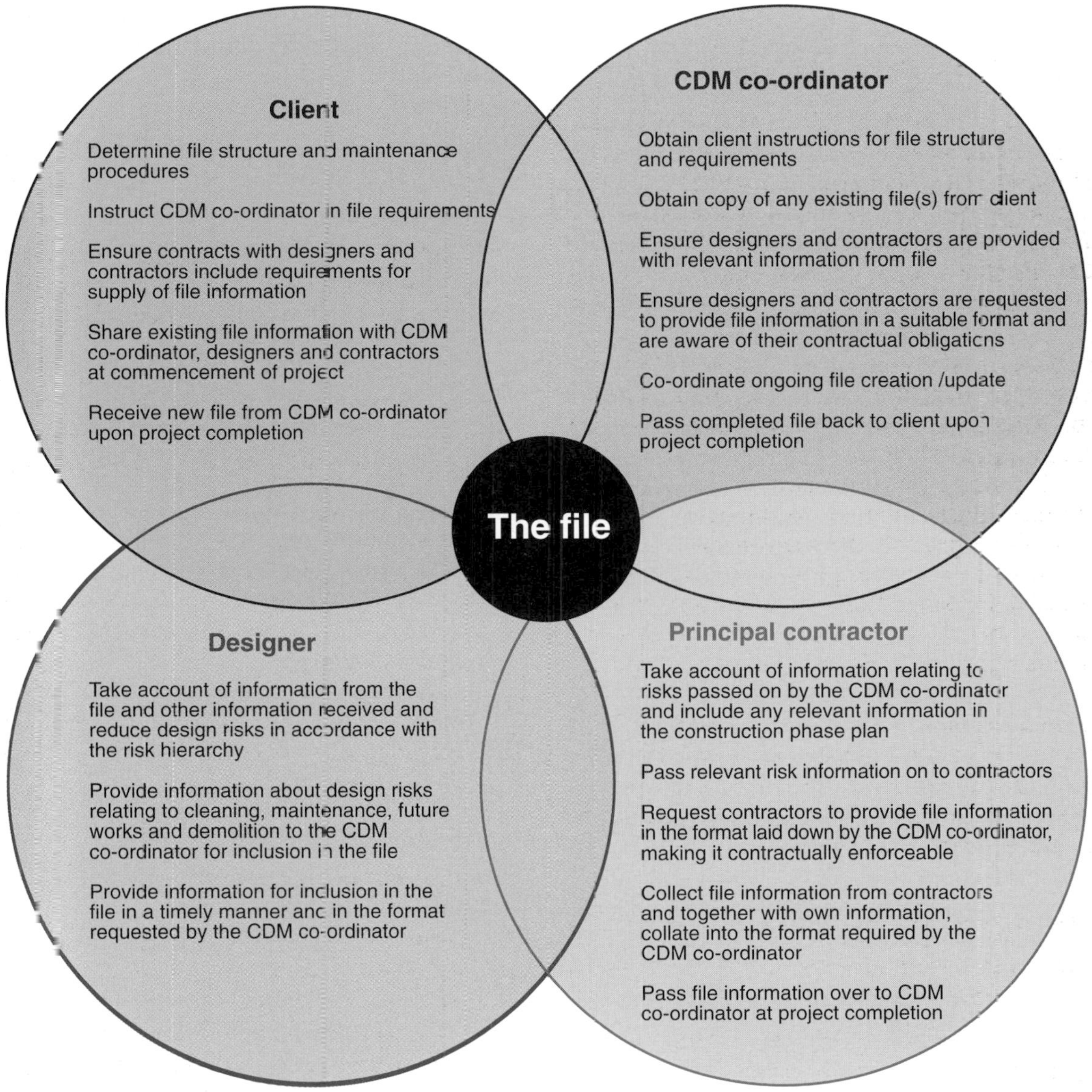

Client

Determine file structure and maintenance procedures

Instruct CDM co-ordinator in file requirements

Ensure contracts with designers and contractors include requirements for supply of file information

Share existing file information with CDM co-ordinator, designers and contractors at commencement of project

Receive new file from CDM co-ordinator upon project completion

CDM co-ordinator

Obtain client instructions for file structure and requirements

Obtain copy of any existing file(s) from client

Ensure designers and contractors are provided with relevant information from file

Ensure designers and contractors are requested to provide file information in a suitable format and are aware of their contractual obligations

Co-ordinate ongoing file creation /update

Pass completed file back to client upon project completion

The file

Designer

Take account of information from the file and other information received and reduce design risks in accordance with the risk hierarchy

Provide information about design risks relating to cleaning, maintenance, future works and demolition to the CDM co-ordinator for inclusion in the file

Provide information for inclusion in the file in a timely manner and in the format requested by the CDM co-ordinator

Principal contractor

Take account of information relating to risks passed on by the CDM co-ordinator and include any relevant information in the construction phase plan

Pass relevant risk information on to contractors

Request contractors to provide file information in the format laid down by the CDM co-ordinator, making it contractually enforceable

Collect file information from contractors and together with own information, collate into the format required by the CDM co-ordinator

Pass file information over to CDM co-ordinator at project completion

Figure 15: CDM duty holders' responsibilities in relation to the file.

WHO SHOULD PRODUCE THE FILE?

There was much debate under the old CDM Regulations as to who should produce the file – this being largely dependent upon the contractual arrangements agreed by the client.

The planning supervisor only had to ensure that the file was prepared: it was open to any of the duty holders, or even for a party to be contracted in to produce the file. Without clear and unequivocal arrangements in place at the outset, disputes could, and did, arise as to the production of the file, and even over who should supply the information required for the file.

The requirements under CDM 2007 more closely reflect the requirements set out in Articles 5 and 6 of Directive 92/57/EEC.

EC Directive 92/57/EEC of 24 June 1992: Temporary or mobile construction sites

Article 5 – Project preparation stage: duties of co-ordinators
'(c) prepare a file appropriate to the characteristics of the project containing relevant safety and health information to be taken into account during any subsequent works.'

Article 6 – Project execution stage: duties of co-ordinators
'(c) make, or cause to be made, any adjustments required to the safety and health plan referred to in Article 5 (b) and the file referred to in Article 5 (c) to take account of the progress of the work and any changes which have occurred;'.

The Directive talks of the file being produced during the project preparation stage: and clearly places this as a duty upon the co-ordinator. The requirements under CDM 2007 do not differentiate between the project preparation and execution stages, merely stating that the CDM co-ordinator should prepare the file.

The duties of the CDM-C in respect of the file are set out in regulation 20(2)(e).

CDM 2007 regulation 20 – General duties of CDM co-ordinators
'(2)(e) prepare, where none exists, and otherwise review and update a record ('the health and safety file') containing information relating to the project which is likely to be needed during any subsequent construction work to ensure the health and safety of any person, including the information provided in pursuance of regulations 17(1), 18 (2) and 22(1)(j); and
(f) at the end of the construction phase, pass the health and safety file to the client.'

'Prepare, where none exists, and otherwise review and update a record ("the health and safety file") containing information relating to the project' – no doubt this phrase will also be open to interpretation. Whilst it is clearly the responsibility of the CDM-C to prepare, or 'make ready for use' the file, there is no contractual relationship (apart from that with the client) between the CDM-C and the parties who are required to provide the information for the file.

Without this direct link the planning supervisor (under CDM 1994) often found some difficulty in eliciting information from both designers and contractors and it is likely that the same conditions will prevail under CDM 2007.

In most instances (apart from those cases where the client instructs other contractors directly), it is the principal contractor who has direct links with the subcontractors and is able to rely upon contractual remedies in those instances where file information is not forthcoming from contractors.

Even so, with current trends for work to be subcontracted further down the supply chain, and the direct link broken, there are still likely to be some problems in ensuring that all of the requisite information is gathered in.

CONTRACTUAL LIABILITY FOR PROVISION OF FILE INFORMATION

With CDM 2007 the client is still at liberty to decide where contractual liability for provision of information and production of the file should rest.

To a certain extent this question is academic: as stated in the introduction to this chapter the more important issue is that adequate arrangements are made in the first place to secure production of the file.

Almost all parties involved in the project will have some hand in the production of information for the file and it is important that the procedures for project managing the project facilitate flows of information between the respective parties (see below) and that as each stage of the project is completed the requisite information is provided.

Contributors to the file

The CDM-C is responsible for preparing the file and ensuring that it is handed over to the client.

However, the majority of the information included in the file will be provided by other duty holders.

Contributor	CDM 2007 Regulation
Client	Regulation 10(2)(d) and 17(1)
Designer	Regulation 18(2)
Principal contractor	Regulation 19(2)(a)(iii)
Contractor	Regulation 19(2)(a)(iii) and 22(1)(j)
Specialist contractor	Regulation 19(2)(a)(iii) and 22(1)(j)

The whole of CDM is characterised by flows of information: initially from the client and designers to allow the contractor to price the work and understand the health and safety and risk management issues associated with the project.

The principal contractor will provide other contractors with information in respect of various works packages and as works are completed information will then flow back to the main contractor and then ultimately back to the client in the form of the health and safety file.

At the same time information will flow to and fro between the designers, suppliers and contractors with ultimate capture of information for the 'file'.

Much of the information will be included in the building, mechanical and electrical and the various specialists manuals produced for the project.

Clients and their advisors should be clear as to the distinction between the requirements of operating and maintenance (O&M) manuals and those of the health and safety (H&S) file.

This can be summarised as shown in the comparison table below.

How can the client ensure that the file is produced on time?

The ACOP recognises that it can be difficult to obtain information for the file after designers or contractors have finished their work and even suggests (in paragraph 107 of the ACOP) that the client may need to provide incentives in order to ensure that information is provided to the CDM-C.

The file needs to be available at practical completion or handover in order to satisfy contractual obligations as well as to achieve compliance with the Regulations.

This also includes the provision of mechanical and electrical manuals, specialists' manuals, and user operating instructions, certificates, guarantees and warranties.

Once designers and contractors have moved onto new projects it is difficult to motivate them to return their attention to outstanding issues on previous projects, especially in those cases where the client has allowed practical completion to take place in the knowledge that the file is incomplete (or even non-existent).

It is essential that the procedures and arrangements for setting up the file and obtaining information are dealt with right at the start of the project and that these procedures and arrangements are adequately reflected in the contractual arrangements between the client and all of the duty holders.

If all parties are obliged to provide information in accordance with clearly set out contractual obligations the client is able to impose financial penalties on both designers and contractors, by withholding payment of fees to designers and withholding final payment to the contractor or by withholding a significant sum by way of retention until the file information is produced.

Where the CDM-C has set up the file at an early stage in the life of the project, he or she can track the provision of information and provide status reports at regular intervals to the client, or at project/progress meetings. (See example on page 110.)

O&M manual	H&S file
Relates to procedures for maintaining, commissioning, testing, starting up, checking, shutting down the plant or equipment	Relates to management issues associated with these tasks
Provides information for the person(s) undertaking these tasks	Relates to the person(s) managing the tasks
Identifies risks, etc.	Identifies key hazards, etc.
Relates to detailed information for emergency shutdown procedures	Relates to management procedures necessary to achieve a safe and effective emergency shutdown
Contains COSHH data and safety information	Relates to procedures and safe systems of work in respect of hazardous substances

HEALTH AND SAFETY FILE INFORMATION STATUS REPORT

Project:					
Date of meeting	Works packages completed to date	Information available/required	Date produced	Checked	Comments

PROCEDURES AT PRACTICAL COMPLETION

CDM 2007 regulation 20 – General duties of CDM co-ordinators
'(2)(f) at the end of the construction phase, pass the health and safety file to the client.'

The Regulations are clear that at practical completion (the end of the construction phase) the file should be handed over to the client. As part of this process the CDM-C should ensure that the handover is recorded and that there is physical evidence that the CDM-C has discharged his or her duty under regulation 20(2)(f).

The CDM-C should also provide the client with advice with regard to the client's ongoing duties: this will normally be noted in the file but can also be confirmed by letter when the file is handed over.

It is also of some benefit if the CDM-C discusses with the client exactly who within the client organisation will be responsible for the file and ensuring that relevant information is passed on to those persons who will need such information throughout the life of the building or structure.

Ideally these persons should be appraised of the purpose and content of the file by the CDM-C when the file is handed over, but if this is not physically possible, then they should be made aware of these matters by the client.

The client has a duty to pass on information contained in the file and to hand over the file to purchasers, etc.

The ACOP deals with various situations including disposals and part disposals (see paragraph 265) and also where all or part of the structure is leased (see paragraph 266).

CDM 2007 regulation 17 – The client's duty in relation to the health and safety file

ACOP paragraph 265:

'... Where clients dispose of their entire interest in a structure, they should pass the file to the new owners and ensure that they are aware of the nature and purpose of the file. Where they sell part of the structure, any relevant information in the file should be passed or copied to the new owner.'

ACOP paragraph 266:

'If the client leases out all or part of the structure, arrangements need to be made for the health and safety file to be made available to leaseholders. In some cases, the client might transfer the file to the leaseholder during the lease period. In other cases, it may be better for the client to keep the file, but tell leaseholders that it is available. If the leaseholder acts as a client for future construction projects, the leaseholder and the original client will need to make arrangements for the file to be made available to the new CDM co-ordinator.'

ACOP paragraph 267:

'In multi-occupancy situations, for example, where a housing association owns a block of flats, the owner should keep and maintain the file, but ensure that individual flat occupiers are supplied with health and safety information concerning their home.'

ACOP paragraph 268:

'A development may include roads and sewers that will be adopted by the local authority or water company. It is generally best to prepare separate files covering each client's interests.'

PURCHASER'S RESPONSIBILITIES IN RESPECT OF CDM

Where a client disposes of all or part of the completed building or structure and hands over the complete health and safety file or the relevant parts thereof, in compliance with regulation 17(4) (see below), the purchaser who receives the file is **not** a client under CDM and therefore has **no** duties in respect of CDM.

CDM 2007 regulation 17(4)
'It shall be sufficient compliance with paragraph (3)(a) by a client who disposes of his entire interest in the structure if he delivers the health and safety file to the person who acquires his interest in it and ensures that he is aware of the nature and purpose of the file.'

The client does have a duty to ensure that the purchaser is aware of the nature and purpose of the file, and it is then up to the purchaser to look after the information that has been handed over – it is no longer the client's responsibility.

WHAT SHOULD THE FILE CONTAIN?

The client needs to understand the purpose of the health and safety file and how this accords with its business requirements and the operational requirements for the premises.

Files are also required for structures (which might include bridges, highways or other engineering projects) and the file requirements need to be tailored to the particular requirements for the project.

The legal requirements relating to the health and safety file are set out in the regulations.

Regulation 20(2)(e):

'… a record ("the health and safety file") containing information relating to the project which is likely to be needed during any subsequent construction work to ensure the health and safety of any person, …'.

This is, by necessity, a fairly broad description as to what might be required because the file will cover all types of construction projects from the smallest office refurbishment to a major engineering structure such as a railway bridge or tunnel.

The ACOP expands on what the contents of the health and safety file might be, but notes that the information should be relevant and that 'the level of detail should allow the likely risks to be identified' (see ACOP paragraph 263).

A strict interpretation of the Regulations suggests that the file is only required for future construction works, and indeed at paragraph 264 it states:

'(a) The file does not need to include things that will be of no help in planning future construction work, for example

…

(c) details about the normal operation of the completed structure;'.

It should be clear that the file is a document that contains information that can assist in the safety of future operations by the provision of relevant information gained during the course of design and construction.

ACOP paragraph 263
'When putting together the health and safety file, you should consider including information about each of the following where they are relevant to the health and safety of any future construction work. The level of detail should allow the likely risks to be identified and addressed by those carrying out the work:

(a) a brief description of the work carried out;
(b) any residual hazards which remain and how they have been dealt with (for example, surveys or other information concerning asbestos; contaminated land; water bearing strata; buried services, etc.);
(c) key structural principles (for example, bracing, sources of substantial stored energy – including pre- or post-tensioned members) and safe working loads for floors and roofs, particularly where these may preclude placing scaffolding or heavy machinery there;
(d) hazardous materials used (for example, lead paint; pesticides; special coatings which should not be burnt off, etc.);
(e) information regarding the removal or dismantling of installed plant and equipment (for example, any special arrangements for lifting, order or other special instructions for dismantling, etc.);
(f) health and safety information about equipment provided for cleaning or maintaining the structure;
(g) the nature, location and markings of significant services, including underground cables; gas supply equipment; fire fighting services, etc.;
(h) information and as-built drawings of the structure, its plant and equipment (for example, the means of safe access to and from service voids, fire doors and compartmentalisation, etc.).'

The file is not intended to be used as a document for the day-to-day running of the premises or client's business activities: there are other documents that fulfil these requirements (health and safety policy, management arrangements and procedures documentation).

The ongoing activities of the business are also covered by other sets of legislation such as the *Management Regulations* 1999, RRFSO, and the *Workplace Regulations* 1992 which require an assessment of the operational risks.

It should also be noted that the HSE states that the file only needs to be reviewed and updated when future construction projects are notifiable. In other words there is no requirement for the file to be updated for non-notifiable projects (although we would suggest that where significant risks are introduced to the premises or structure, for example, a new high voltage cable is laid across the car park, such information should be noted in the file together with any relevant drawings).

Finally, the 'file' should not be confused with the manuals: the file is not a replacement for the operating and maintenance (O&M) manuals – these two documents complement each other.

Where plant is installed or replaced then O&M manuals may be produced even where the project is of short duration and non-notifiable.

For example, under PUWER 1998 and LOLER 1998 there are statutory requirements for the manufacturer/supplier to provide full operating and maintenance instructions with all plant and equipment installed, and the employer (client) is required to pass this information on to those employed to operate and maintain the plant and equipment. Also, some plant and equipment is subject to statutory test and inspection requirements or maintenance regimes. These statutory requirements must be complied with, even if there is no requirement under CDM to produce a health and safety file.

FAILINGS OF FILES

Where clients have not been clear about their requirements the quality of files has varied, especially where insufficient funds or resources have been allocated for the production of the files (and, incidentally, the manuals).

Files supplied by contractors often comprised the construction phase health and safety plan, relabelled as the 'file' containing method statements for construction works but little relevant to the future maintenance, repair or cleaning of the occupied building or structure.

HOW SHOULD THE FILE BE FORMATTED

What is it to be used for?

Some thought needs to be given to the precise requirements for the file and how it fits with the client's business requirements. For the one-off client the format of the file may not be so important, but, where a client has a large property portfolio, the opportunity should be taken to provide a standard and consistent approach to file production.

This can only be achieved if clients provide a clear brief as to their precise requirements for production of both files and manuals for all of their projects. Where such a brief exists it is then much easier to ensure that a consistent approach is applied to the production of tender documentation, including specifications, employer's requirements and the actual contract (in which the requirements for the file are set out).

Late appointment of the CDM co-ordinator

Where the CDM-C is appointed late, the terms and conditions for production of file information may already have been spelt out in the tender documents without any reference to the CDM-C.

However, it should be noted that for the purposes of CDM 2007, the client will be deemed to have undertaken the role of CDM-C and will retain the duties of the CDM-C until such time as a formal appointment has been made.

Use of standard specifications

Where standard specifications have been used for the project then the requirements for the file will be dependent upon the documents that have been produced by the person administering the contract.

Documents such as *NBS Specification* contain sections relating to the production of manuals and files.

Where such documents have been used, prior to the appointment of the CDM-C, then the client will be contractually bound by such requirements.

If subsequently the client wishes to alter the way in which the file is to be presented, then this may prove to be outside the contractual requirements and, even though the production of the file is a statutory requirement, it may involve the client in additional costs.

The client also needs to decide upon the format in which the file is to be presented, e.g. hard copy or in electronic format. In the case of larger or more complex premises or structures some input from those involved in the day-to-day running of the facility (facilities managers) may be required: additional information may need to be captured or systems may be already in place, such as Building Management Systems (BMS), that require a particular format or electronic system to be adopted by the client.

VERSION CONTROL

Clients are inclined to require multiple copies of the file: one to remain in a secure location (perhaps retained with the title deeds), one to be made available to whoever is managing the premises and a further copy kept on site.

Copies of the file may be in the hands of several different organisations (or several departments of the same company or organisation) and unless adequate procedures exist, individual copies may be updated for later projects while other copies are not.

Where a series of relatively small-scale projects are undertaken over a period of time significant disparities can arise in the information contained within each of the files, either in the text or the record drawings (or both).

It is important that the information contained in the file is accurate and up to date and that adequate procedures are in place within the client organisation to allow this to happen.

The same applies to the initial issue of the document at the end of the construction phase (or practical completion) when the CDM-C should have adequate procedures in place for issue of the document – it should be quite clear that the document issued is the 'final issue' with a document control sheet containing:

- the version number;
- the number of documents issued;
- their status;
- who they have been issued to; and
- procedures for updating future amendments, alterations and major works.

Version control

Control copy

This document is a **controlled copy** of the original <document> produced by [*company name*] in respect of the <health and safety file> for the project detailed below.

Project: <name of project>

Job no: <123>

Doc. ref: HSF

Doc. issued:-   14 May 2004

Doc. status: Draft/Information/Revised/Issued

[highlight whichever status level applies]

Any person who undertakes a modification, alteration or revision to this document must ensure that:

- all copies of this document are also updated;
- all persons affected by the revision are informed; and
- the 'Table of versions issued' below is updated.

Quality control unique reference number: C192.MM.040514:000

Issue	Ref	Version	Issued to	Date
V 1.0	D	Draft – For comment and approval		14 April 2004
V 2.0	O	Original	A&T Projects Ltd	14 May 2004
	C001	Controlled Copy	Client	14 May 2004
	UC	Uncontrolled Copies	xyz	14 May 2004

COPYRIGHT

This document is the copyright of [*company name*] and shall not be reproduced in whole or in part without the prior written agreement of [*company name*].

The electricity cable case study illustrates the importance of maintaining control over the issue of documents and ensuring that adequate procedures are in place for updating all copies of the file.

Case study – electricity cable

As part of an upgrade of the electrical supply to an industrial estate a new 11,000 volt cable was routed across part of the site crossing over an overflow car park.

The project was not deemed to be a CDM project (under CDM 1994) and information relating to the project was not recorded; neither was it passed on to the person who held the health and safety file.

Subsequently, excavations for a new extension took place in the overflow car park and a workman struck the live cable. He sustained significant burns and the damage to the cable disrupted electrical supplies to a number of buildings until repairs could be effected.

SELECTION OF INFORMATION TO INCLUDE IN THE FILE

CDM 2007 only requires certain information to be included in the file, i.e. the information required as indicated at paragraph 263 of the ACOP. This information only relates to health and safety.

Of equal importance to the client are drawings produced for Planning and Building Regulations (the stamped up drawings that have been approved by building control or the planning authority). There may be other sets of drawings included for grant approval under various schemes, such as lottery funding or agricultural grant schemes.

There is no requirement to include these drawings within the health and safety file but these are clearly of equal importance to the client. It is therefore appropriate to discuss with the client if, and how, these should be retained and stored, and whether it would be beneficial to include these in the file.

Some documents may require storage in secure conditions (e.g. legal documents – tenancy agreements, way leaves and access agreements, discharge consents, etc.) and discussion should take place with the client as to whether copies should be included in the file or whether these documents need to be cross-referenced in the file.

Original construction drawings

Drawings showing the original construction details should not be discarded without some thought being given to their continued usefulness. They will often contain useful information and detail that has not been shown on drawings produced for later alteration or refurbishment schemes.

Site services information should be dealt with in a similar fashion. Where detailed investigations have been undertaken to ascertain the nature and location of services prior to construction some of the information provided is excluded from the 'record drawings' produced at completion of the project.

Standard file format

Paragraph 258 of the ACOP states:

'**The scope, structure and format for the file should be agreed between the client and co-ordinator at the start of a project**. There can be a separate file for each structure, one for an entire project or site, or one for a group of related structures. The file may be combined with the Building Regulations Log Book, or a maintenance manual providing that this does not result in the health and safety information being lost or buried. What matters is that people can find the information they need easily and that any differences between similar structures are clearly shown.'

Exclusions and constraints

Where the project information applies to only part of a site or development, it is important to note any exclusions in the file where there is a potential for future users of the file to make false assumptions as to the extent of the information contained within the file.

Similarly, where restraints have been placed upon the project by outside parties, especially where such constraints may be ongoing and affect future projects, the information should be properly recorded, either in the file or in the manuals.

Exclusions

Projects may only cover part of a site and the surveys and investigations carried out may have been restricted to those parts of the site where development is to take place.

Commissions for ground investigations, site services information, and/or Type 3 asbestos surveys may have been restricted to the area covered by the specific project.

Refurbishment projects may appear to have involved the complete renewal of electrical and plumbing services but it is possible in some cases for the existing service risers to have been retained (e.g. water, gas) and this fact should be recorded.

In the case of electrical installations it is possible

that sections of old wiring have been retained that do not comply with the new colour codings: this type of information needs to be recorded.

Underground fuel tanks may have been left in place but not recorded as part of the project information.

The premises may contain voids, cellars, vaults below pavements, storm water drains and culverts, which were excluded from the works or were located in areas where no works were undertaken.

It is easy to assume at a later date that just because there is a health and safety file in place that it is complete and covers all of the information that might have been available in respect of the site, structure or premises.

It is vitally important that where the information provided relates only to a part of the site, structure or premises this is quite clearly stated at the beginning of the document.

There is also a risk that where stand-alone documents are produced for further projects that these become separated or lost and vital health and safety information is lost if there is not an overall control document that lists the individual projects undertaken.

(**Note** It is also important to consider whether the file should be for the **project** or the **premises** – see the section on this below.)

Constraints

Where restraints have been placed on the project by outside parties this information should be recorded for future reference.

Conflicts between safe design and conservation have often arisen in the past between various government agencies such as the local authority planning department, or others concerned with design and amenity issues.

The most obvious examples are those where the constraints placed by English Heritage upon Listed Buildings have led to conflicts with other statutory authorities, such as the fire authority over issues relating to the fire integrity of the building.

Where designers have not been allowed to cover existing moulded ceilings with an additional layer of plasterboard to increase the fire rating, or raise the height of balustrading to current levels, then these constraints upon design need to be recorded in the health and safety file.

There are obvious issues relating to future users of the building where restrictions have been placed upon proposed measures to provide safe access to certain areas of the building, but the planners have objected to the proposals.

Conflicts often arise over height restrictions, where a developer wishes to maximise the number of floors in a building and the provision of plant and equipment at roof level compromises the roof profile and overall roof height acceptable to the planners.

Such conflicts can result in designers reducing either the height or the size of the plant room, leading to issues relating to poor access for both routine maintenance and part replacements or to issues relating to edge protection where the provision of railings/balustrading to provide adequate edge protection is not acceptable to the planners, thus compromising the safety of those working at roof level.

CDM co-ordinators should make sure that these types of issues are well documented and noted in the file.

What happens if the CDM-C comes across a file that is inadequate?

The general duties of CDM co-ordinators under regulation 20(2)(e) include the duty to 'otherwise review and update' the health and safety file (where the CDM-C has been appointed by the client in respect of a notifiable project).

The CDM-C may come across instances where he or she considers that the existing file handed over by the client to be completely inadequate (e.g. it fails to meet accepted standards, such as the HSE ACOP or industry guidance).

In these circumstances the CDM-C should identify that he or she considers the file to be inadequate and advise the client accordingly: the CDM-C cannot be expected to produce a new file in these circumstances.

There is a requirement to amend and update the file to take account of the current project but not to produce a complete new file. The deficiencies should be noted and confirmed to the client in writing. The problems should obviously be discussed with the client and instructions sought as to how the issue should be rectified.

An important consideration is whether the file should be for the project or the premises – see below.

PROJECT FILE OR PREMISES FILE?

Traditionally, under CDM 1994, most files were project based and the clear intent of the Regulations was that a file should be produced for each project.

This notion was reinforced by the requirement for the client to provide any file that had been produced for the property or structure on a previous project and then for a new file to be produced at the end of the current project.

Where project based files are produced then it is possible to end up with numerous files for the same building.

This can happen when multiple projects are undertaken within a building or complex with different sponsors and project teams and a variety of contractors, none of whom are working to common standards or templates for document production.

Ultimately, unless the client has adequate systems in place for tracking projects the whole process becomes untenable – in extreme cases where the client has not demanded a consistent approach for the production of file information then it can become almost impossible to find relevant information when required.

In these circumstances it is essential that adequate procedures are put in place for document control, cross referencing and tracking of projects, especially where significant mechanical and electrical (M&E) projects are undertaken and changes to the asset register occur. This can have a knock on effect on future planned maintenance and inspection regimes.

Even where projects only affect part of the structure or premises there can be components of the works which affect systems across the whole of the building or structure, such as fire detection and alarm installations.

Where there are multiple files produced works may overlap and essential information may be lost or difficult to access.

Premises file – the advantages

There are significant advantages to be gained by producing a single file for the premises or structure rather than creating a new file for each project and this approach is explored below.

This requires considerable input initially, inasmuch as the structure of the documentation and procedures has to be thought through, templates produced and the system has to be strictly adhered to throughout the lifetime of the building or structure. See *Premises file – format and content*.

Effort is required to induct all of the building users into the use and advantages of the system and for the system to be properly managed.

Where clients operate an Integrated Management System (IMS) or Quality Assurance (QA) system then the premises file will probably provide the best route for integrating health and safety information into the rest of their system.

In a single tenant occupancy, the building owner or occupier is probably in a position to maintain effective control over all projects and works undertaken within the premises.

Where the building is effectively in multiple occupations, either by virtue of multiple tenancies or by works being let out by sponsors within the same organisation, then adequate systems must be set up and maintained for controlling the premises file.

Where there are multiple tenancies within the same building or complex, managing agents (and facilities managers) will normally deal with such matters – either by way of the tenancy agreement (lease) or licences to carry out alterations.

Leases need to make provision for lessees to provide information for the file where alterations are under-

taken and also for access to existing information to be made available where works are being planned.

Where several properties are owned, or large estates are managed, the advantages of setting up a standardised system become apparent. It is necessary to structure all documentation in accordance with the standard template but the use of a standardised and systematic approach does allow information to be recorded into the system and found much more easily than where a random approach to documentation is used.

This is especially relevant for organisations such as housing associations, where they are managing large estates (perhaps as many as four or five thousand properties) and robust systems need to be in place.

Premises file – format and content

The **file** should be regarded as the overall control document for the building or structure; should contain information that relates to the main health and safety issues; and should make reference to other documents that form an integral part of the safe operation of the building.

By linking the file into other documents such as the asbestos register, the fire risk assessment (required under the RRFSO) and the asset register, a single document can provide a valuable tool in ensuring that the building owner is aware of and able to fulfil his or her statutory duties under health and safety and other associated legislation. (This will include environmental, ecological and any other restrictions or requirements placed upon clients by bodies such as English Heritage and the Environment Agency.)

In taking this approach the file is regarded as a permanent document that records significant events and changes that occur throughout the lifetime of the building or structure and retains its relevance by recording events such as major refurbishments, extensions or the incorporation of new plant, equipment or systems: it is not replaced every time a new project is undertaken.

For this approach to succeed it is necessary to undertake a fundamental review of how the file is set up in the first place.

The document needs to be structured in such a way that it will be maintained throughout the lifetime of the building or structure and be capable of incorporating and recording the additional information that becomes available, not only when new projects are undertaken but when new regulations or codes of practice occur in the future.

The file is linked to the structure, building or premises rather than to the client and therefore is easily transferred with the premises when the premises are sold.

In addition, the use of a single permanent file does mean that valuable information is not lost every time a new file is created when a major project is undertaken.

Project file

Although there is an undeniable case for files to relate to the premises, or the structure as a whole, there will nevertheless be instances where a file will be prepared on a project-by-project basis.

For example, if a project relates to only part of a building (say a single floor, or part of one floor of a multi-storey building) then the file would only contain information relating to that part of the building. Where no works have been undertaken in the rest of the building then **no** file is required for the rest of the building.

If the building or structure was erected prior to 1994 then **no** file would exist anyway, although there may be information available from other sources such as maintenance logs, records and manuals.

Difficulties can also arise where the freeholder is not the client for the purpose of CDM and is not under a contractual obligation to provide information to lessees. This situation can occur where the freeholder has purchased the property from a previous owner who had the work carried out and the freeholder is not deemed to be a client under the CDM Regulations.

From a practical point of view the CDM-C might not be entitled to access other areas of the building, and where commissioned to undertake a project by a tenant who occupies only part of the building the client would have no interest in the remainder of the building.

As noted earlier, a lessee might be under a contractual obligation to provide information to the freeholder.

Where the project is undertaken for the building owner, again it is only necessary to deal with health and safety issues from the project undertaken.

Regardless of the contractual obligations or the requirements of CDM, common sense dictates that it is in the interest of all parties to ensure that relevant information is both recorded and made available to all those who might need it.

It should also be borne in mind that the general requirements of health and safety law in respect of both employees and others will still apply to the activities of those in control of the premises.

UTILITIES

Where works have been undertaken within the highway or where the development includes roads that will be adopted by the Highways Authority then any services will need to be recorded in accordance with the requirements of the *Street Works (Records) (England) Regulations* 2002 (SI 2002/3217).

Procedures for placement and recording of services should be agreed with the client/utility companies at the outset.

National Joint Utilities Group (NJUG)

At the time of writing the National Joint Utilities Group (NJUG) is working on a set of procedures and guidance notes which it is hoped will be adopted by the various bodies representing the utility companies.

The guidance should include protocols for liaising with clients and CDM co-ordinators in respect of CDM procedures and documentation.

OTHER INFORMATION, E.G. ENVIRONMENTAL

Other information may be gathered during the course of the project which, although strictly speaking is not health and safety information, nevertheless may have significant impact upon future projects. For example, a Water Discharge Consent will have conditions attached which severely limit materials and substances which can be discharged into a watercourse. This type of information needs to be made available to contractors and others undertaking future works at the premises.

Where this information is relevant to future construction works, or to ongoing maintenance or cleaning contracts, then there is a valid case for the inclusion of such information in the health and safety file, or at least a reference to where such information can be found.

Where the premises contain a private sewage treatment plant or petrol interceptors, then this information may be included with the manual for the particular item of plant.

Typical information may include:

- Tree Preservation Orders (TPOs);
- Water Discharge Consents;
- protection of watercourses – streams and rivers and canals.

DIFFERENCE BETWEEN FILES AND MANUALS

It should be noted that there is a distinct difference between a file and a manual.

The former is the document required to satisfy the requirements of CDM 2007 as set out above.

The latter may contain additional information that might not be strictly required for inclusion in the file but nevertheless might prove useful to the client at a later date, e.g. decorative finishes (shade and batch numbers).

Clients need to be advised on the requirements for information that needs to be available in the various manuals that are produced for components, plant and equipment and what is required by way of certification.

Too often the manuals contain manufacturers' literature for entire product ranges and very little, or inadequate information about the actual component, plant or equipment that has been installed.

The manuals are not a register of materials: they are (as indicated by their title) documents which will support the operation and maintenance of a structure and the services within.

They should include information about the actual component, plant or equipment that has been installed together with information on spares, frequency of inspections and routine maintenance, access, shutdown procedures, etc.

The small print contained on warranties and guarantees issued by suppliers and manufacturers often provides valuable information in respect of the requirements and recommendations for future inspection and maintenance regimes that needs to be captured and included in the file information.

This type of information should be obtained before materials are specified, or orders placed, as often decisions made by designers and specifiers are based on incomplete information.

A roofing material that is advertised as maintenance free, and guaranteed for 20 years may well require annual inspections and cleaning, and even recoating at specified intervals.

Cladding warranties may require removal and cleaning of seals, otherwise the warranty may be voided by failure to comply with the warranty terms and conditions.

Such requirements may well inform the designers as to the provision of edge protection, the installation of man-safe systems, or the requirement for hard standings to enable the use of cherry pickers (MEWPs – mobile elevated work platforms) in order to undertake such tasks safely.

Once the installation is complete, warranties and guarantees should be signed and dated and the information recorded and retained in the manuals in order that the client and those undertaking future maintenance are provided with accurate information about the defects liability period and the expiry of the warranty or guarantee period.

WHO REQUIRES ACCESS TO INFORMATION CONTAINED WITHIN THE FILE AND MANUALS

Provision of information to end users

There is a gap in the requirements placed upon clients (in the Regulations and the ACOP) and the transfer of information to those who actually operate and manage premises after the finished buildings or structures have been handed over at completion of the project.

The information contained within the various manuals produced for the project will include information relating to health and safety issues that might affect:

- those involved in the day-to-day operation of plant and equipment and routine maintenance; and
- those undertaking future works involving replacement of components, plant or equipment.

Specific information relating to health and safety issues must be provided to all those who might be affected, and this might involve different levels of information being provided to satisfy the differing requirements of those involved.

At the lowest level, i.e. the end user, clear and relatively simple operating instructions should be provided. For example, in the case of a tenant occupying rented accommodation provided by a housing association, the instructions for electrical apparatus would state that in the event of a failure the circuit breaker should be reset and, in the event that this does not clear the problem, the tenant must contact the emergency telephone number provided and report the fault.

Where maintenance personnel are employed to carry out day-to-day maintenance tasks the instructions might include start up and close down procedures, simple tasks such as filter replacements and emergency shutdown procedures.

For those engaged in more complicated tasks a full technical manual would be provided.

Essential safety issues – information

Manuals may contain information about potentially hazardous events that could affect the safety of persons entering a plant room or area containing plant or equipment, especially where they are unfamiliar with the particular environment or operation of the plant or equipment. This could include, for example, surveyors or other consultants undertaking inspections, or painters and decorators tasked with a refurbishment project.

In these circumstances it is essential that safety issues are highlighted both in the manuals and in the file.

Typical examples might include:

- machinery starting up automatically;
- venting off steam or compressed gases, etc.;
- double-sourced power supplies; and
- position and access to isolation valves and procedures for locking off plant whilst being worked on.

CDM co-ordinators need an understanding of these issues in order to be capable of advising clients on the requirements for the file, even though the M&E consultants will advise on the general requirements for production of the manuals.

Access to the file information

Access to the file information will be needed by various parties, including contractors and others, such as the client's own employees, who will be undertaking future construction works and maintaining and cleaning the structure.

Clients also owe a duty of care to persons, such as those in the emergency services, who might need access to the premises in the event of an emergency, such as fire, flood, gas leaks, the release of toxic fumes or chemical spillages.

Apart from the normal HAZCHEM signage, information including accurate up to date drawings giving the location of plant, lifts, services, shutdown procedures and the position of valves and stopcocks should also be made available. (See Premises Information Box on the next page.)

Those who might need access to file information

At various stages within the life cycle of the structure or premises the following groups of people may require access to information contained within the file.

Routine cleaning, repairs and maintenance:
- the client's own employees including facilities managers, cleaning and maintenance personnel and supervisors;

- contractors and their employees;
- engineers and those carrying out routine inspections of plant, equipment and machinery;
- insurers.

Future construction works:
- surveyors and others carrying out inspections or surveys;
- designers;
- CDM co-ordinators;
- contractors including surveyors and estimators.

Emergency personnel:
- the Fire Service.

Others:
- HSE Inspectors;
- Environmental Health Officers.

The above list is not intended to be exhaustive, but to give some indication of the range of persons who might require access to information contained within the file. Some thought should be given as to how this information is provided – normally the master copy should be retained in a secure place – copies of relevant sections of the file may need to be copied to ensure that the integrity of the file is maintained. Clients will need to consider how this is to be done and set up appropriate procedures.

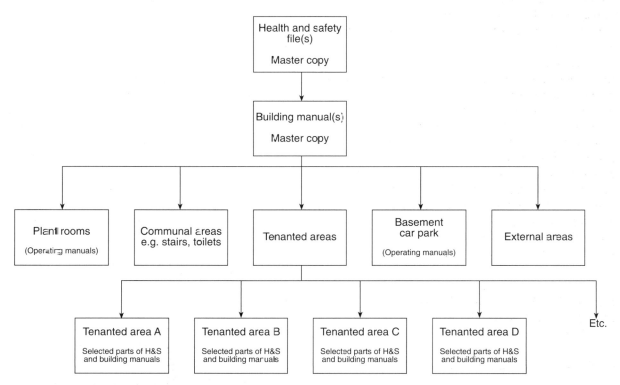

Figure 16: Health and safety document distribution

London Fire Brigade – Premises Information Box

London Fire Brigade has recently pioneered a new approach to facilitate the provision of information to fire brigade personnel attending premises in response to an emergency alarm call.

LFB have recognised a need for information to be made readily available to fire-fighters attending incidents involving buildings with:

- fire-engineered solutions;
- complex layouts; and/or
- complex fire-fighting facilities and/or controlling equipment.

They have produced a Guidance Note, Fire Safety Guidance Note Number 70 *LFB Premises Information Box*, which sets out the format and type of information which should be made available.

The information is contained within a Premises Information Box which is located at a designated point within the building or on the exterior of the building and which is readily accessible to the Fire Brigade.

More information on the Premises Information Box system can be found at www.premisesinfobox.info

Facilities management tool?

Potentially the information contained in the file can provide a useful tool for efficient management of the assets created by the construction project, but in far too many cases the benefits are lost by the file being stacked on a shelf and forgotten.

For the enlightened client, however, the file can be a source of much valuable information that can be taken into the day-to-day running of the facility and ensure that future maintenance can be properly planned. This applies to both the operational plant and equipment and the fabric of the building or structure.

For larger complexes, such as shopping centres and multi-tenanted office buildings the information contained within the files and manuals can be critical to the efficient running of the premises, especially where there is a requirement for a 24-hour facilities management function.

In such cases the requirements will be well understood, but even in smaller buildings there can be significant advantages in making use of the information contained within the file.

What information is available from the file/manuals?

The file (with the manuals) will include information on:

- details of installed plant and equipment;
- warranty details and guarantee information;
- manufacturers' recommendations for maintenance;
- normal operating procedures;
- start up and close down procedures;
- emergency procedures;
- schedules of parts, spares, lubricants, filters, etc.;
- schedules for maintenance frequency (and inspections); and
- requirements for statutory inspections and records of inspection.

How can this information be used?

The CDM-C should be able to advise the client on how best to make use of the available information or assist in setting up systems and procedures, etc.

In many instances, where the client intends to retain the property within his or her portfolio, the CDM-C will need to liaise with the managing agent or facilities manager already appointed by the client to undertake the future management of the premises.

In such cases, rather than include the information in the file as Word documents, the managing agents may wish the information to be presented in a spreadsheet that can easily be transferred into their existing management systems.

Such requirements need to be built into the initial client brief for the project and early liaison between the CDM-C and the managing agent will assist in this process.

Even where the client is the owner-occupier (or tenant) and is dealing directly with ongoing maintenance, cleaning and repairs, an asset register and properly drawn up schedules (see next page) providing information about cleaning and future maintenance requirements can prove most useful.

Recent cases including the *Barrow Legionella* case highlight the relevance and importance of clients ensuring that adequate procedures are in place for the maintenance of plant and equipment, including cooling towers (and other equipment where legionella might be present); pressure vessels, local exhaust ventilation (LEVs); gas appliances (carbon monoxide poisonings) as well as more conventional plant and equipment such as lifts and fire detection systems.

Although these might be considered operational issues much of this information will be derived from the file information and the O&M manuals produced at the end of the project.

The extent of the ongoing or additional advice will depend upon individual circumstances but it is incumbent upon the project team to deliver appropriate documentation, test certificates and commissioning data to enable the client and the facilities management team to have a fully functioning building from the time the building is handed over.

Company name

Company address

Tel: Fax: Email:

Asset register

Asset ref. no.	Asset name/description	Date of purchase	Comments
AAA:001	Boiler – xy3 Mfr Model 1A	March 1995	
AAA:002	Lift – abc Mfr Model 765:06	Nov 2001	
AAA:003			
AAA:004			
AAA:005			

Company name

Company address

Tel: Fax: Email:

Asset inspection schedule

Asset ref. no.	Asset name/description	Type of inspection	Frequency of inspection
AAA:001	Boiler – xy3 Mfr Model 1A		Annual
AAA:002	Lift – abc Mfr Model 765:06	Statutory	Annual
AAA:003	Man safe systems		Annual
AAA:004	Electrical apparatus		5 years
AAA:005			

11 Construction-related legislation

This chapter includes additional information about some of the Regulations mentioned in earlier chapters and in particular, includes summaries of both the *Workplace (Health, Safety and Welfare) Regulations 1992* and the *Work at Height Regulations 2005*

As previously discussed in Chapter 1 *Introduction,* the relationship between CDM 2007 and various other Regulations needs to be considered as an integral part of the design process, rather than looking at separate pieces of legislation in isolation.

The construction triangle of legislation in figure 17 shows it is important to take the requirements of the *Workplace Regulations* 1992 into account and then see how the *Building Regulations* can satisfy these requirements. At the same time look at the principles of prevention contained within CDM 2007 to see whether the building can be built, maintained and cleaned in a safe manner.

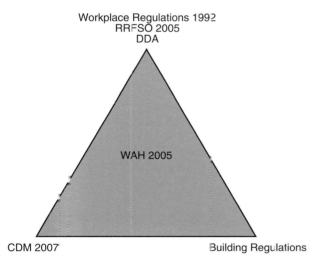

Figure 17: The construction triangle under CDM 2007

This needs to be an intuitive process and a basic understanding of each set of Regulations is required in order for this to be achievable.

We then add into the mix the competing demands of fire legislation, DDA and the ever more complex and demanding requirements of Part L of the *Building Regulations*. We also need to look at how maintenance

and other activities are affected by the *Work at Height Regulations* 2005 (WAH 2005).

The above requirements only relate to the basic design criteria and only cover a small proportion of the legislative requirements that might apply to specific project requirements.

It should be noted that many structures caught within the framework of CDM, such as bridges, tunnels, etc. are outside the scope of the *Building Regulations* and other criteria will apply.

We note below some of the Regulations that are most likely to be encountered on construction-related projects, especially in respect of existing premises and structures.

The CDM-C would be expected to have some understanding of these Regulations, or would need to undertake additional research when such issues arise on a project.

The summary of legislation at the end of this chapter provides an extended list of legislation that might apply and also details of other areas of legislation that might be relevant.

OVERVIEW OF CONSTRUCTION-RELATED LEGISLATION

General health and safety legislation includes:

- the *Health and Safety at Work etc. Act* 1974;
- the *Management of Health and Safety at Work Regulations* 1999;
- the *Provision and Use of Work Equipment Regulations* 1998;
- the *Control of Substances Hazardous to Health Regulations* 2002 (as amended);
- the *Manual Handling Operations Regulations* 1992;
- the *Personal Protective Equipment Regulations* 2002;
- the *Reporting of Injuries, Diseases and Dangerous Occurrences Regulations* 1995; and
- the *Regulatory Reform (Fire Safety) Order* 2005.

Legislation relating to construction activities includes:

- the *Control of Asbestos Regulations* 2006;
- the *Construction (Design and Management) Regulations* 2007;
- the *Work at Height Regulations* 2005;
- the *Lifting Operations and Lifting Equipment Regulations* 1998;
- the *Control of Noise at Work Regulations* 2005;
- the *Control of Lead at Work Regulations* 2002;
- the *Control of Vibration at Work Regulations* 2005;
- the *Dangerous Substances and Explosive Atmospheres Regulations* 2002;
- the *Electricity at Work Regulations* 1989; and
- the *Confined Spaces Regulations* 1997.

The key legislation relating to fire is now:

- the *Regulatory Reform (Fire Safety) Order* 2005.

Legislation relating to office-based activities includes:

- the *Display Screen Equipment Regulations* 1992; and
- the *Workplace (Health, Safety and Welfare) Regulations* 1992.

ASBESTOS

It is essential that information about asbestos is provided by clients and building owners (or occupiers) to any person who is liable to be affected by any asbestos that might be contained within the premises, building or structure, especially to those undertaking minor works of repair and maintenance.

Carpenters, electricians and plumbers are the groups most likely to be affected by uncontrolled exposure to asbestos whilst undertaking works of repair or maintenance.

In 2006 the legislation relating to asbestos was consolidated in a single set of Regulations known as the *Control of Asbestos Regulations* 2006, which came into effect on 13 November 2006 and contain requirements in respect of the identification of the presence of asbestos and notification of work with asbestos.

Asbestos – the Control of Asbestos Regulations 2006 (SI 2006/2739)
These Regulations (CAR 2006) consolidate and replace all of the previously existing legislation in respect of asbestos. Although similar provisions applied under the old legislation these Regulations provide clarity on the requirements relating to construction works in existing premises.

The following regulations are of especial importance to those involved with construction projects:

CAR 2006 regulation 5 – Identification of the presence of asbestos
'An employer shall not undertake work in demolition, maintenance, or any other work which

exposes or is liable to expose his employees to asbestos in respect of any premises unless either:

(a) he has carried out a suitable and sufficient assessment as to whether asbestos, what type of asbestos, contained in what material and in what condition is present or is liable to be present in those premises, or
(b) if there is doubt as to whether asbestos is present in those premises he:
(i) assumes that asbestos is present, and that it is not chrysotile alone, and
(ii) observes the applicable provisions of these Regulations.

CAR 2006 regulation 9 – Notification of work with asbestos
'(1) Subject to regulation 3(2), an employer shall not undertake any work with asbestos unless he has notified the appropriate office of the enforcing authority in writing of the particulars specified in Schedule 1 at least 14 days before commencing that work or such shorter time before as the enforcing authority may agree.'

CDM 2007 also makes explicit reference to asbestos and Appendix 2 of the ACOP (Pre-construction information) includes asbestos at item 3(b)(i).

'3(b) health hazards, including:
(i) asbestos, including results of surveys (particularly where demolition is involved),'.

The client also has a duty to pass on any information relating to asbestos for inclusion in the health and safety file or asbestos register.

It is also important when selecting a contractor to undertake asbestos removal that they are licensed by the HSE for this type of work.

Clients should also be aware of the additional welfare facilities that will be required where asbestos is removed under controlled conditions.

CONTROL OF LEAD AT WORK REGULATIONS 2002

Lead is also recognised as a major issue, particularly in refurbishment work, where it may exist in the form of old layers of lead paint hidden by layers of more recent coatings. Problems arise from the techniques used to remove old paintwork, which may include stripping off with a blow torch or sanding down using an abrasive power tool.

Lead may also be present in pipework, linings to water tanks, flat roof coverings, gutters, cladding to dormers and architectural features, flashings and soakers.

Clients are required to make appropriate investigations where it is known, or suspected, that lead is present within the premises and to provide information to contractors and others who might be affected.

Regulation 5 of the *Control of Lead at Work Regulations* 2002 requires that:

'(1) An employer shall not carry out work which is liable to expose any employees to lead [at work] unless he has:
(a) made a suitable and sufficient assessment [of whether the exposure of any employees to lead is liable to be significant] … '.

The adequacy of the welfare facilities also needs to be considered where work involving lead is to be carried out on a construction project: it may be necessary to provide additional facilities for changing clothes similar to those required for asbestos removal.

WORKPLACE (HEALTH, SAFETY AND WELFARE) REGULATIONS 1992

This set of Regulations formed part of the original '6 Pack' introduced in 1992 implementing EC Directives as Regulations made under the provisions of HASAW 1974.

Although the *Workplace Regulations* have been in place since 1992 they have not always been expressly considered by designers as part of the design process, except where the requirements of the *Building Regulations* have approximated to those contained within the *Workplace Regulations* 1992.

Designers now have an explicit duty under CDM 2007 to deliver a building design that takes account of the requirements of the *Workplace Regulations* 1992, under regulation 11 (Duties of designers).

'(5) In designing any structure for use as a workplace the designer shall take account of the provisions of the *Workplace (Health, Safety and Welfare) Regulations* 1992 which relate to the design of, and materials used in, the structure.'

The ACOP requirements can be found at paragraph 130:

'… This means taking account of risks directly related to the proposed use of the structure, including associated private roadways and pedestrian routes, and risks arising from the need to clean and maintain the permanent fixtures and fittings …'

Contractually this would always have been the case as the client would have been entitled to a building that was fit for purpose.

However, the *Workplace Regulations* 1992 relate to the occupation of the premises and cover such issues as area of workspace, ventilation and lighting, which to a certain extent are dependent upon the occupancy of the premises and can vary with the density of occupation as well as the purpose to which the premises are put.

The main *Workplace Regulations* 1992 issues which designers need to cover are listed below.

Workplace Regulations 1992

Regulation 5 – Maintenance of workplace, equipment, devices, systems
Regulation 6 – Ventilation
Regulation 7 – Temperature
Regulation 8 – Lighting (including emergency lighting)
Regulation 10(1) – Room dimensions and space
Regulation 12 – Condition of floors and traffic routes
Regulation 14 – Windows
Regulation 15 – Windows, skylights and ventilators
Regulation 16 – Ability to clean windows, etc. safely
Regulation 17 – Organisation of traffic routes
Regulation 18 – Doors and gates
Regulation 19 – Escalators/moving walkways
Regulations 21–25 Welfare facilities
Note: Regulations 13(1), (2), (3) and (4) Falls or falling objects were revoked by WAH 2005.

Workplace Regulations 1992

In this section we examine in greater detail the obligations placed upon the occupier of the building (whether it be the owner-occupier or a tenant) in respect of the detailed requirements of the Regulations as they affect those who are actually using the building.

Temperature

For example, the requirements relating to temperature dictate that in an office or shop the minimum temperature must reach 16°C within 1 hour of the shop or office being open.

This obligation is placed upon the occupier of the premises, not on the designer.

The designer does, however, if this requirement is placed within the brief (i.e. the mechanical services scope of works), need to ensure that the design will deliver a heating package that can meet this requirement. The lead designer will need to ensure that the other aspects of design, i.e. insulation, ventilation, etc. allow the mechanical services design to be integrated into the overall design in order to achieve this.

(With innovative design there are now a number of buildings being constructed which rely upon natural features to heat and ventilate the building. The recently completed Brighton Library is a good example of this modern approach.)

Floors – slips and trips

Taking floors as another example, there is a requirement for the floors to be even and in good condition. This duty to keep and maintain the floor in good condition clearly lies with the occupier who owes a duty of care not only to his or her employees but also to customers and other visitors to the premises. This duty also applies to trespassers under the provisions of the *Occupiers Liability Act* 1984.

Where designers are asked to specify or design a floor finish then it is the duty of the designer or specifier (this could include quantity surveyors or contractors where they are involved in the selection process) to ensure that the floor finish that is specified is fit for purpose.

In other words, the designer or specifier needs to take account of the circumstances in which the premises will be used (and the 'workplace' can include external areas) and provide a suitable surface to meet the requirements of the user.

The range of floor finishes is immense including carpet, linoleum, vinyl tiles, non-slip flooring for use in kitchen and food preparation areas, natural stone including flagstones, slate and marble slabs or tiles, brick and block paving; and in residential accommodation natural timber floors and tiled floors to kitchen and bathrooms.

The HSE has commissioned research into accidents due to slips and trips and there are well established techniques for measuring the slip resistance of floor finishes.

CIRIA has published two guidance documents which provide invaluable advice and guidance for designers and CDM co-ordinators.

CIRIA Guide C652 Safer surfaces to walk on – reducing the risk of slipping

In the foreword to the publication, Joyce Edmond-Smith, at the time HSC Commissioner with responsibility for slips, trips and falls, stated:

'Slipping accidents cause many thousands of occupational major injuries each year, more than 90 per cent of which involve broken bones, and much pain, suffering and financial loss for society. Yet the perception by the public, the workforce and those who design or manage floors in buildings is that these accidents are inevitable. The reality is that sensible precautions could eliminate the majority of these accidents. As with many problems, we believe that if the problem is explained, and sensible solutions are suggested, then people will start to manage the risks more effectively.'

This publication goes a long way to satisfy these aims.[44]

The above quote is reproduced from CIRIA Guide C652, Safer surfaces to walk on – reducing the risk of slipping (CIRIA, London, 2006, www.ciria.org) with permission from CIRIA.

CIRIA SP165 Safer surfaces to walk on – reducing the risk of slipping: an introduction

The CIRIA publication SP165 comprises an eight page introduction, including sections on terminology, selection of walking surfaces, a useful flow chart, and *Questions for the client and the planning supervisor*. This short guidance provides a very useful introduction to the larger document, and provides an essential read for CDM co-ordinators.

DUTIES OF BUILDING OWNERS (FREEHOLDERS)

The duty of care in respect of the common parts in a building largely rests with the 'building owner'. The duty of care extends to:

- tenants and their employees and visitors;
- contractors engaged to undertake works of cleaning, maintenance or repairs to the common parts or external areas of the building which are not included in the demise of the tenant; and
- external areas within the curtilage of the premises, including car parks, private access roads and pathways and steps.

It will also include lifts in common use, shared toilet accommodation and any other areas that are not leased out to individual occupiers and are commonly accessible.

It should be noted that where, for example, a contractor is undertaking works in the common parts of residential premises (including the lift) or is working in the lift motor room (which is not accessible to the public) then the contractor will be deemed to be in a 'workplace' and the Regulations will apply.

It is also of interest that, in the recent case of *PRP Architects v Reid* [2006] EWCA Civ 1119, a lessee was also deemed to have a liability in respect of injuries sustained by their own employee due to a defective lift door mechanism, even though as lessee they had no control over the maintenance of the lift. This civil claim was brought stating a breach of the PUWER 1998, rather than the *Workplace Regulations* 1992 but does demonstrate how civil claims are being pursued in the case of a breach of statutory duty.

Occupiers Liability Acts

An occupier or employer owes a 'common duty of care' to all visitors to his or her premises under the *Occupiers Liability Act* 1957 provided the visitor remains within the area to which they have been invited. Trespassers were not classed as visitors, but under common law the occupier owed them some duties, e.g. not to set deliberate traps.

However, the Act reminds the occupier that the safety of children requires special consideration, especially in the presence of 'allurements', e.g. attractive but poisonous berries or machinery.

In the case of *British Railways Board v Herrington* [1972] UKHL 1, which involved a six-year old boy being seriously injured by contact with a live electrified rail, the findings were that the 'common duty of care' was breached by British Railways Board's failure to repair damaged fencing.

This case led to the enactment of the *Occupiers Liability Act* 1984 (OLA 1984) which extends an occupier's 'common duty of care' to trespassers.

BUILDING REGULATIONS

The *Building Act* 1984 provides the framework for the *Building Regulations*.

Application of Building Regulations

It should be noted that these Regulations only apply to building work as defined under regulation 3 of the *Building Regulations* 2000 (SI 2000/2531).

'3 (1) In these Regulations "building work" means:
(a) the erection or extension of a building;
(b) the provision or extension of a controlled service or fitting in or in connection with a building;
(c) the material alteration of a building, a controlled service or fitting, as mentioned in paragraph (2);
(d) work required by regulation 6 (requirements relating to material change of use);
(e) the insertion of insulating material into the cavity wall of a building;
(f) work involving the underpinning of a building.'

Purpose of the Building Regulations

It should also be noted that the origins of the current *Building Regulations* date back to the HASAW 1974 – Part 3 (sections 61 to 76) which were revoked and replaced with the *Building Act* 1984.

These origins are reflected in regulation 8 (Limitation on requirements) of the *Building Regulations* 2000 (SI 2000/2531) which states:

'Parts A to K and N of Schedule 1 shall not require anything to be done except for the purpose of securing reasonable standards of health and safety for persons in or about buildings (and any others who may be affected by buildings, or matters connected with buildings).'

Approved Documents

The Secretary of State is empowered by the *Building Act* 1984 to approve and issue documents containing practical guidance with respect to the requirements contained in the *Building Regulations*.

- Approved Document A – Structure
- Approved Document B – Fire Safety
- Approved Document C – Site preparation and resistance to moisture
- Approved Document D – Toxic substances
- Approved Document E – Resistance to the passage of sound
- Approved Document F – Ventilation
- Approved Document G – Hygiene
- Approved Document H – Drainage and waste disposal
- Approved Document J – Combustion appliances and fuel storage systems
- Approved Document J – 2002 Edition: Guidance and Supplementary Information on the UK Implementation of European Standards for Chimneys and Flues
- Approved Document K – Protection from falling, collision and impact
- Approved Document L1A – Conservation of fuel and power (New dwellings)
- Approved Document L1B – Conservation of fuel and power (Existing dwellings)
- Approved Document L2A – Conservation of fuel and power (New buildings other than dwellings)
- Approved Document L2B – Conservation of fuel and power (Existing buildings other than dwellings)
- Approved Document M – Access to and use of buildings
- Approved Document N – Glazing – safety in relation to impact, opening and cleaning
- Approved Document P – Electrical safety – dwellings
- Approved Document to support regulation 7 – Materials and workmanship

It should be noted that where the requirements of the *Building Regulations* are met, then this will normally be enough to satisfy the requirements of the *Workplace Regulations* 1992.

However, designers do need to ensure that they understand the interrelationship between the two sets of Regulations and to be satisfied that the requirements of both are adequately discharged.

DUTIES UNDER THE WORKPLACE REGULATIONS 1992

The duties outlined below are those of the employer in relation to his or her employees and others who may visit the 'workplace'.

As noted previously, the assumption must be that designers would, in their design, take account of the requirements of the *Workplace Regulations* 1992, as the occupier of the premises would require premises that achieved compliance with these Regulations.

CDM 2007 now makes this requirement explicit: however, it should be remembered that the *Workplace Regulations* apply to employers rather than clients and that designers may only be involved with part of the design (for example, as the designer of the master plan for a development, or as the designer of the shell and core) and not actually involved with the final fit-out of the premises or structure.

It should also be borne in mind that the design might only relate to the shell and core with others being involved in the fit-out of individual floors (or parts of the premises) or of the whole building.

Until such time as the overall occupancy requirements have been established the finer detail cannot be brought into the equation.

Generally, in office premises, where a developer is involved only in the completion of the shell and core, the development will be based upon industry standards for the type and quality of the development and could vary considerably dependent upon the location and type of tenant, or purchaser, that is likely to be attracted.

Likewise, with a development of light industrial units or warehousing, the developer will only provide a shell with perhaps basic welfare provision, i.e. a washroom and toilet, leaving the tenant to fit-out the premises as appropriate to the type and scale of occupation.

Under the *Workplace Regulations* 1992 it is the employer that has the duty to comply with these Regulations and ensure that the facilities are provided.

In addition, where people have control of a workplace, for example, the owner or landlord of business premises, they will have duties and responsibilities in respect of those parts of the premises within their control.

In a typical scenario the landlord of an office block with multiple tenancies should ensure that the common parts that are within their control comply with the Regulations. Typically this might include the entrance lobby, staircase and landings, shared toilets within the core area provided for use by tenants, basement car parks and access routes into the building and external areas including roads and footpaths.

A building owner who is in control of plant (for example, lift installations and mechanical (mechanical ventilation) and electrical plant and equipment) would be liable for these areas.

Case study – identical buildings

Two identical buildings were built on a new commercial/industrial estate.

The first of these premises were fitted out for use as a switch centre (or other remote operations) where the premises were populated by machines, rather than people.

In this case the *Workplace Regulations* 1992 are largely irrelevant – other criteria will come into play, such as provision of enhanced security, fire detection systems and fire suppression, or CCTV with remote monitoring.

The second building was to be occupied as offices and the requirements of the *Workplace Regulations* 1992 would need to be taken into account – they would include requirements for adequate lighting, temperature, ventilation and for the provision of washrooms, toilets, etc.

A checklist is shown below to indicate the main requirements that designers might be required to take into account when designing for the office fit-out.

Checklist of requirements under the Workplace Regulations 1992

The following requirements that might affect design for office premises are:

- sufficient space around plant and equipment for maintenance and inspection access is required (regulation 5);
- ventilation – for an office should be provided at a rate of 5 to 8 litres per second per occupant of fresh or purified air (regulation 6) – the mechanical and electrical designer should consult with the company communications specialist to ensure that adequate ventilation is provided for computer and communications equipment as well as employees;
- a minimum temperature of 16°C is required (regulation 7), this applies in most circumstances;
- lighting (regulation 8) should be suitable and sufficient – for office work a minimum illuminance of 320 lux – natural light is preferable. However, with most employees using DSE equipment, reflections and glare must be taken into account – coating windows with an anti-UV and anti-glare film and provision of blinds to block direct sunlight should be considered;
- emergency lighting should be at sufficient illuminance within 15 seconds to facilitate escape from the building and should last for at least an hour;
- floors, walls, ceilings, stairs and doors must be finished with a surface layer that can be cleaned easily on a regular basis (regulation 9);
- the minimum space allowance per person (for office use) is 11m^3 (regulation 10);

- floors should be level, without steps or ramps, to minimise the risk of slips, trips and falls (regulation 12);
- adequate storage for files, books, computer listings, etc. taking into account risk of being struck by objects falling from high shelves (regulation 13) or musculoskeletal injuries;
- transparent partitions, windows and doors of a suitable material that will not shatter and will be clearly marked to prevent people attempting to walk through them (regulation 14);
- windows should be compliant with regulations 15 and 16 in respect of window cleaning;
- doors must be suitably constructed (regulation 18) with safety glass panels to permit sight through the door to avoid collisions and fitted with self-closing devices;
- sanitary and washing provisions (regulations 20 and 21);
- requirement to provide drinking water for employees (regulation 22);
- cupboards suitable for outdoor clothes storage are required (regulation 23);
- appropriate food preparation area (regulation 25).

CDM 2007 PART 4 – DUTIES RELATING TO HEALTH AND SAFETY ON CONSTRUCTION SITES

Contractors carrying out construction work or persons controlling the way in which construction work is carried out are required to comply with regulations 26 to 44 and Schedules 2 and 3 of CDM 2007.

Part 4 of CDM 2007 basically comprises the *Construction (Health, Safety and Welfare) Regulations* 1996 apart from a few amendments and some minor changes in word order, although some sections had already been previously revoked upon the implementation of the *Work at Height Regulations* 2005 (WAH 2005).

There are also about a dozen significant amendments to the old CDM Regulations including a new regulation 34 (Energy distribution installations) and the removal of the requirement for demolition works to be supervised by a competent person (although CDM 2007 regulation 4 does require the appointment of competent persons).

Although mention is made in CDM 2007 of the requirements to consider the *Workplace Regulations* 1992, no mention is made about the importance of giving consideration to the requirements of the *Work at Height Regulations* 2005.

WORK AT HEIGHT REGULATIONS 2005

Falls from height have consistently been one of the primary causes of fatalities in construction work, and also a significant cause of accidents in both the cleaning and maintenance sectors.

Designers need to have regard to how both the fabric of the building can be cleaned and maintained and how fittings such as light bulbs can be changed without the necessity of working at height, or at least making provision for suitable safe access.

From the building owner's point of view (and the facilities manager's) badly sited light fittings can become a financial burden, especially when mechanical plant has to be hired in on a regular basis to change the lamps.

As mentioned elsewhere, whole life-cycle costing will often reveal the true expense of poor design decisions, often based on savings in initial costs (or just poor siting of fittings) without proper consideration for future requirements for working at height.

WAH summary and changes

The *Work at Height Regulations* 2005 (SI 2005/735) implement EC Directive 2001/45/EC of 27 June 2001 amending EC Directive 89/665/EEC concerning the minimum health and safety requirements for the use of work equipment by workers at height (the *Temporary Work at Height Directive*).

Legislation covering work at height was previously contained within those sections of the *Construction (Health, Safety and Welfare) Regulations* 1996 dealing with scaffolds (regulation 6), falling objects (regulation 7), fragile roofs (regulation 8), and Schedules 1 to 5.

Those sections of CHSW 1996 were replaced by the new *Work at Height Regulations* 2005 (WAH 2005), which have been effective since 6 April 2005.

Regulations 13(1) to (4) of the *Workplace (Health, Safety and Welfare) Regulations* 1992, which dealt with falls, slips and working on roofs and the requirements relating to provision of fencing to roofs, have also been revoked and incorporated into WAH 2005.

This section summarises the requirements of WAH 2005 and also highlights the change in emphasis from the requirements of previous legislation, i.e. CHSW 1996.

Summary of WAH 2005

Duty holders must ensure that:

- all work at height is properly planned, organised and supervised;
- work is carried out in a manner which is, so far as is reasonably practicable, safe;
- those involved in work at height are competent;
- risks are assessed and appropriate work equipment is selected and used;
- objects are prevented from falling and as necessary, areas below are adequately protected or access is restricted;

- risks from fragile surfaces are avoided or, if necessary, properly controlled;
- equipment for work at height is properly inspected and maintained;
- there is planning for emergencies and rescue.

Hierarchy

The following hierarchy should be adopted for managing and selecting work equipment for working at height:

1. Avoid work at height where possible.
2. Use work equipment or other measures to prevent falls where work is necessary. This will include guardrails and safe working platforms.
3. Where the risk of a fall cannot be eliminated, use work equipment or other measures to minimise distance and consequences of a fall. This may include the use of passive restraint such as nets and airbags to minimise the consequences of a fall. The use of personal harnesses should be a last resort.

The Regulations also include Schedules giving details of requirements for existing places of work and means of access for work at height, collective fall protection, collective fall arrest, personal fall protection, rope access techniques and the selection and use of ladders.

Changes of emphasis within WAH 2005

Considerable change has occurred in the changeover from CHSW 1996 to the WAH 2005 and the following should be noted:

The 2m rule (Schedule 8) – The so called '2m rule' which was previously applied to scaffold/edge protection in the *Construction (Health, Safety and Welfare) Regulations* was withdrawn.

Weather (regulation 4(3)) – 'Every employer shall ensure that work at height is carried out only when the weather conditions do not jeopardise the health or safety of persons involved in the work.'

Competence (regulation 5) – 'Every employer shall ensure that no person engages in any activity, including organisation, planning, and supervision, in relation to work at height or work equipment for use in such work unless he is competent to do so or, if being trained, is supervised by a competent person.'

Avoidance of working at height (regulation 6(2)) – 'Every employer shall ensure that work is not carried out at height where it is reasonably practicable to carry out the work safely otherwise than at height.'

Fragile surfaces (regulation 9(1)) – 'Every employer shall ensure that no person at work passes across or near, or works on, from or near, a fragile surface where it is reasonably practicable to carry out work safely and under appropriate ergonomic conditions without his doing so.'

Where work of this type is required, platforms, covering, and guardrails, should be provided to prevent falls. Warning notices, etc. should be also be displayed.

Falling objects and danger areas (regulations 10 and 11) – '10(1) Every employer shall ... take suitable and sufficient steps to prevent, so far as is reasonably practicable, the fall of any material or object.' Where this cannot be achieved, steps must be taken to ensure that persons cannot be struck by falling objects and materials.

Areas presenting danger of falling or being struck by objects must be clearly marked with entry prevented.

Inspection of work equipment (regulation 12) – Work equipment includes guardrails, toe boards and barriers, working platforms (including scaffolding), nets, airbags and other collective safeguards for arresting falls, work restraint systems, ladders, rope access and positioning techniques and personal fall protection equipment.

Inspection may be such visual or more rigorous inspection by a competent person as is appropriate for safety purposes.

- Work equipment must be inspected in its location before use.
- Work equipment is inspected at suitable intervals or after exceptional circumstances may have jeopardised the safety of the equipment.
- 'Every employer shall so far as is reasonably practicable ensure that the surface and every parapet, permanent rail or other such fall protection measure of every place of work at height are checked on each occasion before the place is used.' (regulation 13).
- Schedule 7 lists the particulars to be included in such a report of inspection.

Inspection of working platforms in construction work (regulation 12)

- Working platforms used for construction work and from which persons could fall more than 2m, must be inspected in their locations before use, or if a mobile working platform, inspected on the site within the previous 7 days.
- Prepare the report before the end of the working period to which it refers and provide a copy of the report to the appropriate person within 24 hrs. This report will be kept on site and thereafter at the office for 3 months after project completion.

Change to height of guardrails (Schedule 2) – 'The top guardrail or other similar means of protection shall be at least 950[mm] ... above the edge ...'. Existing protection already fixed before the Regulations came into force can continue to be used as long as it is at least 910mm high.

Use of ladders (Schedule 6) – (1) 'Every employer shall ensure that a ladder is used for work at height only if a risk assessment ... has demonstrated that the use of more suitable work equipment is not justified because of low risk and:

- the short duration of use; or
- existing features on site which he cannot alter.'

(10) 'Every ladder shall be used in such a way that:

(a) a secure handhold and secure support are always available to the user; and

(b) [this includes stepladders, where if] maintenance of a handhold is not practicable when a load is carried, … [the use must be justified by risk assessment].'

SUMMARY OF KEY HEALTH AND SAFETY LEGISLATION

A summary of construction-related legislation is provided in the remainder of this chapter and includes information about the primary legislation such as HASAW 1974 and Regulations made thereunder.

As noted in Chapter 1, a significant amount of recent legislation has been introduced by the government in order to comply with EC Directives.

Not all of the Regulations will apply to every project but CDM co-ordinators should have a working knowledge of most of the Regulations included in the list, or at least have access to specialist advice where needed.

The text from the *Temporary or Mobile Construction Sites Directive* and other European legislation can be found on the European legislation website (http://eur-lex.europa.eu/en/index.htm).

Revised editions of UK primary legislation (i.e. Acts of Parliament) can be accessed via the internet at www.statutelaw.gov.uk. Unrevised editions of Acts and Statutory Instruments produced since 1988 are published on the Office of Public Sector Information website at www.opsi.gov.uk/stat.htm. UK legislation prior to 1988 may be purchased through The Stationery Office Limited or via www.ukstate.com

Title	SI no. (if applicable)	Short form (if applicable)	Description/key points
European Directives			
EU Directive 89/391/EEC adopted in 1989: Management			This Directive covers the management of health and safety at work. It was implemented in the UK as the *Management of Health and Safety at Work Regulations* 1992, which were amended four times between 1992 and 1997, then revoked and replaced by the *Management of Health and Safety at Work Regulations* 1999. The Directive can be found at: http://eur-lex.europa.eu/LexUriServ/LexUriServ.do?uri=CELEX:31989L0391:EN:HTML
EU Directive 92/57/EEC of 24 June 1992: Temporary or mobile construction sites			This Directive covers the implementation of minimum safety and health requirements at temporary or mobile construction sites – it was implemented in part, in the UK, as the *Construction (Design and Management) Regulations* 1994 (CDM 1994). Requirements under Articles 9 and 10 and Annex IV were implemented as the *Construction (Health, Safety and Welfare) Regulations* 1996. CDM 2007 brings these requirements into one set of Regulations. The Directive can be found at: http://eur-lex.europa.eu/LexUriServ/LexUriServ.do?uri=CELEX:31992L0067:EN:HTML
UK legislation			
Building Regulations 2000			This covers all aspects of construction methods and materials – it is used in conjunction with health and safety legislation to ensure that premises are safe for use, especially in areas like Approved Document B relating to fire safety.
Environment Act 1995			This covers issues relating to sustainable development, contaminated land and abandoned mines and requirements to make them safe, national parks and air quality.
Environmental Protection Act 1990			This covers issues relating to pollution of land, air or water by industrial processes and classification of pollutants.
Regulatory Reform (Fire Safety) Order 2005	2005/1541	(RRFSO) (Sometimes also known as RRO or the Fire Safety Order.)	This legislation repeals and replaces the following legislation: ● *Fire Precautions Act 1971*; and ● *Fire Precautions (Workplace) Regulations 1997* and incorporates the fire safety requirements which have been removed from the following legislation: ● *Management of Health and Safety at Work Regulations 1999*; and ● *Dangerous Substances and Explosive Atmospheres Regulations 2002.*
UK health and safety Acts and Regulations			
Health and Safety at Work etc. Act 1974		HASAW 1974	This Act lays down general duties, upon employers and those controlling work activities or premises, to protect the health and safety of employees and others. This Act is the UK framework legislation under which health and safety regulations are enacted and most instances of non-compliance are prosecuted.
Confined Spaces Regulations 1997	1997/1713	CSR	This covers safe working in confined spaces, i.e. where there is a risk of death or serious injury from hazardous substances or dangerous conditions (e.g. lack of oxygen).

Regulation	Abbreviation	SI number	Description
Construction (Design and Management) Regulations 2007	CDM 2007	2007/320	These Regulations lay down requirements for health and safety management, mainly through risk assessment, for all aspects of construction work, including design, fabrication, construction, repair and maintenance activities. They revoke and replace the *Construction (Design and Management) Regulations 1994* (CDM 1994) (SI 1994/3140), the *Construction (Design and Management) (Amendment) Regulations 2000* (SI 2000/2380) and *Construction (Health, Safety and Welfare) Regulations 1996* (CHSW 1996).
Construction (Head Protection) Regulations 1989	CHPR	1989/2209	These Regulations ensure provision and use of adequate head protection.
Construction (Health, Safety and Welfare) Regulations 1996	CHSW 1996	1996/1592	These were the previous Regulations about practical safety requirements on site – replaced by CDM 2007 and the *Work at Height Regulations 2005*. This legislation and CDM 1994 are revoked and replaced by the *Construction (Design and Management) Regulations 2007*.
Control of Asbestos Regulations 2006	CAR 2006	2006/2739	These Regulations relate to the control of exposure to asbestos and replace previous legislation regarding asbestos.
Control of Lead at Work Regulations 2002	CLAW	2002/2676	These Regulations relate to the control of exposure to lead.
Control of Noise at Work Regulations 2005	CNWR	2005/1643	These Regulations relate to the control of health risks from noise.
Control of Substances Hazardous to Health Regulations 2002 (as amended)	COSHH	2002/2677, 2003/978 and 2004/3386	These Regulations relate to the control of health risks.
Control of Vibration at Work Regulations 2005	CVWR	2005/1093	These Regulations relate to the control of health risks from vibration.
Dangerous Substances and Explosive Atmospheres Regulations 2002	DSEAR	2002/2776	These Regulations relate to the control of risks from fire and explosion due to dangerous substances.
Electricity at Work Regulations 1989	EWR	1989/635	These Regulations relate to the control of exposure to electricity.
Health and Safety (Consultation with Employees) Regulations 1996	HSCER	1996/1513	These Regulations relate to the provision of consultation for those employees who have no safety representative.
Health and Safety (Display Screen Equipment) Regulations 1992	*Display Screen Equipment Regulations 1992*	1992/2792	These Regulations relate to the use of display screen equipment.

Title	SI no. (if applicable)	Short form (if applicable)	Description/key points
Health and Safety (Enforcing Authority) Regulations 1998	1998/494	HSEAR	These Regulations relate to the demarcation between HSE and local authorities for enforcing health and safety law.
Health and Safety (First Aid) Regulations 1981	1981/917	HSFAR	These Regulations relate to first aid requirements.
Ionising Radiations Regulations 1999	1999/3232	IRR	These Regulations relate to requirements for protection from ionising radiation at work.
Lifting Operations and Lifting Equipment Regulations 1998	1998/2307	LOLER	These Regulations relate to requirements regarding the use of lifting equipment.
Management of Health and Safety at Work Regulations 1999 (as amended)	1999/3242	*Management Regulations 1999*	These Regulations relate to the general management of health and safety, including availability of health and safety advice and risk assessment.
Manual Handling Operations Regulations 1992	1992/2793		These Regulations relate to the control of risks from handling heavy and/or awkward loads.
Personal Protective Equipment Regulations 2002	2002/1144	PPER	These Regulations relate to the provision and use of personal protective equipment at work.
Provision and Use of Work Equipment Regulations 1998	1998/2306	PUWER	These Regulations relate to machinery, vehicle and other work equipment suitability and safety, including safety helmets.
Reporting of Injuries, Diseases and Dangerous Occurrences Regulations 1995	1995/3163	RIDDOR	These Regulations relate to duties to report accidents, diseases and dangerous occurrences.
Safety Representatives and Safety Committees Regulations 1977	1977/500		These Regulations relate to the right of employees to participate, be consulted and represented on health and safety issues, including the appointment of safety representatives by recognised trade unions.
Work at Height Regulations 2005	2005/735	WAH	These Regulations relate to requirements regarding work at height and preventing falling objects – previously covered by CHSW 1996.
Workplace (Health, Safety and Welfare) Regulations 1992	1992/3004	*Workplace Regulations 1992*	These Regulations relate to general workplace issues, including some design requirements for commercial buildings. They implement most provisions of the EC Workplace Directive (89/654/EEC).

NB – this list is not intended to be exhaustive.

12 Enforcement and lessons to be learned

INTRODUCTION

This chapter briefly summarises the potential consequences of incidents involving breaches of health and safety legislation including non-compliance with the CDM and other construction-related Regulations, HSE enforcement, the common law 'duty of care' and details of a number of court cases brought by the HSE and local authorities where both contractors and clients (or their managing agents) have been prosecuted.

ENFORCEMENT ACTION

In recent years the Health and Safety Executive has undertaken a number of 'construction blitzes' where they have concentrated resources in a particular area and visited as many sites as possible over a period of a week or more.

Falls from height always feature in these inspections, more often than not in the form of inadequate or missing edge protection, inadequate work platforms, etc and the HSE will take action on sites even where no workers are in the area of danger.

In recent blitzes up to 25 per cent of the sites have been served with prohibition notices requiring them to stop work until such time as safe conditions are provided throughout the site.

Prosecutions have been brought on a number of sites even though no injuries have occurred.

A similar campaign was initiated in Scotland, the North West and Newcastle upon Tyne (see Chapter 2) involving designers and it is now generally the case that where incidents occur on sites that the HSE will examine the role of other duty holders, and where necessary, take appropriate action to deal with any shortcomings that may have contributed to the failings on site.

HSE POWERS OF ENFORCEMENT

The enforcement of health and safety legislation is covered under the provisions of the *Health and Safety at Work etc. Act* 1974 which is the enabling, or 'umbrella' Act for all subsequent Regulations.

Sections 18, 19 and 20 of HASAW 1974 set out the arrangements for enforcement: by either the HSE or by local authorities, the appointment of inspectors, and the powers of inspectors.

The powers to serve an improvement notice are covered by section 21 and the powers to serve a prohibition notice are dealt with in section 22.

Improvement notices (HASAW 1974, section 21)

An inspector will make use of an improvement notice in situations where there is a breach of legislation, and there is reason to believe that the contravention is likely to continue or be repeated.

The notice will provide details of the breaches and the steps that must be taken in order to comply with the inspector's requirements and the period of time allowed for the improvements to be implemented.

If the notice is not complied with in the specified timescale, the persons or organisation committing the breach are guilty of two offences:

- failure to comply with the improvement notice; and
- breach of the legislation.

There is a procedure for appeal (see the Appeal section later in this chapter) and in those cases where an appeal has been lodged the 'notice' is suspended until such time as the appeal has been heard.

Example improvement notice

The specimen improvement notice which follows is an HSE document and copyright is held by the HSE. The notice is reproduced here with permission from the HSE.

HSE

**Health and Safety
Executive**

Health and Safety at Work etc Act 1974, Sections 21, 23 and 24

Improvement Notice

Serial Number
I

Name

Address

Trading as*

I, *(Inspector's full name)*

one of Her Majesty's Inspectors of *(Inspectors official designation)*
Being an Inspector appointed by an instrument in writing made pursuant to section 19 of the said Act and entitled to issue the notice

of *(Official address)*

Telephone number

hereby give you notice that I am of the opinion that:
at *(Location of premises or place of activity)*

you, as an employer* / self employed person* / person wholly or partly in control of the premises* / other* *(capacity of duty holder)*

are contravening* / have contravened in circumstances that make it likely that the contravention will continue or be repeated* the following statutory provisions:

The reasons for my said opinion are:

and I hereby require you to remedy the said contraventions or, as the case may be, the matters occasioning them by
(and I direct that the measures specified in the schedule which forms part of this notice
shall be taken to remedy the said contraventions or matters).*

Signature   Date

An Improvement Notice is also being served on*

of

related to the matters contained in this notice.

This is a relevant notice for the purposes of the Environment and Safety Information Act 1988   Yes* / No*
This page only will form the register entry.*

Signature   Date

LP1 (rev 11.06)   **SEE NOTES OVERLEAF**   * *delete as appropriate*

1.   Failure to comply with this Improvement Notice is an offence as provided by section 33(1)(g) of the Health and Safety at Work etc Act 1974 and section 33(2A) of this Act renders the offender liable on summary conviction to imprisonment for a term not exceeding 6 months, or to a fine not exceeding £20,000, or both, or, on conviction on indictment, to imprisonment for a term not exceeding 2 years, or a fine, or both.

2.   An Inspector has power to withdraw Prohibition Notice, or extend the period specified in the notice, before the end of the period specified in it. If you wish this to be considered you should apply to the Inspector who issued the notice, but you must do so before the end of the period given in it. Such an application is not an appeal against this notice.

3.   The issue of this notice does not relieve you of any legal liability for failing to comply with any statutory provisions referred to in the notice or to perform any other statutory or common law duty resting on you.

4.   You can appeal against this notice to an Employment Tribunal. Details of the method of making an appeal, a form to use (ETS19) and information about where to send it are contained in booklet URN 05/998 which will be provided by the Inspector with this notice. Copies are also available from the Employment Tribunal Enquiry Line (Tel: 0845 795 9775).

Time limit for appeal

A notice of appeal must be sent to the Employment Tribunal within 21 days from the date of service on the appellant of the notice, or notices, appealed against, or within such further period as the tribunal considers reasonable in a case where it is satisfied that it was not reasonably practicable for the notice of appeal to be presented within the period of 21 days. If posted the appeal should be sent by recorded delivery.

The entering of an appeal suspends the Improvement Notice until the appeal has been determined, but does not automatically alter the date given in this notice by which the matters contained in it must be remedied.

The rules for the hearing of an appeal are given in The Employment Tribunals (Constitution and Rules of Procedure) Regulations 2004 (SI 2004 No 1861), and the Employment Tribunals (Constitution and Rules of Procedure) Regulations 2001 (SI 2001 No 1171) for England and Wales and the Employment Tribunals (Constitution and Rules of Procedure) (Scotland) Regulations 2001 (SI 2001 1170) for Scotland to the extent those Regulations remain in force.

PUBLIC AVAILABILITY OF INFORMATION ON ALL ENFORCEMENT NOTICES

1.   The Health and Safety Executive (HSE), for its own purposes, records and monitors trends in the enforcement action it takes, and in the convictions and penalties imposed by the Courts. It is HSE's policy that this information should be brought to the public's attention. HSE also has a statutory obligation under the Environment and Safety Information Act 1988 to maintain a public register of certain notices. Details from this notice will therefore be stored on an electronic database, which is available on HSE's Website (www.hse.gov.uk).

2.   Information on a notice will not be entered onto the database until after the right of appeal against the notice has expired. Where a notice is withdrawn or cancelled on appeal no entry will be made. Entries will be kept on the database for a period of 5 years from the date of issue. Notices served on individuals under the age of 18 will be removed sooner.

3.   Information will be withheld where, in HSE's belief, its disclosure would:

   *   cause harm or prejudice; or

   *   be in breach of the law.

4.   Personal information is dealt with in accordance with the Data Protection Act 1998. Where disclosure of personal information would be incompatible with the Act it will not be included on the database.

5.   If you are not satisfied with the information contained in the entry you have a further right to appeal to the HSE in the first instance.

Prohibition notices (HASAW 1974, section 22)

An inspector will make use of a prohibition notice in situations where activities are being carried out which involve or, as the case may be, will involve, a risk of serious personal injury.

The prohibition notice may come into immediate effect if the risk is imminent, or alternatively may be deferred, for example, to allow a continuous process to come to completion.

Failure to comply with the notice is an offence.

In the event of an appeal the prohibition notice remains in force until such time as the appeal has been heard.

Example prohibition notice

The specimen prohibition notice which follows is an HSE document and copyright is held by the HSE. The notice is reproduced here with permission from the HSE.

HSE

**Health and Safety
Executive**

Health and Safety at Work etc Act 1974, Sections 22, 23 and 24

Prohibition Notice

Serial Number

P

Name

Address

Trading as*

I, *(Inspector's full name)*

one of Her Majesty's Inspectors of *(Inspectors official designation)*
Being an Inspector appointed by an instrument in writing made pursuant to section 19 of the said Act and entitled to issue the notice
of *(Official address)*

Telephone number

hereby give you notice that I am of the opinion that the following activities namely:

which are being carried on by you* / likely to be carried on by you* / under your control* at: *(Location of premises or place of activity)*

involve* / or will involve*, a risk of serious personal injury, and that the matters which give rise* / will give rise* to the said risks are:

and that the said matters involve* / will involve* contravention of the following statutory provisions:

because

and hereby direct that the said activities shall not be carried on by you or under your control immediately
after   unless the said contraventions and matters have been remedied.
I further direct that the measures specified in the schedule which forms part of this notice shall be taken to remedy the said
contraventions or matters.*

Signature   Date

A Prohibition Notice is also being served on*

or

related to the matters contained in this notice.

This is a relevant notice for the purposes of the Environment and Safety Information Act 1988   Yes* / No*
This page only will form the register entry.*

Signature   Date

LP2 (rev 11.06)   **SEE NOTES OVERLEAF**   *delete as appropriate*

1.   Failure to comply with this Prohibition Notice is an offence as provided by section 33(1)(g) of the Health and Safety at Work etc Act 1974 and section 33(2A) of this Act renders the offender liable on summary conviction to imprisonment for a term not exceeding 6 months, or to a fine not exceeding £20,000, or both, or, on conviction on indictment, to imprisonment for a term not exceeding 2 years, or a fine, or both.

2.   Except for an immediate Prohibition Notice, as Inspector has power to withdraw a notice or extend the period specified in the notice, before the end of the period specified in it. If you wish this to be considered you should apply to the Inspector who issued the notice, but you must do so before the end of the period given in it. Such an application is not an appeal against this notice.

3.   The issue of this notice does not relieve you of any legal liability for failing to comply with any statutory provisions referred to in the notice or to perform any other statutory or common law duty resting on you.

4.   You can appeal against this notice to an Employment Tribunal. Details of the method of making an appeal, a form to use (ETS19) and information about where to send it are contained in booklet URN 05/998 which will be provided by the Inspector with this notice. Copies are also available from the Employment Tribunal Enquiry Line (Tel: 0845 795 9775).

Time limit for appeal

A notice of appeal must be sent to the Employment Tribunal within 21 days from the date of service on the appellant of the notice, or notices, appealed against, or within such further period as the tribunal considers reasonable in a case where it is satisfied that it was not reasonably practicable for the notice of appeal to be presented within the period of 21 days. If posted the appeal should be sent by recorded delivery.

The entering of an appeal does not have the effect of suspending this notice. Application can be made for the suspension of this notice to the Employment Tribunal, but the notice continues in force until a tribunal otherwise directs.

An application for suspension of the notice must be in writing and must set out:

(a) the case number of the appeal, if known, or particulars sufficient to identify it; and

(b) the grounds on which the application is made. (It may accompany the appeal).

The rules for the hearing of an appeal are given in The Employment Tribunals (Constitution and Rules of Procedure) Regulations 2004 (SI 2004 No 1861), and the Employment Tribunals (Constitution and Rules of Procedure) Regulations 2001 (SI 2001 No 1171) for England and Wales and the Employment Tribunals (Constitution and Rules of Procedure) (Scotland) Regulations 2001 (SI 2001 1170) for Scotland to the extent those Regulations remain in force.

PUBLIC AVAILABILITY OF INFORMATION ON ALL ENFORCEMENT NOTICES

1.   The Health and Safety Executive (HSE), for its own purposes, records and monitors trends in the enforcement action it takes, and in the convictions and penalties imposed by the Courts. It is HSE's policy that this information should be brought to the public's attention. HSE also has a statutory obligation under the Environment and Safety Information Act 1988 to maintain a public register of certain notices. Details from this notice will therefore be stored on an electronic database, which is available on HSE's Website (www.hse.gov.uk).

2.   Information on a notice will not be entered onto the database until after the right of appeal against the notice has expired. Where a notice is withdrawn or cancelled on appeal no entry will be made. Entries will be kept on the database for a period of 5 years from the date of issue. Notices served on individuals under the age of 18 will be removed sooner.

3.   Information will be withheld where, in HSE's belief, its disclosure would:

*   cause harm or prejudice; or

*   be in breach of the law.

4.   Personal information is dealt with in accordance with the Data Protection Act 1998. Where disclosure of personal information would be incompatible with the Act it will not be included on the database.

5.   If you are not satisfied with the information contained in the entry you have a further right to appeal to the HSE in the first instance.

Impact on duty holders

Both types of notice are available to HSE inspectors to deal with shortcomings identified in the management arrangements of any of the duty holders, i.e. clients, designers, CDM co-ordinators and contractors.

In practice it is more likely that the shortcomings of clients, designers or CDM co-ordinators will be dealt with by way of an 'improvement notice' whereby the client is given a specified period in which to remedy the failings within the company or practice and to introduce new procedures and arrangements for the management of CDM (and where applicable any other Regulations where contraventions are found).

These measures could include:

* The appointment of a 'competent person' to assist with health and safety advice in accordance with the requirements of regulation 7 of the *Management Regulations* 1999 (this could be an internal appointment or be provided by an external consultant).
* A requirement for the duty holder to attend a suitable training course specific to their role, e.g. a designer would be required to attend a health and safety training course and/or a course on CDM for designers.
* A requirement to introduce procedures within the company to ensure that CDM procedures are implemented and followed in future.
* A requirement for the duty holder to provide information, instruction and training for all employees engaged in design.

It should be clear that there will be an impact on the business in terms of time, money and effort in achieving compliance with the 'notice'.

Where this is dealt with in a positive frame of mind, and taken as a 'wake-up call' then the business can benefit by being better prepared, especially if the opportunity is taken to improve all aspects of the company's management arrangements.

Dealing with a notice

The service of an improvement notice or a prohibition notice is most likely to arise following an incident on a project with which the client is involved, or, following a routine visit to one of the duty holders on a client's project where shortcomings have been identified in the management arrangements or the failure to provide information in accordance with the requirements of the CDM Regulations.

Whatever the circumstances that have led to the service of the notice, clients do need to respond whether it has been served upon a member of their project team or on their own company or organisation.

Where the notice has been served on a designer appointed by the client organisation or on the CDM co-ordinator then the client must review his or her selection procedures to ensure that he or she understands issues relating to competence. The client should also review his or her management arrangements to ensure that he or she understands the issues relating to the implementation of the CDM Regulations.

Similar issues will arise where the notice has been served upon the principal contractor.

Where the notice has been served upon the client organisation then it is important that the notice is acted upon within the timescales set out in the notice.

Failure to comply with a notice can lead to a prosecution being sought by the HSE for failure to comply with the terms of the notice: it is therefore important that the measures required to comply with the notice are fully understood and implemented within the allotted timescale.

It is also important that these issues are dealt with at a senior management level within the organisation and that the necessary measures are implemented throughout the whole of the client organisation.

In smaller companies or organisations this may not prove too difficult to achieve, as the management will be directly involved throughout the process. In larger companies, especially where there are a number of divisions, or operations are conducted from a number of offices, then it is especially important that the review of procedures takes in all parts of the company or organisation and that the new procedures are communicated and implemented throughout.

Where will advice be obtained?

Where the issues relate to CDM then the CDM-C may be able to offer some advice, but generally the requirement will be for the company or organisation either to source advice from within their own organisation, i.e. from the competent person appointed by the company or organisation (under regulation 7 of the Management Regulations) or to bring in additional external expertise.

The CDM-C will be required to provide suitable and sufficient advice in respect of the requirements relating to a specific project for which he or she has been appointed but is not required to provide advice on the general business activities of the company or organisation which has engaged him or her to provide CDM services for a specific project.

Where it is felt that the CDM-C has sufficient knowledge and experience to advise on these issues, beyond that required to fulfil the CDM-C role, then the company or organisation may wish to obtain that person's services in respect of the additional advice required in order to deal with their overall health and safety management. Generally, additional qualifications would be required, such as the NEBOSH Diploma, or Chartered Safety and Health Practitioner (Chartered Membership of IOSH).

Where the CDM-C does not have these additional qualifications, knowledge or experience then additional resources will need to be brought in.

Appeals against notices

Clients and their advisors should note that the mechanism for appealing against an improvement notice or a prohibition notice is to an Employment Tribunal (formerly an Industrial Tribunal): and on such an appeal the tribunal may either cancel or affirm the notice. If it affirms the notice, it may be either in its original form or with such modifications as the tribunal may in the circumstances think fit.

The appeal must be brought within a prescribed period (which is indicated on the notice – essentially within 21 days).

In the case of an appeal against an improvement notice then the operation of the notice is suspended until such time as the appeal is finally disposed of, or if the appeal is withdrawn, then until the withdrawal of the appeal.

In the case of an appeal against a prohibition notice, the operation of the notice can only be suspended on application by the appellant to the tribunal and then only from the giving of the direction by the tribunal to suspend the notice.

Information relating to improvement notices and prohibition notices is now held on a register open to the public (www.hse.gov.uk/notices).

An appeal against the decision of the Employment Tribunal is to the Employment Appeals Tribunal (EAT).

Prosecutions under HASAW 1974

Although a number of prosecutions have been brought against clients, planning supervisors, designers and contractors under the CDM Regulations, the majority of cases are prosecuted under sections 2(1) and 3(1) of HASAW 1974.

Section 2 relates to the general duties of employers to their employees.

'2(1) It shall be the duty of every employer to ensure, so far as is reasonably practicable, the health, safety and welfare at work of all his employees.'

Section 3 relates to the general duties of employers and the self-employed to persons other than their employees.

'3(1) It shall be the duty of every employer to conduct his undertaking in such a way as to ensure, so far as is reasonably practicable, that persons not in his employment who may be affected thereby are not thereby exposed to risks to their health or safety.'

The duties placed upon employers are all-embracing and will between them cover any breach of health and safety legislation.

The provisions as to offences are covered under section 33 of HASAW 1974 and section 37 deals with 'offences by bodies corporate', i.e. companies and corporations.

It is a tenet of health and safety law that:

'… it shall be for the accused to prove (as the case may be) that it was not practicable or not reasonably practicable to do more than was in fact done to satisfy the duty or requirement…'.

In other words, the defendant is required to establish that they did all that was necessary in order to comply with the law (reverse burden of proof – section 40, HASAW 1974).

Other authorities also have enforcement powers which may affect construction – see Chapter 2.

APPROVED CODES OF PRACTICE

In criminal proceedings under health and safety law Approved Codes of Practice (ACOPs) have a special status conferred upon them by virtue of sections 16 (Approval of codes of practice by the Commission) and 17 (Use of approved codes of practice in criminal proceedings) of HASAW 1974.

Status of ACOP

The status statement regarding the ACOP can be found on the reverse of the title page:

'This Code has been approved by the Health and Safety Commission, with the consent of the Secretary of State. It gives practical advice on how to comply with the law. If you follow the advice you will be doing enough to comply with the law in respect of those specific matters on which the Code gives advice. You may use alternative methods to those set out in the Code in order to comply with the law.

However, the Code has a special legal status. If you are prosecuted for breach of health and safety law, and it is proved that you did not follow the relevant provisions of the Code, you will need to show that you have complied with the law in some other way or a Court will find you at fault.'

It should be noted that there are a number of Approved Codes of Practice and Guidance that apply to construction and related activities, for example, *Safety in the installation and use of gas systems and appliances*[45] and *Control of substances hazardous to health* (COSHH)[46], including issues relating to cooling towers and legionella.

Clients should be aware that although this book is primarily concerned with CDM and the application of CDM and other legislation throughout a construction project, there are areas of legislation that will affect and apply to their continuing business activities and ownership and occupation of premises.

The *Workplace Regulations* 1992 have already been mentioned but others such as PUWER 1998 and LOLER 1998 also apply and clients may need to make reference to the Approved Codes of Practice and Guidance from time to time.

Both designers and CDM co-ordinators should be aware of these publications and be able to either provide information or advise the client in respect of its continuing obligations (for example, in respect of gas safety in rented accommodation).

Some of this information should be made available in the health and safety file, e.g. information relating to the need for inspections of gas appliances and the arrangements for managing cooling towers and the control of legionella.

ENFORCING AUTHORITIES

Sections 18, 19 and 20 of HASAW 1974 set out the arrangements for enforcement.

Enforcement of CDM 2007 will be consistent with the existing *Health and Safety (Enforcing Authority) Regulations* 1998 which are amended as per Schedules 4 and 5 of CDM 2007.

Enforcement by HSE inspectors

The HSE is the enforcing authority for construction work carried out on construction sites, or at HSE enforced premises (for example, factories, quarries or mines).

The HSE is also the enforcing authority for construction works carried out at premises normally within the jurisdiction of local authorities (i.e. offices, shops, etc.) if the construction works are carried out by persons who do not normally work at the premises if:

- the project is notifiable;
- all or part of the work is to the external fabric of the building or structure; or
- the work is carried out in a physically segregated area (i.e. where the normal business activities have been suspended in order to enable the construction works to take place).

Enforcement by local authority inspectors

The local authority will be the enforcing authority for construction works at premises normally within the jurisdiction of local authorities (i.e. offices, shops,

etc.) if the construction works are carried out by persons who do not normally work at the premises if:

- the project is not notifiable; and
- all of the work is internal; and
- the work is carried out in an area which is not physically segregated.

The local authority will be the enforcing authority for all construction works at premises normally enforced by the local authority, if works are carried out by persons who normally work at those premises.

In these circumstances the works would be under the control of the employer (or occupier) and the arrangements for undertaking risk assessments and managing the works would have to comply with the *Management Regulations* 1999.

Enforcement by the Office of Rail Regulation

The enforcing authority for construction works carried out on the rail infrastructure is the Office of Rail Regulation by virtue of regulation 3(1) of the *Health and Safety (Enforcing Authority for Railways and Other Guided Transport Systems) Regulations* 2006.

WORK-RELATED DEATH PROTOCOL

Employers, including duty holders under CDM, should be aware of recent developments in the way in which fatalities within the workplace are now dealt with.

Such incidents are now handled in accordance with *Work-related Deaths: A Protocol for Liaison* (MISC491, see www.hse.gov.uk/pubns/misc491.pdf), that has been developed by the HSE and the Police Service for the investigation of work-related deaths, and the ongoing deliberations that may lead to manslaughter charges being preferred by the Crown Prosecution Service (CPS) or health and safety charges brought by the HSE.

This applies not only to fatalities that occur on construction sites but also to any death that occurs within the workplace and would include, for example, an employee killed whilst inspecting or undertaking surveys of premises or potential development sites, or a contractor engaged in cleaning activities or repairs and maintenance.

Major incidents on the railways, such as the Hatfield and Paddington rail crashes, were investigated under this protocol and more recently, incidents such as the crane collapses at Canary Wharf, Worthing, Battersea and Liverpool have been dealt with in this way.

In the past the police would have been content to focus their attention on frontline workers who were directly involved in the incident. However, the emphasis has changed and it is the management chain that will come under scrutiny. As the HSE's *Successful health and safety management* (HSG65)[5] says:

'Accidents, ill health and incidents are seldom random events. They generally arise from failures of control and involve multiple contributory elements. The immediate cause may be a human or technical failure, but they usually arise from organisational failings which are the responsibility of management.'

© *Crown copyright material is reproduced with the permission of the Controller of HMSO and Queen's Printer for Scotland.*

Thus the investigation will be more concerned about the underlying causes:

- were there management failings;
- were these failings known; and
- had any attempts been made to put right these failings.

It is the failures in process safety and management procedures rather than the failings of individuals that are the major contributor to accidents.

Case study – legionella

In 2005 Gillian Beckingham was tried at Preston Crown Court for gross negligence manslaughter in relation to an outbreak of legionnaires disease in which seven people died. Her employers, Barrow Borough Council, were also prosecuted for manslaughter with Beckingham as the embodiment of the Council.

Beckingham, a qualified architect, was employed as head of design services. She was in charge of the air-conditioning unit at an arts centre which contained the bacteria.

Barrow Borough Council pleaded guilty to a breach of section 3 HASAW 1974 but denied gross negligence manslaughter on the basis that Beckingham was not a directing mind. Following an application at the conclusion of the prosecution's case the judge ruled that on the evidence she was not an embodiment of the Council.

Beckingham was convicted of a breach of section 7 of HASAW 1974 but there was a hung jury in respect of the manslaughter prosecution. At a subsequent retrial the jury returned a 'not guilty' verdict.

R v Balfour Beatty Rail Infrastructure Services Ltd and Network Rail

R v Balfour Beatty Rail Infrastructure Services Ltd [2006] EWCA Crim 1586; [2007] BUS LR 77 (Old Bailey, October 2005)

This prosecution related to the Hatfield train derailment of 2000 when a rail suffering from gauge corner cracking shattered into many pieces causing the death of four passengers. Balfour Beatty Rail Infrastructure

Services Ltd, the maintenance contractor, was fined £10 million (the company was acquitted of manslaughter) and Network Rail, the infrastructure owner (formerly Railtrack), was fined £3.5 million. Both companies were ordered to pay costs of £300,000 each.

The prosecution related to Balfour Beatty's failure to carry out visual and ultrasonic inspection adequately over a 21 month period. Network Rail's failure related to failing to adequately manage the maintenance contractor. The rail in question had been programmed for renewal which had not occurred. The new rail had been delivered to the track six months before the derailment. The renewal had been contracted to another contractor by Railtrack.

THE COURT SYSTEM

This section provides a brief explanation of the criminal and civil court systems in England and Wales (Scotland having its own legal system and different systems and terminology) and includes information on the types of case that have been brought under CDM 1994.

Figure 18 provides a simplified structure of the system of courts for both criminal and civil cases.

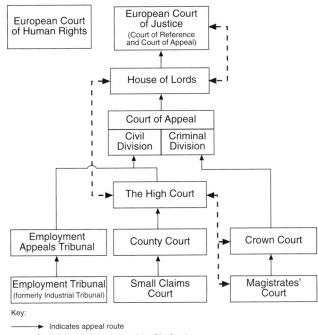

Figure 18: Law court hierarchy (England and Wales).

Criminal courts

Magistrates' Courts
Prosecutions for breaches of health and safety law are initially brought in the Magistrates' Court and may be heard before Magistrates or, in those cases where the defendant elects to be heard before a jury, before the Crown Court.

Where a case is tried in the Magistrates' Court and a plea of guilty is entered, or following trial before the Bench the defendant is found guilty, the Magistrates can impose sentence or refer the case to Crown Court for imposition of a greater sentence.

The maximum penalty for a breach of the *Health and Safety at Work etc. Act* 1974 (and Regulations made under the Act) in a Magistrates' Court is £5,000 and, for those breaches of health and safety legislation where a custodial sentence can be handed down, a custodial sentence of up to six months.

Crown Courts

As noted above, cases can be referred from the Magistrates' Court to the Crown Court for sentencing where the Bench considers that it does not have sufficient powers to impose a greater sentence.

Defendants can also elect to have their case heard before a jury in the Crown Court where they enter a plea of 'not guilty'.

The maximum penalty in a Crown Court for breaches of sections 2, 3 and 7 of HASAW 1974 is an unlimited fine. The Crown Court is also able to impose greater custodial sentences than those handed down in the Magistrates' Court.

In *R v F Howe and Son (Engineers) Ltd* [1999] 2 All ER 249 the Court of Appeal provided guidelines on the sentencing of employers for breaches of HASAW 1974.

It said any fine should reflect the gravity of the offence *and also* the means of the defendant. Since then there has been a marked increase in the level of fines imposed. The court commented:

'There may be cases where the offences are so serious that the defendant ought not to be in business.'

Alternative penalties

The HSC has carried out consultation concerning alternative penalties to fines imposed by the courts (in line with the proposals contained in *Regulatory Justice: Sanctions in a post-Hampton World*). These include the following:

- administrative fines;
- restorative justice;
- conditional cautioning;
- enforceable undertakings;
- fixed penalties;
- remedial orders;
- probation for companies and directors; and
- adverse publicity orders.

Civil cases

Civil cases are heard either in the County Court or the High Court dependent upon the size of the claim.

Civil liability

Personal injury law has evolved through time and the origins of employer's liability can be found in a case dating back to 1837, *Priestley v Fowler* (1837) 3 M&W 1 in which a number of issues were raised:

- the contractual relationship;
- general duty;
- vicarious liability;
- plant and equipment;
- personal responsibility of the employer;
- fault or strict liability; and
- personal responsibility of the employee.

The principle that a breach of statutory duty may create civil liability is generally regarded to date back to a case for an alleged breach of the *Factory and Workshop Act* 1878 in the case of *Groves v Wimborne* [1898] 2 QB 402.

As noted in the section on regulation 45, civil liability claims can be made where breaches have occurred under CDM 2007, resulting in loss or injury on the part of the person bringing the claim.

CIVIL LIABILITY UNDER CDM AND THE *MANAGEMENT REGULATIONS* 1999

Breach of statutory duty

A breach of statutory duty may give rise to a claim under civil law except where such a claim is debarred by statute.

Where an injured party has suffered an injury or loss due to the actions of another party then under civil law the claimant may bring an action against the defendant for negligence.

Where a breach of statutory duty has occurred, the claimant may also bring a case for breach of statutory duty in addition to the claim for negligence (double-barrelled action). In order to establish a claim for breach of statutory duty, the claimant must be able to establish in proceedings that:

- the defendant was in breach of their statutory duty;
- the breach caused the injury or loss;
- the claimant was a class of person the statute was intended to protect; and
- the type of injury was of a type that the statute was intended to prevent.

The defendant is able to employ various arguments in defending the case that would include that there was no breach of statutory duty and that it had done everything that was required.

The defendant might also be able to establish that the injured party was not entitled to claim for breach of statutory duty because no duty was owed to them, for example, where the duty only applies to an employee and the claimant is a visitor to whom no duty was owed.

A further defence might be that the harm done was not covered, or that there was no causal connection between the breach and the loss suffered.

Statute barred

However, many civil claims are statute barred, i.e. the legislation does not allow an action to be brought by a claimant for a breach of statutory duty. This can apply to both Acts of Parliament and Regulations brought under the Acts.

Health and Safety at Work etc. Act 1974
Section 47 of HASAW 1974 states that civil liability is excluded for sections 2 to 7 of the Act, and this also applies to any contravention of section 8.

CDM 2007
Regulation 45 of CDM 2007 deals with the question of civil liability and limits the right of action to those who are covered by the Regulations apart from a breach of duty under certain specified Regulations (see below).

Regulation 13(6) refers to the duty of contractors to ensure that reasonable steps have been taken to prevent access by unauthorised persons to that site.

> **CDM 2007 regulation 45 – Civil liability**
> 'Breach of a duty imposed by the preceding provisions of these Regulations, other than those imposed by regulations 9(1)(b), 13(6) and (7), 16, 22(1)(c) and (l), 25(1), (2) and (4), 26 to 44 and Schedule 2, shall not confer a right of action in any civil proceedings insofar as that duty applies for the protection of a person who is not an employee of the person on whom the duty is placed.'

The cases of *Moon v Garrett* indicates how the courts are interpreting the law in this type of case and the definition of '**at work**'.

Moon v Garrett
Moon v Garrett and Others [2006] EWCA Civ 1121
This case involved a Mr Moon, a delivery driver, who in the course of his work made a delivery of building materials (blocks) to a property owned by Mr Garrett at which construction works were being undertaken. During the course of the delivery (which involved the unloading of the blocks, in a particular place specified by Mr Garrett), the plaintiff, Mr Moon, fell into a pit and injured his back.

Mr Moon brought proceedings under the *Occupiers Liability Act* 1957, and claimed that CHSW 1996 applied to him whilst making the delivery.

It was found that Mr Moon was within the definition of 'a person at work' and that CHSW 1996 applied; and accordingly the homeowner owed the delivery driver a similar duty of care to that which would be owed by a professional builder.

PRP Architects v Reid
PRP Architects v Reid [2006] EWCA Civ 1119
A recent case involving a firm of architects in the City of London has raised some interesting issues over the extent of an employer's liability where injuries were sustained by an employee in an area comprising the common parts of multi-occupied office premises.

The injury (to the employee's hand, which was caught in the lift doors) was due to a faulty sensor which failed to prevent the lift doors closing.

Responsibility for lift maintenance would normally rest with the landlord: the tenant being responsible for payment of a service charge which covered, amongst other things, the cost of lift maintenance.

Even though PRP Architects did not have exclusive use of the lift, only sharing it in common with other occupiers of the building, the Court found that the company was in breach of regulation 5(1) of the *Provision and Use of Work Equipment Regulations* 1998 (PUWER), which requires employers to maintain work equipment so as to ensure employee safety.

The Court also held that the employee was 'at work' for the purpose of the Regulations even though the lift was located in the common parts of the building and outside the premises demised to the defendant company.

Vicarious liability

An important aspect of negligence is the law relating to vicarious liability whereby the employer is liable for the wrongdoings of the employee acting in the course of his or her employment ('respondeat superior') and there are a number of reported decisions.

Within the construction industry the question will normally revolve around which of a number of potential employers is the employer of the particular employee for the purposes of vicarious liability.

In the **leading case** of *Mersey Docks and Harbour Board v Coggins & Griffith (Liverpool) Ltd and Another* [1947] AC 1, the harbour authority let out a mobile crane together with a driver, but the contract with the firm of stevedores who were to use the crane stipulated that the driver would be, albeit it temporarily, a servant (or employee) of the firm.

This type of case is especially relevant to the construction industry with its practice of hiring in plant and machinery, with or without drivers, and for lifting operations to be undertaken either under hire or under contract.

Woolf Report (Civil Procedure Rules)

A radical overhaul of the procedures for dealing with personal injury claims came into being following the review by Lord Woolf (The Woolf Report). The new *Civil Procedure Rules* were introduced on 26 April 1999 and apply to both the High Court and the County Court. Cases are managed by the court; Alternative Dispute Resolution (ADR) is encouraged and strict timetables must be adhered to. Lord Irvine stated that this was:

'the first serious attempt to set effective and enforceable standards for the efficient conduct of pre-action litigation'.

Clients need to be aware of the ramifications of the *Civil Procedure Rules* in the event of a claim. Claims cannot be ignored and clients (when placed in the position of **defendant**) need to respond to claims within 21 days, otherwise they are at risk of a claim being awarded against them because they have failed to comply with the strict procedures that now apply.

The *Civil Procedure Rules* can be found at: www.dca.gov.uk/civil/procrules_fin/index.htm

Aims of Woolf

The aims of Woolf were to enable:

- more pre-action contact between the parties;
- better exchange of information;
- better pre-action investigation:
  - to allow for early and fair settlements;
  - to reduce litigation – and hence to allow more efficient litigation;
  - to allow predictability in the time needed;
  - to standardise the disclosable documentation.

(Disclosable documentation – there are 83 separate items on the Standard Disclosure List.)

Clients should be aware that the pursuit of civil claims by both employees and third parties represents a greater risk to the company than the threat of prosecution for breaches of health and safety legislation.

The Woolf Report has driven the need for organisations to develop more effective health and safety systems and to introduce and implement adequate procedures and documentation in order to satisfy the disclosure of information requirements.

Technology Court

The Technology Court is a division of the High Court and deals with cases arising from contract law where the specialist knowledge of judges in construction and contract law is required to give judgement on highly technical matters.

Coroners' Courts

All cases involving fatalities will involve an inquest that takes place at the Coroner's Court.

The Coroner has the power to call witnesses and determine the cause of death and cases may be heard before a jury.

The Centre for Corporate Accountability (www.corporateaccountability.org) maintains a database of cases where workers have been fatally injured during the course of their employment.

PROSECUTIONS BROUGHT UNDER CDM

The first prosecution brought under CDM 1994 was against a firm of demolition contractors, Oakwood Demolition, in August 1995. They were involved with the demolition of a church, in North West London, which suffered an uncontrolled collapse and led to their subsequent prosecution for breaches under CDM.

Prosecutions have been brought against each category of duty holder, with the first prosecution against an architect being the case against Taylor Young partnership in November 1995 at West Bromwich Magistrates' Court.

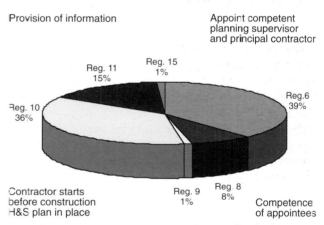

Figure 19: Successful CDM client prosecutions April 1995 to March 2006 (total 144 cases)

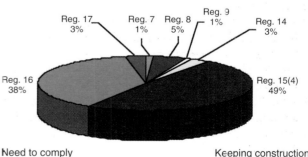

Figure 20: Successful CDM principal contractor prosecutions April 1995 to March 2006

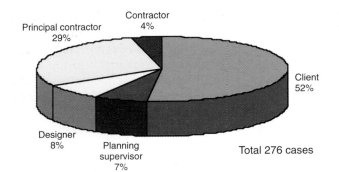

Figure 21: Successful CDM prosecutions (all categories) April 1995 to March 2006 (total 276 cases)

The following pages give examples of the types of prosecution and penalties arising for a number of cases.

The HSE publishes details of HSE cases which resulted in successful prosecution at www.hse.gov.uk/prosecutions

Accidents on construction sites

The cases on the following pages involve various incidents involving accidents on construction sites with prosecutions brought by both the HSE and local authorities, as well as cases brought by the Crown Prosecution Service, where manslaughter charges have been preferred.

Architect hit by first safety rules fine

The first prosecution under CDM 1994 resulted in a £500 fine for a Manchester firm of architects following a site incident at a West Bromwich cash-and-carry store.

The Taylor Young Partnership was prosecuted at West Bromwich Magistrates' Court in November 1995.

On 3 August 1995, contractors preparing the site of an extension to Batley's warehouse struck an 11,000 volt electricity cable, causing an explosion. No one was injured.

Taylor Young was the architect for the warehouse, when it was built eight years previously, and also designed the new extension.

The HSE alleged in court that Taylor Young failed to advise Batley's that a planning supervisor needed to be appointed, and assumed the role of 'safety co-ordinator' itself, without a proper appointment.

The practice was therefore prosecuted under section 13(1) for failing to inform the client of their duties under CDM.

HSE prosecution of Neil Vesma

This case concerned an architect, Neil Vesma, who designed an extension to a factory, and also took on the role of planning supervisor. He specified solid concrete blocks, weighing 36 kilograms each, for the wall construction.

The HSE alleged that the blocks were too heavy, and that as planning supervisor he should have identified the potential risks arising from the use of such heavy blocks, when standard practice within the construction industry was not to use blocks in excess of 20 kilograms.

Mr Vesma pleaded guilty and was fined £500 and ordered to pay the HSE's prosecution costs amounting to £1,000.

The Warrington case

The HSE prosecuted seven different parties following the death of untrained demolition worker David Moran who fell eight metres to his death when he stepped on a fragile roof light in Warrington on 20 September 2002. David and another untrained demolition worker were using the roof to access another roof on the site.

At a hearing at Warrington Crown Court, David's employer, Elmsgold Haulage Ltd, and John McSweeney, the Managing Director of Elmsgold Haulage Ltd, pleaded guilty to two charges under section 2(1) of HASAW 1974, in that they failed to provide a safe system of work and failed to ensure that people working on site were properly trained and supervised, and a third charge under regulation 9(3) of the *Lifting Operations and Lifting Equipment Regulations* 1998 in that they failed to ensure that lifting equipment was properly examined and inspected.

Demolition contractor Excavation & Contracting (UK) Ltd, the principal contractor for the project, and the company's former Managing Director, Bernard O'Sullivan, pleaded guilty to a charge under section 3 (1) of HASAW 1974, in that they each failed to ensure that risks to non-employees were adequately controlled.

The company pleaded guilty at Warrington Magistrates' Court with the case transferred to Warrington Crown Court for sentence.

Dennis O'Connor, the site foreman, pleaded guilty to a charge under section 7 of the *Health and Safety at Work etc. Act* 1974, in that he failed to ensure the safety of other employees.

At an earlier hearing at Warrington Magistrates' Court on 31 January 2006, John Edge of Knight Frank, a Manchester-based property management company acting for the owner of Chesford Grange and planning supervisor for the project, pleaded guilty to two charges under regulation 15 of CDM 1994 for which Knight Frank was fined a total of £7,000 plus full prosecution costs of £4,500.

(Knight Frank operated as a partnership, which does not constitute a legal entity for the purposes of prosecution, and therefore the case was taken against one of the partners, John Edge.)

The Bootle case

In a case brought by the HSE and heard at Liverpool Crown Court, KDP Capita Property Services Limited were fined a total of £30,000 with additional costs of £37,860 awarded to the HSE for breaches of section 3(1) of HASAW 1974.

A demolition worker was killed and two other site

operatives seriously injured, following the collapse of two properties at the end of a three storey brick-walled Victorian terrace undergoing demolition works in windy conditions.

The defendant company was employed as the planning supervisor for the project.

HSE v JMPI Limited and TSL Hygienic Limited
A panel installer died when he fell 2.5 metres from a scaffold platform while trying to access a ladder. The installer had been working on the installation of panels on the expansion of a dairy complex.

A scaffold with two polythene-wrapped working platforms accessed by ladder had been erected so that panels could be installed on to structural steel work. The front edge of the platform on which the victim had been working was open on one side leaving an unguarded gap. The aluminium ladder was not tied and did not extend high enough above the platform to make it safe. The victim fell from the platform on to the concrete floor below. He died from severe head injuries. The ladder was knocked sideways.

JMPI Limited was fined £6,000 for breaching regulation 6(6) of CHSW 1996, for not ensuring the stability of a ladder.

TSL Hygienic Limited was charged with a breach of regulation 6(6) and also with a breach of regulation 6(1) of CHSW 1996. They were fined £5,000 for the latter with no penalty for the 6(6) charge.

Both defendants were required to pay £5,000 each for HSE costs.

Lincoln City Council v Charles Ian Helmrich
(See www.lincoln.gov.uk/news_det.asp?sec_id=468&id=3249)

This is a case known as the Fatty Arbuckles' case, which concerns a prosecution brought by the local authority following an incident in a restaurant located in Lincoln.

A 17 year old student, on a summer vacation job, was scrubbing the floor with water and a long handled scrubber, which came into contact with an item of faulty electrical equipment which was in an unsafe condition. The student suffered a fatal electric shock.

The company, Fatty Arbuckles, went into receivership and the Crown Prosecution Service declined to prosecute, although an inquest jury returned a verdict of unlawful killing.

Lincoln City Council brought a successful prosecution before a district judge, against the company's health and safety manager, Charles Helmrich under sections 7(a), 33(1)(a) and 37(1) of HASAW 1974.

This case illustrates the need for those offering health and safety advice, such as persons undertaking the CDM co-ordinator role to ensure that advice and procedures are properly followed.

Clay v AJ Crump & Sons Ltd
Clay v AJ Crump & Sons Ltd [1964] 1 QB 533
This case involved an architect, a demolition contractor and a building contractor.

The architect failed to carry out his duties in respect of the demolition works and allowed a wall to remain in place standing on a precipice of some five to seven feet high. After a period of several weeks during which time the wall remained unsupported one of the employees of the building contractor was injured when the wall fell on top of him.

The architect was held to be largely to blame.

R v Hatton Traffic Management Ltd
R v Hatton Traffic Management Ltd [2006] EWCA Crim 1156

This concerns a case taken to the Court of Appeal where Hatton Traffic Management Ltd appealed against their conviction in the lower Court for offences under HASAW 1974.

The Court of Appeal made an important ruling that allows employers to put forward a defence that by provision of safe systems of work, training and instructions they have followed the requirements of the law, even where employees have not followed the correct procedures.

Incidents relating to cleaning, maintenance and repair

The following cases involve prosecutions brought by the enforcing authorities following incidents where premises were being cleaned or premises were not maintained in good repair.

Crawley Borough Council v County Mall Management (Crawley) Limited, and Crawley Borough Council v Mitie Cleaning South East Limited at Lewes Crown Court
An operative fell 25 feet from an elevated platform whilst cleaning the outside of the County Mall Shopping Centre in Crawley, West Sussex. The cage to the MEWP was incorrectly attached by the operative and became detached when it struck the wall of the building. The cage and the operative plunged 25 feet to the ground leaving the worker severely injured and confined to a wheelchair.

The operative's employer, Mitie Cleaning South East Limited failed to ensure that their employee received suitable training.

The company operating the shopping centre, County Mall Management (Crawley) Limited, had undertaken a risk assessment which concluded that a permit to work should be issued to workers before they used the spider lift to check that they were competent. They failed to do so and, in their defence, stated they had expected Mitie to send properly trained workers to operate the equipment.

County Mall Management (Crawley) Limited was fined £25,000 under section 3(1) of HASAW 1974 and regulation 9 of PUWER 1998.

Mitie Cleaning South East Limited was fined £40,000 under section 2(1) of HASAW 1974, and regulation 9 of PUWER 1998.

Wiltshire District Council v Warminster One and Two Limited and Hartnel Taylor Cook

A driver arrived at a Red Cross shop in Warminster to collect clothing. The shop had a first floor walkway at the rear from which bags were dropped on to lorries below. As the driver leaned over to drop some bags the parapet railing collapsed causing him to fall 12 feet to the ground below. He sustained serious injuries including a broken back and has been unable to work since.

The owner of the premises, Warminster One and Two Limited, was fined £2,000 with £500 costs under section 4(2) of HSWA for failing to take measures to ensure safe means of access to and exit from the premises. The managing agents, Hartnel Taylor Cook, were fined £8,000 with £1,381 costs for the same charge.

Crown Prosecution Service v Mr Harper, Managing Director of Harper Building Contractors Ltd

This case involved a fragile surface and resulted in a custodial sentence.

After a joint investigation between the police and the HSE, the CPS decided to prosecute Mr Harper following the death of one of his employees. The employee was removing and replacing a roof to a warehouse when he stepped backwards on to a fragile roof light, which gave way. The employee fell approximately 6.75 metres, landing on the floor below. There was no safe system of work in place and the equipment to prevent people falling through fragile materials was not provided.

A member of the HSE commenting on the case said:

'There was a fundamental failure to recognise that the roof included fragile roof lights that will not bear a man's weight. Moreover, the equipment to prevent people falling through fragile materials is readily available and relatively cheap. A sensible, straightforward approach to health and safety in managing the risks on this job should have prevented this tragic death.'

Mr Harper received a 16-month custodial sentence.

LEARNING FROM MISTAKES

A study of the various cases that are reported in the construction press and in the journals produced by the professional safety bodies provides an opportunity to learn from past experience.

There is a consistent pattern in the type of accident that occurs and the type of work (e.g. roofing repairs or maintenance) being undertaken and clients should be able to translate that knowledge to their own projects.

The following issues should be considered:

- **Fragile surfaces** – prevention of workers falling through asbestos cement sheeting or through fragile roof lights when undertaking maintenance works, cleaning out gutters or clearing blockages in gulleys on roofs with asbestos cement roofing materials and/or glazed roof lights. Clients should be aware of the type and condition of any such roof and the dangers of working on this type of roof.
- **Falls from height** – includes falls from ladders and also use of improvised means of access whilst workers carrying out work at height; falls involving lack of edge protection to lift shafts, stairwells, floor slabs, balconies, flat roofs and pitched roofs both during construction and whilst future works of maintenance and repair are being undertaken.
- **Trips and slips** – although rarely fatal, trips and slips have now overtaken falls from height as the cause of the largest number of injuries. They often lead to serious injury (such as broken hips) and prolonged absence from work (leading to significant civil claims for compensation).
- **Collapse of structures** – collapses of partially complete structures during construction (cases recorded include collapse of metal columns, precast flooring during new build); collapse or partial collapse of buildings during refurbishment or demolition; and collapses of scaffolding due to high winds or inadequate design.

The HSE publishes accounts of major incidents (e.g. the Port Ramsgate Walkway collapse[29]) and also provides alerts to the construction industry via the Construction Infonet.

These reports together with the material published in the professional safety journals provide a valuable resource to those undertaking the role of CDM co-ordinator.

Appendices

Appendix A: Agenda for an initial client meeting

1 Client brief

Ascertain requirements for the project from the client – the client brief (should include information relating to the use of the premises or workplace – the *Workplace Regulations*).

2 Notification of construction project

Ascertain who the client(s) for the project will be – there may be one or more clients involved in the project, or there may be a separate company set up specifically for the purpose of undertaking the development (PFI project, SPV etc.).

Discuss requirements relating to the signing of the declaration on the notification of the project to the HSE (Form F10 or other method of providing the particulars noted in Schedule 1 to CDM 2007).

Discuss who will be acting as the client 'sponsor' or 'representative' from within the client organisation.

Discuss requirements relating to the time allowed for planning and preparation (the 'mobilisation period').

3 Provision of welfare facilities

Discuss requirements in respect of provision of welfare facilities throughout the course of the construction phase.

4 Project 'gateways'

Discuss how the various project 'gateways' or key stages will be incorporated into the project programme and the procedures for ensuring that any identified requirements are monitored and met.

5 Pre-construction information

Discuss requirements relating to pre-construction information (PCI): provision of information and information flows throughout the project.

6 Commencement of construction phase

Discuss the mechanism for dealing with the requirements of regulation 16 and allowing construction to commence on site.

7 The health and safety file

Discuss requirements for the health and safety file and the manuals and liaison with end users (e.g. Facilities Manager) in order to allow input and feedback.

8 Contractual arrangements

Discuss the contractual arrangements for ensuring that information is provided by designers, contractors, etc.

- at various stages throughout the project; and
- at practical completion.

This could include discussion with cost consultants/contract administrator as to how financial mechanisms can be used to ensure compliance with requirements for provision of information (e.g. practical completion only being achieved if health and safety file has been issued).

9 Competence

Discuss arrangements for ensuring compliance with regulation 4 (competence):

- use of pre-qualification questionnaires;
- use of third-party accreditation; and/or
- use of competence packs for suppliers.

10 Management arrangements

Discuss arrangements for compliance with regulation 9 (management arrangements).

11 General client duties

Discuss the general duties of the client under both Part 2 and Part 3 of CDM 2007.

Appendix B: Insolvency and CDM

The text of *Insolvency and CDM* was written by David Jones FCIOB FASI MRICS MaPS of London Borough of Bromley and is reproduced here with permission.

A core essential of CDM is the provision of adequate resources. The 'client' is the essential provider of the funds to undertake any project. Indeed, without a financially solvent client providing the essential resource of money, there can be no project at all. Thus it can be seen the important role the client plays in the procurement chain. The client is the only duty holder that has a continuous influence throughout the span of the project. Essentially, in this regard, the client could be regarded as a 'bank' – and this simple idea helps to clarify exactly who is the client where complex procurement and partnerships or other groupings come together in common purpose to undertake construction. The 'rule' often used to test the identity of the client is 'follow the money trail back up the chain'. The client is thus discovered where the money trail stops. Under CDM 2007 the client is prevented from employing an agent as under CDM 1994 so this will add help to clarify the role even more, and additionally, under CDM 2007 a collective group of clients are able to formally agree for one person or organisation to act for all the others – further clarifying the identity of the client.

The client has a number of key statutory duties under CDM – the appointment of the planning supervisor (CDM co-ordinator) and the appointment of the principal contractor. The law requires the client only to appoint those person(s) and/or organisations who are competent to undertake their respective CDM roles and who have the necessary resources to undertake the statutory duties of these roles. The law also requires the appointees to be able to show they have the resources and will apply all that is necessary to the project in the interests of safety and health. Finally, the law is clear on the client's duty not to allow the project works on site to commence until and unless adequate resources are assured to be in place. This has been the case under CDM 1994 and is now strengthened even more under CDM 2007. Once appointed, the client must maintain the appointments throughout the span of the particular project. It would be unlawful for a client to allow any work requiring to comply with CDM to proceed during the construction phase without the existence of a principal contractor.

So, let us look at what the term 'insolvency' means.

Insolvency is defined as having insufficient assets to meet all debts, or being unable to pay debts when they are due. Bankruptcy takes a longer term view of being a cash free zone than insolvency does. In other words, to be considered bankrupt, we need to be in the state of not only having enough cash, but of having no prospect of getting the cash! It is important to understand that, even in the defined area of insolvency and with the prospect of eventual recovery, that situation can still have dire consequences for the provision of safety and health on a construction project.

The study of the law around insolvency and bankruptcy is not part of this study. This text is to assist to understand the appropriate considerations that should be made in assessing what actions will need to be taken under CDM in order to stay within compliance of the law when it becomes clear that there are insufficient assets provided to maintain a safe place to work and/or to progress the project safely.

Bankruptcy, receivership, liquidation

Bankruptcy relates to individuals and not organisations. Receivership is when the control of a company is passed over to an insolvency practitioner to operate. Liquidation means that a company ceases to exist and there are three types of liquidation:

1. Members voluntary liquidation: the company liquidates but it is expected that the creditors, employees, taxes and shareholders will all be paid any money owing to them.

2. Creditors voluntary liquidation: it is expected here that the company cannot pay all of its bills, so a meeting of creditors is held to discuss the liquidation of the company.

3. Compulsory liquidation: here, a creditor creates an action against the company where it is clear that a debt cannot be paid: providing the debt is at least £750. The grounds on which a company may be wound up by the court include: a special resolution of the company that it be wound up by the court; that the company is unable to pay its debts; that the number of members is reduced below two; or that the court is of the opinion that it would be just and equitable for the company to be wound up.

Insolvency practitioners are clearly involved in all of the three states of liquidation and the timings of relevant actions are crucial to the legal process – but the state of insolvency is far less defined or obvious. Any sign of insolvency and/or cash flow problem around the principal contractor at any time during the span of the construction phase of the project must be regarded very seriously by the client – as this changed state will mean that there are insufficient resources being applied to keep the construction phase safe. In these circumstances the client has limited choice of action – to either make the principal contractor solvent or remove the appointment and **immediately** appoint a new principal contractor.

It is not sufficient or lawful for the client to just allow matters to 'free-fall' during the difficult period when appointed contractors are having financial difficulties. The usual scenario when financial difficulty strikes a project is for the work to cease entirely when, say, all the subcontractors pull off site. Even worse, when subcontractors providing safety measures and equipment, e.g. protective fencing around excavations, remove their equipment thus leaving the site in a dangerous vulnerable condition. When this happens the client must take robust control of the works and make the site safe.

When work has ceased in this way, it is comparatively straight forward for the client to terminate the appointment of the ailing principal contractor in writing (recorded delivery to registered address). Clients then have a choice – either to appoint themselves as the principal contractor if they are competent to undertake the role, or appoint another to act. As soon as it becomes apparent the principal contractor is in difficulty and the health and safety plan is no longer suitable the client could ask the planning supervisor to undertake an assessment of the hazards and advise on what measures need to be put in place to maintain and ensure the works and site are safe. CDM 2007 is clear that the client is the principal contractor in the event there is no valid appointment and the CDM co-ordinator has an automatic duty to advise the client – thus the HSE have made the law clearer.

The client will inevitably have to expend considerable amounts of money to put back the safety to the site and maintain the site in a safe state until other contractors can be found to complete the project. The site is particularly vulnerable during these periods. The client does not have an option but to maintain safety.

However, the client does perhaps have the right to apply the rules of set-off to recover all the additional expenditure on safety – the exact amount that can be set-off in this financial period is determined by the manner of the insolvency and how it was revealed. If the principal contractor had concealed the poor financial state of affairs from the client, this could then allow the client to take the whole amount of additional

cost over the period of concealment from any outstanding monies. However, if the principal contractor serves notice of insolvency or winding up then the rules of apportionment and having to prove debt in liquidation and the bankruptcy date and resulting liability period is far clearer.

Rule 4.90 of the Insolvency Rules 1986 is headed 'Mutual credit and set-off' and provides:

'(1) This rule applies where, before the company goes into liquidation there have been mutual credits, mutual debts or other mutual dealings between the company and any creditor of the company proving or claiming to prove for a debt in the liquidation.'
'(3) An account shall be taken of what is due from each party to the other in respect of the mutual dealings, and the sums due from one party shall be set off against the sums due from the other.'
'(8) Only the balance (if any) of the account is provable in the liquidation. Alternatively [(as the case may be) the amount] shall be paid to the liquidator as part of the assets … .'

When the conditions of the rule are satisfied, a set-off is treated as having taken place automatically on the bankruptcy date. The original claims are extinguished and **only the net balance remains owing one way or the other**: *Stein v Blake* [1996] 1 AC 243.

The effect is to allow the debt which the insolvent company (principal contractor) owes to the creditor (the client) to be used as security for its debt to him or her. The creditor is exposed to insolvency risk only for the net balance.

Not all jurisdictions recognise this kind of security in bankruptcy. The judgment of Sir Richard Scott VC in *In re Bank of Credit and Commerce International S.A. (No. 10)* [1997] 2 WLR 172 illustrates the problems caused by the fact that English law, as the law of the ancillary liquidation, recognises such a set-off but the law of the principal liquidation (Luxembourg) does not.

In English law, it is **strictly limited to mutual claims existing at the bankruptcy date**. It is vital the client maintains accurate chronology of the site operations and what information was available at any particular time. This type of approach often eases difficult negotiations the client may subsequently be involved in with insolvency practitioners acting for the ailing or failed principal contractor.

There can be no set-off of claims by third parties, even with their consent. To do so would be to allow parties by agreement to subvert the fundamental principle of pari passu distribution of the insolvent company's assets: see *British Eagle International Airlines Ltd v Compagnie Nationale Air France* [1975] 1 WLR 758.

Appendix C: Pre-construction information checklist

The pre-construction information checklist is based on the list given in Appendix 2 of the ACOP.

© *Crown copyright material is reproduced with the permission of the Controller of HMSO and Queen's Printer for Scotland.*

A template for a *Schedule of pre-construction information* has been included (see Appendix D) to illustrate how the list can be developed into project specific checklist.

Because the range of construction projects is so vast – from civil engineering projects such as bridges and tunnels to new build shops, offices, schools, hotels down to refurbishments and small extensions – any checklist needs to be designed to reflect the nature and complexity of the project.

Most CDM co-ordinators will need to develop a range of checklists and schedules to reflect the type of projects covered.

Client: _____

Project: _____

Ref	Task	Date	√	Ref./comment
1	**Description of project**			
1.1	Brief project description			
1.2	Programme details – key dates (including planned start and finish of the construction phase)			
1.3	Programme details – the minimum time to be allowed between appointment of the principal contractor and instruction to commence work on site (mobilisation period)			
1.4	Details of clients, designers, CDM co-ordinator and other consultants			
1.5	Whether or not the structure will be used as a workplace (if so, the finished design must take account of the *Workplace Regulations* 1992)			
1.6	Extent and location of existing records and plans			
2	**Client's considerations and management requirements**			
2.1	Arrangements for: (i) planning for and managing the construction work: include any health and safety goals for the project, (ii) communication and liaison between client and others, (iii) security of the site, (iv) welfare provision.			

Ref	Task	Date	√	Ref./comment
2.2	Requirements relating to the health and safety of client's employees/customers or those involved in the project such as; (i) site hoarding requirements, (ii) site transport arrangements or vehicle movement restrictions, (iii) client permit-to-work systems, (iv) fire precautions, (v) emergency procedures and means of escape, (vi) 'no-go' areas or other authorisation requirements for those involved in the project, (vii) any areas the client has designates as confined spaces, (viii) smoking and parking restrictions.			
3	**Environmental restrictions and existing on-site risks**			
3.1	Safety hazards, including: (i) boundaries and access, including temporary access – e.g. narrow streets, lack of parking, turning or storage space, (ii) any restrictions on deliveries or waste collection or storage, (iii) adjacent land uses – e.g. schools, railway lines or busy roads, (iv) existing storage of hazardous materials, (v) location of existing services particularly those that are concealed – water, electricity, gas, etc. (vi) ground conditions, underground structures or water courses where this might affect the safe use of plant, e.g. cranes, or the safety of groundworks, (vii) information about existing structures – stability, structural form, fragile or hazardous materials, anchorage points for fall arrest systems (particularly where demolition is involved), (viii) previous structural modifications, including weakening or strengthening of the structure (particularly where demolition is involved), (ix) fire damage, ground shrinkage, movement or poor maintenance which may have adversely affected the structure, (x) any difficulties relating to plant and equipment in the premises, such as overhead gantries whose height restricts access, (xi) health and safety information contained in earlier design, construction or 'as-built' drawings, such as details of pre-stressed or post-tensioned structures.			
3.2	Health hazards including: (i) asbestos, including results of surveys (particularly where demolition is involved), (ii) existing storage of hazardous materials,			

Ref	Task	Date	√	Ref./comment
	(iii) contaminated land, including results of surveys, (v) existing structures containing hazardous materials, (⌐) health risks arising from client's activities.			
4	**Significant design and construction hazards**			
4.1	Significant design assumptions and suggested work methods, sequences or other control measures			
4.2	Arrangements for co-ordination of ongoing design work and handling design changes			
4.3	Information on significant risks identified during design			
4.4	Materials requiring particular precautions			
5	**The health and safety file**			
5.1	Describe its format and any considerations relating to its content			

Ref	Task	Date	√	Ref./comment

Appendix D: Schedule of pre-construction information

Project: _____

	Type of information	Requested From	Requested Date	Available √	Available N	Date received	CDM-C comments	Further actions
1	Existing health and safety file	Client						
2	Asbestos survey							
3	Ground investigations							
4	Soil reports							
5	Desk-top study:							
	History of site							
	Land usage data							
	Liable to flooding, etc.							
6	Condition survey							
7								
8								
9								
10								
11								
12								

Distribution list:

Date of issue:

The manner in which this type of schedule is formatted must depend on the type and complexity of the project being undertaken.

The requirements for a fairly basic office refurbishment will be vastly different from what might be required for a major civil engineering project.

We have indicated ways in which such a schedule might be drawn up but both the format and the information must be based upon the particular demands of the actual project for which the schedule is being drawn up.

Appendix E: Construction phase plan checklist

The construction phase plan checklist is based on the list given in Appendix 3 of the ACOP.

© Crown copyright material is reproduced with the permission of the Controller of HMSO and Queen's Printer for Scotland.

Client: _____

Project: _____

Ref	Task	Date	√	Ref./comment
1	**Description of project**			
1.1	Brief project description			
1.2	Programme details – key dates including actual start and finish of the construction phase			
1.3	Details of clients, designers, CDM-C, PC and other consultants			
1.4	Extent and location of existing records and plans that are relevant to health and safety on site, including information about existing structures as appropriate			
2	**Management of the work**			
2.1	Management structure and responsibilities			
2.2	Health and safety goals for the project and arrangements for monitoring and review of health and safety performance			
2.3	Arrangements for: (i) regular liaison between parties on site, (ii) consultation with the workforce, (iii) the exchange of design information between the client, designers, CDM co-ordinator and contractors on site, (iv) handling design changes during the project, (v) the selection and control of contractors, (vi) the exchange of health and safety information between contractors, (vii) site security, (viii) site induction, (ix) on site training, (x) welfare facilities and first aid, (xi) the reporting and investigation of accidents and incidents including near misses, (xii) the production and approval of risk assessments and written systems of work.			

Ref	Task	Date	√	Ref./comment
2.4	Site rules (including drug and alcohol policy)			
2.5	Fire and emergency procedures			
3	**Arrangements for controlling significant site risks**			
3.1	Safety risks, including: (i) delivery and removal of materials (including SWMPs*) and work equipment taking account of any risks to the public, e.g. during access to or egress from the site, (ii) dealing with services – water, electricity and gas, including overhead power lines and temporary electrical installations, (iii) accommodating adjacent land use, (iv) stability of structures whilst carrying out construction work, including temporary structures and existing unstable structures, (v) preventing falls, (vi) work with or near fragile materials, (vii) control of lifting operations, (viii) the maintenance of plant and equipment, (ix) work on excavations and work where there are poor ground conditions, (x) work on wells, underground earthworks and tunnels, (xi) work on or near water where there is a risk of drowning, (xii) work involving diving, (xiii) work in a caisson or compressed air working, (xiv) work involving explosives, (xv) traffic routes and segregation of vehicles and pedestrians, (xvi) storage of materials (particularly hazardous materials) and work equipment, (xvii) any other significant safety risks.			
3.2	Health risks, including: (i) the removal of asbestos, (ii) dealing with contaminated land, (iii) manual handling, (iv) use of hazardous substances, particularly where there is a need for health monitoring, (v) reducing noise vibration, (vi) work with ionising radiation, (vii) exposure to UV radiation from the sun, (viii) other significant health risks.			
4	**The H&S file**			
4.1	Layout and format			
4.2	Arrangements for the collection and gathering of information			
4.3	Storage of information			

* **Note:** Contractors will be required to produce site waste management plans (SWMPs) in the future.

Appendix F: F10 Notification of construction project

The specimen F10 form which follows is an HSE document and copyright is held by the HSE. The form is reproduced here with permission from the HSE.

It can be found at www.hse.gov.uk/forms/notification/f10.pdf

Guidance Notes for completion of form F10 - Notification of construction project

What should this form be used for

- To notify the enforcing authority for the Construction (Design and Management) Regulations 2007 of any project that is likely to last longer than 30 days or involve more than 500 person days of construction work.
- Any day on which construction work is carried out (including holidays and weekends) should be counted, even if the work on that day is of short duration.
- A person day is one individual, including supervisors and specialists, carrying out construction work for one normal working shift.
- Construction work for a domestic client is **not** notifiable.

Who should use this form

- The CDM co-ordinator for the project.

Where to send the completed form

- The HSE area office covering the site where construction work is to take place. You can get the address by contacting HSE's Infoline, Tel: 0845 345 0055.

When to send this form

- As soon as practicable after the CDM co-ordinator for the project is appointed by the client.

Notification of construction project

1. Is this the initial notification of the project or are you providing additional information not previously available?

☐   Initial notification   ☐   Additional information

2. What is the date of forwarding this notification or provision of additional information?

3. What is the exact address of the construction site? *(Full address, including postcode)*

4. What is the name of the Local Authority where the site is located?

5. Give a brief description of the project and the construction work it includes.

6. Client contact details *(name, full address, postcode, telephone number and any email address)*
(If more than one client, please attach details on a separate sheet)

Name		Email address	
Address			
Postcode		Telephone number	

7. Please give the name and address of any designer already engaged
(name, full address, postcode, telephone number and any email address)
(If more than one designer, please attach details on a separate sheet)

Name		Email address	
Address			
Postcode		Telephone number	

F10 (rev 04.07)

8. CDM co-ordinator contact details *(name, full address, postcode, telephone number and any email address)*

Name

Email address

Address

Postcode

Telephone number

9. Principal contractor contact details *(name, full address, postcode, telephone number and any email address)*

Name

Email address

Address

Postcode

Telephone number

10. What is the time allowed by the client to the principal contractor referred to in regulation 15(b) for the planning and preparation for construction work?

11. Please give your estimates of the following:

Please indicate if these estimates are: Original   Revised

a.   The planned date for the start of the construction phase

b.   The planned duration of the construction phase

c.   The maximum number of people at work on the site at any one time

d.   The planned number of contractors on the site

12. Please give the name and address of any contractor already appointed
(name, full address, postcode, telephone number and any email address)
(If more than one contractor, please attach details on a separate sheet)

Name

Email address

Address

Postcode

Telephone number

13. Declaration of client

I hereby declare that I am aware of my duties under the Construction (Design and Management) Regulations 2007 (S.I. 2007/320).

Signed by or on behalf of the organisation

Print name   Date

Appendix G: Useful sources of information

CDM2007.org

For the London Borough of Bromley scheme for the public sector comprising an accreditation scheme and a modular learning package see www.CDM2007.org

Construction Infonet

This is a bulletin prepared by the HSE Construction Division, initially as a local initiative from the Luton office, but now available nationally.

Subscription (free) to the Construction Infonet can be made via the HSE construction web pages www. hse.gov.uk/construction/infonet.htm

Construction Skills

For more information on Construction Skills see www. citb-constructionskills.co.uk/healthsafety/cdmregulations

European Union

Information in all the official languages of the European Union is available on the internet. It can be accessed through the Europa server (http://europa. eu.int).

Information and publications in English on the European Union can be obtained from the following addresses

European Parliament Offices

Ireland
European Union House
43 Molesworth Street,
Dublin 2
Tel: (353–1) 605 79 00
Fax: (353–1) 605 79 99
Email: EPDublin@europarl.eu.int

United Kingdom
2, Queen Anne's Gate
London
SW1H 9AA
Tel: (40–20) 72 27 43 00
Fax: (40–20) 72 27 43 02
Email: EPLondon@europarl.eu.int

Scotland
9 Alva Street
Edinburgh
EH2 4PH
Tel: (44–131) 225 20 58
Fax: (44–131) 226 41 05

European Commission
Directorate-General for Education and Culture
Publications Unit,
Rue de la Loi/Wetstraat 200,
B-1049 Brussels

European Agency for Safety and Health at Work
The EASHW is based in Bilbao and was set up to provide information and promote health and safety throughout the Member States.

Information and publications can be obtained from the following address:
European Agency for Safety and Health at Work
Gran Via, 33,
E-48009
Bilbao
SPAIN
Tel: (34) 944 79 43 60

The European Agency also operates an electronic newsletter called OSHmail.

Website: http://agency.osha.eu.int

F10 form

The F10 Notification of construction project can be found at www.hse.gov.uk/forms/notification/f10.pdf

HSE Books

Website: www.hse.gov.uk/pubns/index.htm

Legislation

Revised editions of primary legislation (i.e. Acts of Parliament) can be accessed via the internet at www.statutelaw.gov.uk.

Unrevised editions of Acts and Statutory Instruments produced since 1988 are published on the Office of Public Sector Information website at www.opsi.gov.uk/stat.htm. UK legislation prior to 1988 may be purchased through The Stationery Office Limited or via www.ukstate.com

NEBOSH qualifications

NEBOSH
Dominus Way
Meridian Business Park
Leicester
LE19 1QW
Tel: 0116 263 4700
Website: www.nebosh.org.uk

Northern Ireland

Stationery Office Bookshop
16 Arthur Street
Belfast
BT1 4GD
Telephone: (028) 9023 8451

The Health and Safety Executive for Northern Ireland
83 Ladas Drive
Belfast
BT6 9FR
For general enquiries – helpline: 0800 0320 121
Tel: 028 9024 3249
Website: www.hseni.gov.uk

RICS Europe

Information on services provided by the Brussels office:
RICS Europe
Rue Ducale 67
1000 Brussels
Belgium
Tel: +32 2 733 10 19
Fax: +32 2 742 97 48
Email: ricseurope@rics.org
Website: www.rics.org/AboutRICS/RICSworldwide/RICSEurope

RICS main offices (UK)

RICS HQ
Royal Institution of Chartered Surveyors
12 Great George Street
Parliament Square
London
SW1P 3AD
Tel: +44 (0)870 333 1600
Fax: +44 (0)207 334 3811
Email: contactrics@rics.org

Coventry
Royal Institution of Chartered Surveyors
Surveyor Court
Westwood Way
Coventry CV4 8JE
Tel: +44 (0)870 333 1600
Fax: +44 (0)207 334 3811
Email: contactrics@rics.org

References

1 Factsheet L7, Legislative Series Revised April 2003, ISSN 014‑4689 (available at www.parliament.uk/documents/upload/L07.pdf)

2 EU legislation can be found at http://europa.eu.int/eur-lex/en/search/search_lif.html

3 *Temporary or Mobile Construction Sites Directive* 92/57/EEC can be found on the European legislation website at http://eur-lex.europa.eu/LexUriServ/LexUriServ.do?uri=CELEX:31992L0067:EN:HTML

To order a paper version, use the online order facility at: http://bookshop.europa.eu/eGetRecords?Template=Test_EUB/en_search_identifiers (the catalogue number to enter into the search box is: PD2599221ENC, you will also need to tick the (search) Archive box).

4 Approved Code of Practice (ACOP), *Managing health and safety in construction: Construction (Design and Management) Regulations 2007*, L144, Health and Safety Executive, 2007, ISBN 978 0 71766 223 4

5 *Successful health and safety management*, HSG65, Health and Safety Executive, 1997, ISBN 0 7176 1276 7

6 *Construction Programme's existing SME work and development of future strategy*, Health and Safety Commission Paper, HSC/07/16 (available at www.hse.gov.uk/aboutus/hsc/meetings/2007/090107/c16.pdf)

7 Commission of the European Communities v United Kingdom of Great Britain and Northern Ireland, *Case C-127/05*

8 Dr. Klaus-Dieter Borchardt, *The ABC of Community Law* (5th edition), Office for Official Publications of the European Communities, ISBN 92 828 7803 1, an electronic version of this publication can be viewed at http://ec.europa.eu/publications/booklets/eu_documentation/02/txt_en.pdf

9 *Statistics of fatal injuries 2005/06* can be viewed on the HSE website at www.hse.gov.uk/statistics/overall/fatl0506.pdf

10 *Self-reported work-related illness in 2004/05: results from the Labour Force Survey* can be downloaded from www.hse.gov.uk/statistics/swi/swi0405.pdf

11 *An investigation of reporting of workplace accidents under RIDDOR using the Merseyside Accident Information Model*, HSE Report RR528, Health and Safety Executive, 2007, see www.hse.gov.uk/research/rrhtm/rr528.htm

12 *Constructing Better Health pilot*, see www.fit-builder.com/index01.html

13 *Highways Economic Note No1* (HEN1), see the DFT website: www.dft.gov.uk/stellent/groups/dft_rdsafety/documents/page/dft_rdsafety_610642.hcsp

14 *Movement for Innovation (M4i) Demonstration Projects*, 2006, see www.constructingexcellence.org.uk//resources/az/view.jsp?id=290 or *Demonstration Projects* www.constructingexcellence.org.uk/resources/demonstrationprojects/default.jsp

15 *Designer Initiative 2005 – Report*, Health and Safety Executive (Construction Division), Scotland, Northwest and Newcastle upon Tyne offices, see http://products.ihs.com/Ohsis-SEO/718427.html

16 *The health and safety system in Great Britain* (3rd edition), Health and Safety Executive, 2002, ISBN 0 7176 2243 6 (also available at www.hse.gov.uk/pubns/ohsingb.pdf)

17 *Framework Directive* 89/391/EEC, can be found at http://eur-lex.europa.eu/LexUriServ/LexUriServ.do?uri=CELEX:31989L0391:EN:HTML

18 European Foundation for the Improvement of Living and Working Conditions, *From Drawing Board to Building Site: Working Conditions, Quality, Economic Performance*, HMSO, London, 1991

19 *The Role of the Client*, Construction Information Sheet 39, Health and Safety Executive

20 *Having Construction Work Done*, MISC193, Health and Safety Executive

21 Turnbull Report, *Internal Control: Guidance for Directors on the Combined Code*, Institute of Chartered Accountants of England in Wales, 1999, ISBN 1 84152 010 1, available at www.icaew.co.uk/index.cfm?route=120907

22 *Principles of Good Governance and Code of Best Practice*, available at www.fsa.gov.uk/pubs/ukla/lr_comcode.pdf

23 *Regina v Paul Wurth SA* [2000] ICR 860, CA (1999 Dec 9 and 2000 Jan 26, Pill LJ, Rougier and Newman JJ)

24 Approved Code of Practice, *Managing Health and Safety in Construction*, HSG224, Health and Safety Executive, 2001, ISBN 0 7176 2139 1

25 *Revitalising Health and Safety in Construction*, Discussion Document 20 (DDE20), Health and Safety Executive, 2002, available at www.hse.gov.uk/consult/disdocs/dde20.pdf

[26] For responses to *Revitalising Health and Safety in Construction*, Discussion Document 20, see www.hse.gov.uk/consult/disdocs/dde20.summary.pdf

[27] *Improving safety and health in construction: the need for action during procurement, design and planning, construction and maintenance*, results of the European Construction Safety Summit, Bilbao, Spain, 22 November 2004, ISBN 92 9191 115 1 (The Bilbao Declaration can be downloaded at: http://osha.eu.int/publications/other20041122/bilbao declaration.pdf). Proceedings from a subsequent event, Brussels Conference 21 September 2006, are available at http://ew2004.osha.europa.eu/closingevent/september.2006

[28] *Designing for Safety in Construction*, see http://www.efcanet.org/pages/news.aspx?item=3358

[29] A report on the investigation into the walkway collapse at Port Ramsgate on 14 September 1994, HSE Books, ISBN 0 7176 1747 5, see www.hsl.gov.uk/casestudies/ramsgate.htm

[30] See page 20 of *Whole-life Costing and Cost Management: Achieving Excellence in Construction Procurement Guide*, 2007, available at www.ogc.gov.uk/document/CP0067AEGuide7.pdf

[31] *A Design Framework for Building Services – design activities and drawing definitions*, BG 6/2006, BSRIA Ltd, 2006, ISBN 978 0 86022 656 7

[32] Jessup, G. 'The emerging model of vocational education and training' in J. W. Burke (ed.) *Competency Based Education and Training*, Lewes: Falmer Press, 1989

[33] Carpenter, J., *Developing guidelines for the selection of designers and contractors under the Construction (Design and Management) Regulations 1994*, 2006, available at www.hse.gov.uk/research/rrpdf/rr422.pdf

[34] *Global Best Practices in Contractor Safety*, Institute of Occupational Safety and Health (IOSH), available at www.iosh.co.uk/files/technical/globalbestpract030502wv.pdf

[35] *Preventing Falls in Scaffolding and Falsework*, SG4:05, see www.nasc.org.uk/publications.shtml

[36] *Guide to Good Practice for Scaffolding with Tube and Fittings*, TG20:07, due to publish in two volumes later in 2007, see www.nasc.org.uk/publications. shtml

[37] *Heritage works – The use of historic buildings in regeneration: A toolkit of good practice*, available as a pdf at www.english-heritage.org.uk/upload/pdf/Heritage_Works.pdf

[38] *Provision of welfare facilities at fixed construction sites*, HSE Information Sheet No 18 (rev1), available at www.hse.gov.uk/pubns/cis18.pdf

[39] *Provision of welfare facilities at transient construction sites*, HSE Information Sheet No 46, available at www.hse.gov.uk/pubns/cis46.pdf

[40] *Fire Prevention on Construction Sites: Joint Code of Practice on the Protection from Fire of Construction Sites and Buildings Undergoing Renovation* (6th edition), Fire Protection Association, 2006, ISBN 0 90216 739 1

[41] Rushton, T., *Investigating Hazardous and Deleterious Building Materials*, RICS Books, 2006, ISBN 1 84219 291 4

[42] *Workplace Exposure Limits: Containing the list of workplace exposure limits for use with the Control of Substances Hazardous to Health Regulations 2002 (as amended)*, EH40, Health and Safety Executive, 2005, ISBN 0 71762 977 5

[43] *Surveying safely*, RICS, available at www.rics.org/AboutRICS/RICSforums/RICSHealthandSafetyForum/surveyingsafely.htm

[44] *Safer surfaces to walk on – reducing the risk of slipping*, CIRIA Guide C652, London, 2006, ISBN 978 0 86017 652 7

[45] *Safety in the installation and use of gas systems and appliances: Gas Safety (Installation and Use) Regulations 1998*, Approved Code of Practice and Guidance, L56, Health and Safety Executive, 1998, ISBN 0 71761 635 5

[46] *Control of substances hazardous to health (5th edition): The Control of Substances Hazardous to Health Regulations 2002*, Approved Code of Practice and Guidance, L5, Health and Safety Executive, 2005, ISBN 0 71762 981 3

Index

vermiculte 94
vicarious liability 146
village store
    client case study 24
volatile organic compounds (VOCs) 94

walking surfaces
    requirements and condition 126
warranties and guarantees
    information in 118
    remedial work under 33, 34
    retaining 118
washing facilities
    regulations covering 129
watercourses
    protection 117
water discharge consent 117
weather conditions
    working at height 130
weather protection 19
welfare facilities
    decontamination facilities 74
    provision of, options 74, 75

requirements 74
welfare units 75
windows
    regulations covering 128, 129
wood preservatives 94
Woolf Report 147
Work at Height Regulations 2005
    changes of emphasis within 130
    duties under 129
    history 129
    managing and selecting work equipment 130
    requirements 1, 3, 124
    summary of 129, 134
workforce
    perceptions about 14
workplace
    definition 3
Workplace Directive (89/654/EEC) 2
Workplace (Health, Safety and Welfare) Regulations 1992
    duties under 128, 129
    requirements 2, 3, 15, 39, 45, 124, 125
    summary 134
work-related ill health *see* ill health
Work-related Death Protocol 143